Flying
The Edge

Flying The Edge

FLIGHT AT THE THRESHOLD OF OPTIMUM PERFORMANCE

Capt. Brian McAllister

Airlife
England

First published in the UK in 1997
by Airlife Publishing Ltd

British Library Cataloguing-in-Publication Data
A catalogue record for this book
is available from the British Library

ISBN 1 85310 865 0

Illustrations by the author.

Typeset by Phoenix Typesetting, Ilkley, West Yorkshire.

Printed in England by Livesey Ltd, Shrewsbury.

Airlife Publishing Ltd
101, Longden Road, Shrewsbury, SY3 9EB, England

This book is dedicated to my late father,
RAPHAEL DILSCHESP McALLISTER MM,
a veteran campaigner,
for what might have been
and to my two grandsons,
JACOB AND BENJAMIN,
for what I hope will be.

Also by Brian McAllister
The Instrument Pilot – PPL and Beyond
Crew Resource Management

God be thy guide from camp to camp;
God be thy shade from well to well;
God grant beneath the desert stars
thou hear the Prophet's camel-bell

Moslem blessing for the traveller

Contents

Author's Introduction

I actually learned to fly by accident, which was amazing really because I can't stand heights. (That statement has raised a few disbelieving smiles among passengers when revealed in a weak moment). That, and large tropical spiders which suddenly decide to hurl themselves off jungle tree branches, with legs spread out in the shape of a parachute; then stop and hang suspended in mid-air on a single, flimsy thread, resembling escapees from a spiders' Jurassic Park. I wondered if they might have discovered something new concerning gravity, or the aerodynamics of flying we don't know anything about.

With STOL flying you get to visit some really out-of-the-way places and often stay in strange accommodation. For instance, an Indian Maharajah's ex-palace, an African prison, a Saharan Bedouin chief's harem, a jungle tree house and an old paddle steamer. Then once in South America, I stayed for several nights in a ranch house guest accommodation surrounded by a steel fence, like an animal enclosure. It was to protect visitors from wandering crocodiles as the house was situated close to the river Orinoco. In fact, you get to see things the average airline pilot can only read about.

I'm saying all this for a valid reason, of course, because STOL pilots have to develop self-reliance and accumulate a whole range of aviation knowledge and skills, as well as diplomacy – if they are going to survive.

A veteran Air America pilot, who was very experienced in STOL operations, once said to me, 'They don't install real solid flap handles in aircraft anymore. They were a real comfort if you felt a bit nervous before a particularly STOL take-off, because you could grab hold of the handle if you saw the obstacle at the far end of the strip looming up fast, then yank hard on it and the aircraft would literally leap off the ground like a startled rabbit!'

I'm not advocating you should try this, by the way, whatever they do in the movies. The reasons will become apparent as you read through this book.

As with everything in aviation, STOL flying has developed over the years, and we have learned and refined the techniques that will see us through the most difficult situations. However, the basics remain the same, and we should always be certain we understand those. And any aspiring STOL pilot worth his gold wings will make sure he knows as much about the subject as possible. Which brings me to the reason for writing this book.

Within its pages, is a broad cross-section of information, tips, mistakes I've made, and 'what to do in the event of' type advice from 40 years experience in aviation. If it helps you become a better pilot, let alone a STOL pilot, then I'll be well satisfied.

Centre of gravity limits, high-lift devices, asymmetric flight, surviving an emergency crash landing and much more, is available for the reading. So with notebook and sharpened pencil at the ready, enjoy. Good luck and safe flying – so turn off that television!

B.M. 1997

CHAPTER 1

PRACTICAL COCKPIT MANAGEMENT

Is anyone flying the aircraft?

PART I: SITUATIONAL AWARENESS

Accidents don't happen by accident! We've all heard that expression I'm sure. They result from a chain of events in which the human element is a vital link. In most cases they have little to do with the type of aircraft being flown.

In recent years, it has become increasingly evident that human error is the prime cause of aviation accidents involving professional pilots; not mechanical failure, electronic malfunctions, bad maintenance or the weather. The problem can be summed up in two words, SITUATIONAL AWARENESS. This takes in the entire spectrum of factors and conditions that affect the aircraft and flight crew during any one specific period of time. In simple terms, knowing exactly what is going on in the operational environment around you, and thinking ahead of the aircraft. This is a concept taught to student pilots from the beginning of flight training.

It therefore follows that there is a direct relationship between situational awareness and SAFETY.

There is no doubt that pilots who have better situational awareness are safer. Therefore it is true to say there is a direct link between the situational awareness of individual crew members and the flight crew as an operating group.

Individual Situational Awareness

As we can see, situational awareness is influenced by the individual. If we take a two pilot crew, for example, one may have a very high level of awareness whilst the other has a lower level of awareness. And of course there will even be small variations of situational awareness between highly aware crew members. So, as we analyse this factor, it is apparent there are variations because every human being is different.

Let's look at an IFR, two-pilot, public transport flight heading for a destination airport surrounded by mountains. The captain has inadvertently descended well below the minimum safe sector altitude and the aircraft is on a collision course with a mountain peak five miles distant.

Imagine what impact situational awareness might have on the outcome. The copilot is young, straight out of flight school with minimum experience, but because of recent training he has a high situational awareness and can see the dangerous position the aircraft is in.

The captain, who is flying the aircraft, has been over the route so many times he has become complacent and bored. We all know about the classic, 'familiarity breeds mistakes' syndrome. There is also another factor adding to the problems. His mind is constantly thinking about a local golf tournament he is playing in the following day, which is important (to him). Here is a combination of circumstances that has lowered his personal situational awareness to the point where he has made a potentially fatal error. Unless immediate action is taken the aircraft will crash. This is because *group* situational awareness is low, limited by the captain.

Group Awareness

To enable the level of group awareness to be raised, the young copilot must intervene and impart the knowledge gained from his high level of situational awareness to the captain so that he will accept it. This is the most vital factor required to achieve group situational awareness in this case. There is no doubt also that communication and a proper understanding of the concepts of command and leadership are essential.

International regulations recognise that 'the pilot in command of an aircraft is directly responsible for, and is the final authority, as to the operation of the aircraft'. But there is a fine line between being in charge and being dictatorial. Unfortunately, there have been instances where captains have crossed that line with disastrous results. Here are two well documented examples.

One of the worst ever aviation accidents, which claimed 581 lives, was in part due to a captain who did not heed the warning of a subordinate flight crew member. It was a prime example of the breakdown of group situational awareness. A KLM 747 was beginning its take-off roll in foggy weather conditions at Tenerife Airport in the Canary Islands, when the flight engineer questioned whether a Pan American 747 which was back taxying down the same runway was clear. The captain ignored his subordinate, for whatever reason, and decided to continue the take-off. The KLM 747 collided with the Pan American aircraft seconds later.

The captain of Air Florida Flight 90 ignored several warnings from his copilot that the engine gauges 'didn't look right' during their take-off roll from snowbound Washington National Airport. The 737 in question crashed shortly after take-off.

Whilst the copilot by definition is the subordinate crew member, or second in command, the captain should not be overbearing, although many are. As a Training Captain of many years' experience, I have checked out scores of pilots. One day I had just completed a young copilot's line training and released him for normal duties. An hour later I accidentally overheard a senior line captain telling the same copilot that when he was on board the aircraft to 'just sit in the (RH) seat, make the radio calls and SHUT UP!'

The captain was certainly not making the situation better for himself. He was actually increasing his own workload and wasting a valuable asset. Such a well-trained copilot could have substantially reduced his workload. Not only that, but the captain's situational awareness would also be lowered, thus decreasing group situational awareness. This self-imposed involvement in task performance, restricts the available time for the important pilot-in-command duties of planning, analysis and decision-making.

Main Elements of Situational Awareness

Every pilot is affected by a number of important elements that make up his level of situational awareness.

Experience and Training

What we mean by experience is the practical knowledge, skill, or increased expertise derived from training or direct observation of particular activities. We use different parts of this experience every time we fly. This experience is stored away in our brain's memory file. It helps us establish how changing conditions and events are interpreted and how we respond to them. We are constantly reaching into this memory file of experience to guide the actions we take while we are flying, and the different situations we face. This wealth of experience allows us to solve our problems more quickly and therefore allocate more time to other tasks which require a pilot's attention.

Experience and training are therefore closely related. Training is much more than the effort to improve our system's knowledge and hone our physical flying skills. Training adds to our bank of experience.

A great many of the problems faced by pilots are actually solved before entering the aircraft. In the air, the constant review of certain emergency procedures are solved from repetitive training experience. For instance, dealing with a simulated engine failure on take-off at V_2 becomes automatic to the well-trained pilot.

Modern simulators allow us to recreate the worst scenario in-flight emergency situations we could face in everyday flying. This contributes to our experience file without risking death or crashing the aircraft. When actual malfunctions occur, we can instantly draw on this experience for correct reactions.

Physical Flying Skills

We can all remember our days as student pilots. I learned to fly in an open cockpit biplane with an ex-RAF WWII bomber pilot as my instructor. His highly developed situational awareness had been forged in the heat of aerial combat. He was a hard taskmaster even at my stage of flying experience.

Virtually all my attention was devoted to simply controlling the aircraft. I had little time to look out for other aircraft, navigate, or mull over the finer points of a developing weather situation. Consequently I can now see that my own level of situational awareness was extremely low. Many of us are only here today because our situational awareness was just capable of coping with the problems faced during this early period.

My salvation was the ex-RAF instructor with his highly developed instinct for survival. His favourite expression was, 'Make that same mistake when you're solo and you'll kill yourself for sure!' He made the point that 'In wartime flying, there was no room for two mistakes'. Believe me, my learning curve in those circumstances was very rapid – especially in a tail dragger with a metal skid, no radio or brakes.

As our physical flying skills improve we are able to devote more time to the mental aspects of flying. We must continue to sharpen these skills to ensure that more of our energies are devoted to other important flying tasks. However much we develop, though, our physical flying skills are still very important.

Health and Motivational Attitude

A great many physical and emotional factors contribute to our ability to reach and maintain a high level of situational awareness. Therefore, our physical and emotional state directly affects our personal view and interpretation of events around us. Even a slight illness, or a combination of personal problems, can have a detrimental effect on our ability to function properly in a demanding flight environment. The stressful interview with the bank manager concerning your overdraft which takes place just one hour before arriving at the airport, must be forgotten. It is a fact that good emotional and physical health are essential for establishing and sustaining high levels of situational awareness.

Also, a good professional attitude allows us to focus our energies in a more positive manner. It is every pilot's own personal commitment to safety, and furthers situational awareness.

How to apply Situational Awareness

If no-one is flying the aircraft or looking out of the cockpit window, situational awareness is severely compromised. Therefore, unattended and uncorrected deviations become a very real possibility. Even when the autopilot is engaged, any aircraft needs a pilot, or pilots, to 'mind the shop' inside and outside the cockpit.

As we have seen, a pilot establishes situational awareness through training and good cockpit management skills. This involves setting specific targets for each and every flight. These targets then become the yardstick by which we measure situational awareness.

Once situational awareness has been established, it is maintained by detecting and correcting any deviations. The key to continuing a high level of situational awareness lies in closely monitoring progress and making sure no problems arise. This is very important, as there is no formal measure of this factor.

It is important for flight crews to recognise the clues that will highlight any actual or possible loss of situational awareness. The following are some of the main ones:

Failure to meet planned targets.

This could mean higher than expected fuel consumption, ETAs not met, or failure to achieve cruise performance. If these are not analysed and acted upon, situational awareness will inevitably be compromised.

Ambiguity.

This takes place any time two or more different sources of information disagree. It can include different readings for the same aircraft system from two separate sources, navigation, electronics, etc, or uncertainty of position, deviating from the flight plan. As long as such ambiguities exist, are ignored or unresolved, situational awareness is in danger.

Mental Confusion.

A sudden increase in unnecessary stress causes doubts which impair judgement. Our conscious mind can suppress our subconscious doubts to a great extent, or our personal ability to handle it. Any doubt can lead to a loss of situational awareness if it cannot be resolved or overcome.

Improper Procedures.

This includes aircraft systems, violation of air traffic control and approach procedures, and operating outside the safe and efficient flight envelope of the aircraft. Whenever improper or totally non-standard procedures are even considered, situational awareness suffers and this can become a major element in aviation safety. Thus, establishing and minimising its loss is accomplished by good cockpit management.

Practical Cockpit Management

Practical cockpit management could equally fall under the heading of *Managing Cockpit Safety*. It is a wide and involved subject with many different facets that every pilot should understand better. Unfortunately, a large percentage of pilots do not give it the attention it deserves and they are the poorer for it.

So whatever emphasis you want to place on this 'management', it goes well beyond the actual physical flying. It includes essential factors of communications, decision making, inter-personal relationships, leadership and the responsibilities of command.

In the aviation industry quest for safety, attention has been focused on the more obvious deficiencies, such as mechanical failures and bad errors in airmanship. Maybe this is an over-simplistic approach to the problems, as you might ask yourself why perfectly competent pilots suddenly make mistakes in misreading approach charts, or unaccountably fly below a sector safety altitude. Flying is a complex, interwoven series of tasks that is constantly subjected to what researchers describe as the human factor in aviation safety.

Theoretically, there are four types of errors:

- Incorrect performance of a required task.
- Performance of a required task at the wrong time.
- Performance of an improper action.
- Failure to perform a required task.

However, in recent years a better understanding of human interaction and behavioural patterns has emerged. This is helping to solve some unanswered questions related to accidents, as well as focusing attention on ways to improve operational safety and efficiency. It has led to a greater understanding of the way people behave individually and collectively, whether under stress or not. Pilots need to be reinformed of the problems and how to manage and overcome them.

There are many important skills which contribute to good cockpit management. These skills can be learned and practised and apply in varying degrees to all pilots irrespective of aircraft type or qualifications. Here are eight major areas relating to cockpit management which would be advantageous for every flight crew member to self study and analyse in relation to their own operation:

- Cockpit distractions – imposed or random.
- Correct use and function of checklists.
- Workload assessment – time and stress management.
- Decision-making relating to sound aviation judgement.
- Inter-personal management skills – communication.
- Managing cockpit resources.
- Flight planning in all its aspects.
- Chain events (pattern recognition).

The Result of Compound Mistakes

In flying, disaster is normally the consequence of compound mistakes. For example, a landing gear fails to extend and, during the trouble shooting period, the aircraft crashes because of a series of unfortunate mistakes by both pilots. Firstly the copilot drops the (emergency) checklist on the cockpit floor and it slides behind the seat out of reach. In the process of trying to retrieve the checklist he accidentally disengages the autopilot. At the same time the impatient, stressed captain – whose prime responsibility is to fly the aircraft – takes unilateral action to deal with the situation without the emergency checklist (forgetting there is one on his side of the cockpit). He inadvertently shuts off the LP fuel cock to the left engine (the most critical on his turboprop aircraft) by mistake; the lever is right next to the emergency gear extension handle (both coloured red). Naturally the left engine stops.

Neither the problem with the landing gear, the dropping of the checklist, or the unexpected disengagement of the autopilot should have caused the aircraft to crash. It was the cumulative effect of stress resulting in panic-induced impatience, resulting in a severe loss of situational awareness and a total breakdown of normal cockpit management which caused the crash. You might say that such a series of mistakes could not happen, but there are many well documented accident reports which highlight similar chains of events.

None of us can say how we will react as individual pilots when faced with a real emergency. This is why repetitive training, and awareness training, are so vitally important. I feel sorry for the over-confident pilot who tells me that all the training he has had to do is an overrated waste of time. *He* hasn't experienced *any* emergency in twenty-five years of flying. In my opinion, that pilot is a potential accident looking for somewhere to happen!

When faced with an emergency, even if you initially simply remember to just fly and control the aircraft until the heart rate is under control, then you are well on the way to survival. Training conditions the mind to react *correctly* to the (emergency) situation; but it is only self-motivation and a positive mental attitude that will lift us into the high state of situational awareness necessary to handle our professional flying responsibilities. As on every take-off – *think* emergency and if it happens you are in a positive mental attitude to deal with it effectively.

There have been classic examples of pilots selecting the fuel tanks in the wrong sequence, and even shutting off the fuel in flight as mentioned in the previous example. There are known instances of pilots failing to do anything at all and consequently running a tank dry. When these errors, or potential errors, are considered and measured against known weaknesses in the aircraft, crew or the operational environment, the pilot is better able to avoid these compound mistakes which cause tragedies. No flight crew is morally responsible for the failures of others. But the cockpit can be regarded as the last line of defence, and a simple review of potential errors can easily highlight the most critical items.

The Safety Window

The rapid changes in aircraft technology have brought about changes for all pilots from that of control manipulator to an information processor. Only with a programme of integrated training can we assimilate new skills and let the new technologies blend in and take the place of old ones. But even with the new technology accidents still occur. Let's look at the most vulnerable phase of flight, in which the majority of accidents happen.

The diagrammatic view at figure 1.1 shows us the SAFETY WINDOW,

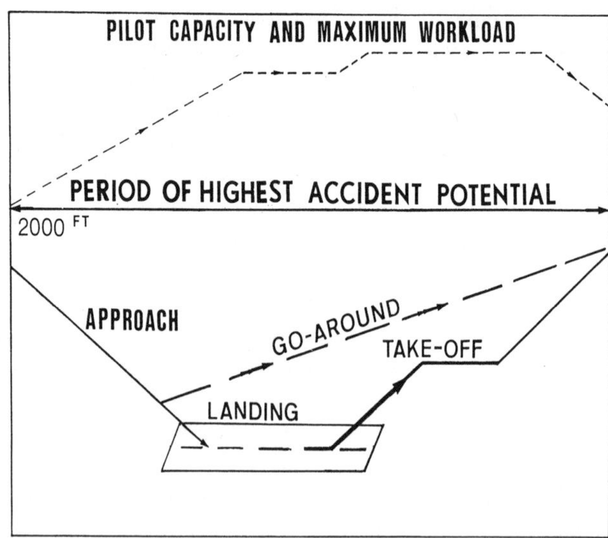

Figure 1.1 The Safety Window

which is a block of airspace extending from ground level to 2,000 feet AGL. This is centred around a runway with the WINDOW beginning at or around a final approach fix, extending to the end of the final segment of take-off climb. As we show, it is also the period of highest accident potential.

A closely interwoven use of cockpit management skills and situational awareness is necessary throughout the Safety Window period.

- For a conventional turboprop or jet aircraft the window is about 4-6 minutes long.
- Of the accidents involving professional pilots, eighty-three per cent occur within this window.
- Ninety per cent of these accidents are generic, meaning their cause is not confined to a specific weight category or particular type. For instance, the failure of the crew to extend the landing gear will result in a wheels-up landing irrespective of aircraft type. Statistics show that generic accidents tend to be caused by pilots, rather than by any technical fault with the aircraft.

The Safety Window period shown in the diagram almost certainly generates the highest pilot workload, and is regarded as the most critical portion of flight. The overall skills of the pilot are under pressure more than at any other time. Altitude changes, aircraft configuration, checklists, communication with air traffic control and instrument interpretation, are all sandwiched together inside the Safety Window.

To summarise, we can see from these observations that the highest pilot workload occurs within the safety window and also the majority of accidents take place within it. However, we can extend this one stage further, and overlay the Safety Window concept on any other part of a flight defining a critical period of time.

There is one other important aspect of our original Safety Window we would be wise to consider. Should the pilot leave the window when something goes wrong, or should he stay and land as soon as possible? How do we arrive at such a decision?

Consider the case of a twin-jet aircraft in the final phase of an IFR approach and cleared to land. Suddenly there is an engine fire warning, but the crew see no abnormalities with any engine instruments. The captain elects to continue to land the aircraft before dealing with the fire warning, rather than initiate a go-around. This is obviously the right decision and no-one would dispute that. In this instance, the best option is to remain in the Safety Window.

Now let's take another scenario; the same aircraft, again in-bound on final approach and the copilot selects gear down and nothing happens. Should the captain continue to hope they can get the gear down at the last moment and land? Of course there is that possibility. But in an IFR environment at a period of highest workload and stress, one or other of the pilots could miss a vital item and unnecessarily compound the initial problem.

The captain informs ATC and initiates the missed approach procedure and is directed to a holding fix outside the Safety Window to sort out the problem. In this case it is clear that leaving the window was the best choice. I know because the incident happened to me and it took several minutes to sort out the problem.

PART II: MANAGEMENT OF FLIGHT RESOURCES

The Concept

Practical cockpit management skills include flight resource management. This is the *effective* use of all available people, information, equipment and consumables that will help to successfully and safely complete a flight. These resources can be either internal or external to the aircraft.

The types and availability of flight resources vary widely and are dependent on factors such as aircraft type and equipment, composition of crew, operating environment and geographical location. All pilots should be familiar with as many types of resources as possible, as this will give them greater influence over the progress of a flight. This in turn can greatly increase situational awareness.

Each pilot has a maximum workload capacity, which is influenced by many factors. These include overall experience, specific training and proficiency level. Then there is the important inter-relationship of motivation and emotional health (marriage, financial pressures, job related stress, promotion/career prospects, illness, etc). In fact anything that reduces piloting skills and situational awareness.

A pilot's maximum workload capacity can therefore vary from day to day and flight to flight, even during a particular flight, if influenced by any combination of the factors already mentioned.

Task Loading

Task loading is the actual cockpit workload required for the safe performance of any phase of flight. We know there is an average pilot task loading, but sometimes this increases sharply and the pilot has to cope with this for the successful completion of the flight. The causes include abnormal or emergency situations, aircraft equipment and adverse weather problems, high density air traffic, plus company pressures.

Regardless of any particular flight phase, it is always possible to overload a pilot. Once this happens an accident potential exists and an adequate safety margin must be restored. This can only happen if *all* the available flight resources are utilised effectively. It might merely require a simple reallocation of duties between two pilots to deal with a one-off abnormal task load. However, a pilot who manages flight resources effectively from the beginning of a flight has greater control over cockpit workload. In this case, task loading is less likely to exceed the pilot's capacity to perform safely.

Proper preflight planning and conformity to predetermined targets helps to establish and maintain high levels of situational awareness. High levels of situational awareness allow a pilot to operate at peak capacity, and combined with keeping task loading under control, helps to maintain an acceptable safety margin throughout all phases of flight.

There are four major categories of flight resources:

- Human.
- Operational.
- Equipment.
- Consumable.

Human Resources

Human resources relate to those people who use their individual skills to provide valuable support and they are the most complex and variable resources available to a pilot. They can be broken down into three main areas:

Technical. Specialist knowledge and ability, and the aptitude to use it productively.

Interpersonal. Interactions between people. The ability to manage others and communicate in ways they understand.

Conceptual. The analysis and integration of all associated activities towards a common objective. In aviation, viewing the flight as a whole and seeing how various phases fit, in relation to the entire profile. These skills include the ability to project, analyse and alter the flight profile accordingly, to ensure a successful outcome.

Human resources are the most complex and can be categorised generally as follows:

- Flight crew
- Ground services
- Flight services

Flight Crew

The most important flight crew resource is one's self. In facing almost any situation or problem, individuals draw upon their own personal skills before turning anywhere else for assistance.

A pilot can draw upon his own actual flying skill, level of training and proficiency. Reaching into one's total experience file of knowledge is an excellent way of recognising pattern development. It gives a pilot the ability to make accurate observations, judgements and decisions. Personal resources are therefore the sum total of a pilot's technical, interpersonal and conceptual skills.

Ground Services

Ground services provide support from preflight to postflight. They are normally only thought of as providing fuel and servicing facilities, but in fact there is far more to it than that.

We can include in these services, meteorologists, engineers, operations personnel, fixed base operators and manufacturers' representatives. These individuals provide a wealth of valuable services and information that is readily available, either personally or through modern communications facilities. They support the crew and ease the task loading in the cockpit.

Flight Services

Air traffic control facilities in the widest sense are the major providers of flight services, and the fastest means of giving routine or emergency assistance to pilots. The range of ATC services includes flight planning, weather briefings, airport traffic control, radar sequencing and enroute airways control, crash and rescue services.

Additional flight services can also be given by the pilots of other aircraft through the relay of operational messages and weather information.

Operational Information

Operational information is a wide range of data that provides the pilot with information needed for planning and decision-making. It includes national and international aeronautical information publications and regulations, operations and flight manuals, technical handbooks, performance, enroute and instrument let-down charts. Some of this information will be carried in the aircraft for easy reference.

Other operational information will be collected as part of preflight preparation, such as weather briefs, flight plans (ATC and navigational), NOTAMS, aircraft load sheets (weight and balance computations) and passenger manifests.

To be effective, operational information must be:

- Current.
- Readily available.
- Applicable to a particular flight and the planned route.

Anything which has expired or is obsolete can only lead to poor planning and decision making, and could become critical to the safety of the flight.

Equipment

To help the pilot operate in a more complex environment, sophisticated equipment has been developed. We can categorise equipment resources as:

- Communications equipment.
- Status indicators.
- Predictors.
- Labour saving devices.

Like all flight resources, these various categories of equipment overlap and support each other. Either individually or collectively, equipment resources help pilots achieve and maintain high levels of situational awareness.

Communications Equipment

Communications equipment facilitates the transfer of information to and from the cockpit. VHF and HF radios, flight phones and transponders connect a pilot with many valuable sources of support. They form an integrated network, providing an up-to-the-second, highly reliable information collecting, processing and disseminating capability.

Radio communications link a pilot with many of the human resources that are available. In addition to receiving instructions and guidance, a pilot can make intentions and needs known to those capable of providing services and support.

Status Indicators

Status indicators are basic building blocks for achieving and maintaining high levels of situational awareness. They provide valuable information on the current status of the aircraft, enhance planning and decision-making. Some examples of status indicators are radar (including weather radar), navigational equipment, flight instruments, systems indicators, annunciator lights and audible warnings.

Predictors

Predictors allow pilots to accurately estimate future needs and plan accordingly. Time-to-station read-outs, fuel management and flight planning computers, inertial navigation systems, GPS and associated equipment, provide timely indications of potential problems, thereby allowing sufficient time for corrective action. Other examples of predictors include stall warning and ground proximity warning systems, and wind shear alerts.

Labour-saving devices

Labour-saving devices reduce pilot workload by assisting load sharing. Trends in aircraft development are towards consolidated flight management and the delegation of routine tasks to automated systems. The benefit of this is to increase situational awareness when a pilot is relieved of many routine cockpit duties.

What we must understand is that these sophisticated systems cannot be responsible for the safety of the flight – that remains the sole responsibility of the pilot-in-command.

Consumable Resources

Consumable resources are those resources used during the course of the flight. Because they are consumable, they impose limits on a flight. The three most important of these resources are fuel, personal energy and time. Efficient management of each one is critical to flight. The key to the effective use of a consumable resource is careful planning:

- How much is required.
- How much is available.
- How to use it efficiently.
- How to ensure sufficient reserves are available.

Personal energy is a consumable resource. Energy fuels the body in the same way an aircraft requires fuel. Not enough attention is given to building up and conserving this resource. Proper rest, nutrition, and utilising relaxation techniques all go towards maintaining good physical condition and high personal energy levels. This will of course help to boost individual situational awareness.

Establishing realistic targets and practising *time management* throughout a flight will help pilots to avoid time-related losses and to manage other consumable resources more effectively. Time lost can never be regained.

Time management and utilisation/integration of flight resources are skills every pilot should develop and refine. We have seen that there is an abundance of flight resources available to a pilot. The effective flight resource manager will take the initiative to learn what they are, where they can be found – and how to use them effectively.

Cockpit Management Essentials

We have looked at many aspects of practical cockpit management, but what about cockpit *safety*? This requires the application of six *skills*:

- Asking the right questions.

- Stating opinions frankly.
- Working out differences.
- Criticising in a constructive manner.
- Making decisions.
- Managing resources effectively.

In addition, there are six *rules* for safe operation within the cockpit.

- The positive delegation of flying and monitoring responsibilities must be a top priority.
- The positive delegation of monitoring responsibilities is just as important as the positive delegation of flying responsibilities.
- The pilot flying the aircraft should avoid performing secondary tasks, unless absolutely operationally essential.
- Whenever there are conflicting interpretations of fact, external sources of information must be used to resolve the problem.
- Whenever there is conflicting information from two sources, cross-checking from an independent source is necessary.
- If any crew member has a doubt about a clearance, procedure or situation, he or she must make that doubt known to other crew members.

Part III: Checklists – Use and Composition

Why have Checklists?

All of us at one time or another have heard a long list of excuses for not using checklists: 'Checklists take too much time', or 'I know my aircraft so well, I don't need the checklist any more', the list is endless. But the one that really stands out in my mind is, 'I fly a simple aircraft, I don't need a checklist!' In my view, this is the most misguided one of all.

It may well be true that there are fewer items to remember when flying less sophisticated aircraft. However, it is also true that simple aircraft don't always have simple procedures, or simple systems. It is just as easy to forget a simple action as it is to forget a more complex one, particularly in times of stress and a high cockpit workload where your attention is divided.

Definition and Purpose of a Checklist

A checklist is an essential tool used to initiate, direct and progress essential operational activities in the cockpit. It establishes a common method of communication between the flight crew and serves as a written aid to accomplish essential crew activities. The checklist, therefore, helps ensure that the crew is prepared, and, if followed religiously, will ensure that the aircraft and its systems are configured correctly for the related phase of the flight. However, it is not to be regarded as a substitute for a thorough knowledge of the aircraft systems and procedures. This final point can never be overstated or repeated too often.

Checklist Discipline is Essential

I have regularly come across pilots who have taken off with pitot-static covers and plugs still in place, cargo doors not latched properly and many other items unchecked. This might well lead only to an aborted take-off and some embarrassed, red-faced pilots, but it could also result in a major accident.

Each year, many aviation incidents and notifiable accidents are caused by failure to use the checklist. One typical extract from an official investigation report: 'The preflight was not conducted in accordance with the aircraft approved checklist, and was a major factor in the resulting accident'.

If you follow the checklist conscientiously each and every time it is required, you are a professional. Deviate from this and you are risking your life. The other important point we can draw from this is, if checklist discipline is lacking, then discipline may be lacking in other areas as well. After all, discipline is a prime factor in reaching and maintaining a high level of competence and professionalism in flying.

FAA regulations require that a cockpit checklist be used during operations under Parts 91, 121 and 135. Certainly all the various civil aviation authorities I have dealt with around the world, require an approved checklist to be used in all professional operations. They are an important ingredient of good cockpit management and therefore contribute to a high level of situational awareness.

Checklist Design

Having trained pilots of many nationalities around the world on various aircraft types, I have found that the checklist is the one item that causes the most arguments.

Each cockpit leads itself to a logical 'flow pattern'. This helps the pilots complete all the procedures and configure the aircraft. The design of the checklist should take this into account. For example, the flow may be from left to right or top to bottom. But, where possible, all actions or cross-checks should be completed on a specific systems panel, or area, before moving on to the next. This gives the checklist a logical progression and cuts out unnecessary further checks in areas already covered. Fewer errors or omissions are the result, as well as faster completion of the checklist.

I have found that the normal procedures checklist cause the most problems. Although these checklists are the most routine, accident and incident investigations highlight the fact that missed normal checklist items often contribute to gear-up landings, fuel-starved engines, incorrect flap or trim settings, and crew induced malfunctions.

What really causes confusion is the actual content; the items that should or should not be included in the checklist, and where. The manufacturer says one thing; the training organisation may state another, so the operator then faces a dilemma and has to find a workable operational solution. In the end though, it is the operators who must decide what works most efficiently for them. The best way is to work with the manufacturer's Technical Field Support Department, which always includes very experienced training pilots. This will provide the operator with the best available information in solving checklist problems.

In my book, the worst kind of pilot is the one who performs his own 'surgery' on the established checklist, thinking his version saves time and gets the job done just as well. No prizes for guessing what can happen as a result.

Checklists have evolved over many years and have been organised into categories and sub-categories. These have proved to be the most effective way to carry out desired procedures. They include NORMAL, ABNORMAL and EMERGENCY checklists.

Abnormal checklists.

These contain procedures for non-standard conditions that do not represent an *immediate* threat to the safety of the aircraft or its occupants. Failure of one part of an electrical, navigation or communications system, would fall into the category.

Emergency Checklists.

These are used to isolate and compensate for failed or malfunctioning systems to protect the aircraft from immediate or critical harm involving the safety of flight. For instance, an engine or electrical fire would be associated with the emergency checklist.

The checklist should be limited to the minimum number of items considered to be essential to aid the pilot in an emergency. They should also be in a concise, abbreviated form, designed to remind pilots of items to check without providing details concerning the operation of any one system.

In precise terms there will be:

- IMMEDIATE or INITIAL ACTIONS (memory items) when sequence is essential to safety.
- SUBSEQUENT ACTIONS (challenge and response) read items for two pilot operation, or an 'Item' and 'Condition' list for single pilot aircraft. For example:

Challenge or Item	Response or Condition
Generator	Cross-couple

This is to provide pilots with a better understanding of the reasons behind their IMMEDIATE actions. Completion of this is designed to contain the emergency and isolate the malfunctioning system.

Well designed checklists:

- Contain only those items necessary to accomplish the task or resolve the problem.
- Have items listed in the correct order.
- Are arranged so as not to interfere with the flying of the aircraft.

Therefore, we can see that checklists are constructed to assist, not hinder operations. The best checklists have a natural flow pattern and contain only the items necessary to accomplish the task.

However, the use of checklists does not necessarily mean that items won't be missed, but there are established techniques that will help prevent this happening. The main point to remember is the importance of using checklists in exactly the same sequence and pattern. Doing it this way makes it more likely that missed items or deviations will be detected.

Finally, a word of warning. Any checklist is only as good as the flight crew member using it. Disciplined, self-motivation in going through each item will ensure nothing is missed. The answer is to gather the maximum concentration of mind and body in the process of using the checklist. Familiarity and inattention called, 'Checklist Lassitude', is the greatest enemy.

Challenge and Response Technique

One proven and effective way of running a checklist is the challenge and response technique. It has been used for many years by professional pilots for normal, abnormal and emergency checklists to assure accuracy and good communication.

One pilot initiates each checklist item verbally, stating exactly what is written, i.e. the challenge. A second pilot, who is responsible for performing the item, responds accordingly.

A sample extract from a two-pilot checklist is given below:

After Engine Start Checklist

			READ BY	ANSWERED BY
1	Start Master	Normal	RP	LP
2	Ignition L & R	Off	RP	LP
3	Electrical Master	Internal	RP	LP
4	Generators	On	RP	LP
5	Volts & Amps	Checked	RP	LP
6	Shedding Bus R & L	Normal	RP	LP
7	External Supply	Disconnected	RP	LP
8	All MIs	Check vertical	RP	LP
9	Fuel Levelling Valves	Shut/MI vertical	RP	LP
10	Flaps	Set & Check	RP	LP
11	Warning Lights	Standard Three	RP	LP/RP
12	Engine Instruments	Checked	RP	LP/RP
13	Air Conditioning	As Required	RP	RP
14	Emergency Brakes	Normal	RP	LP
15	Parking Brakes	Off	RP	LP

			READ BY	ANSWERED BY
16	Toe Brakes	Exercise	RP	LP
17	Parking Brakes	Set	RP	LP
18	Cabin Clear	Received	RP	LP
19	Wheel Checks	Removed	RP	LP
20	Taxi Clearance	Received	RP	RP
21	Parking Brakes	Off	RP	LP
22	Taxi Light	On	RP	RP
			Checklist Complete	

This system has proven effective whether two pilots are involved, or one pilot issues both the challenge and the response.

A useful way to improve the effectiveness of challenge and response is to SAY, LOOK and TOUCH.

Saying each item out loud stimulates the sense of hearing and helps focus attention. From this, a pilot can monitor his own actions and prevent confusion and distraction in high-stress situations.

LOOKING helps ensure that variation between the checklist instruction and the control position or instrument reading, will show up immediately.

TOUCHING involves the third 'doing' sense. The physical act of the pilot touching the item, whether operating or checking it, completes the focus of attention.

Using the challenge and response method is useful in countering stress, fatigue, divided attention and the old enemy, complacency.

Pacing the Checklist

Using the checklist to the best advantage can be accomplished by proper pacing:

- Complete appropriate checklists as soon as possible to avoid interference caused by high density traffic, bad weather, minor aircraft technical problems and stress.
- Don't let attention-dividing situations put you behind the aircraft.

Pacing is extremely important when using abnormal and emergency checklists. Going through a critical checklist too fast can have very serious consequences. There are many recorded instances where perfectly good engines have been shut down by flight crews rushing into the emergency checklist before the real problem was identified. Few emergencies require *immediate* action.

The first and primary objective when faced with an emergency situation is to fly and control the aircraft. Then you can safely identify the problem, perform any memory items and use the appropriate emergency checklist methodically and accurately.

The points made here apply equally well to single-pilot operations. An effective self-challenge and response technique is very helpful to ensure all checklist items are covered. In fact, whether you are flying single or multiple crew, if you talk to yourself and begin hearing answers, then you have learned well, you are not going crazy!

Limitations to Checklists

One important point that should be clearly understood is well worth restating. The checklist is not a substitute for lack of knowledge of systems, aircraft performance and operating conditions. Without the knowledge, even the meticulous use of the checklist can lead to a great many problems. A technical malfunction may be incorrectly identified and the wrong checklist used to deal with it. This might easily compound the problems, make the emergency much worse, and could easily lead to serious consequences that would endanger the safety of the aircraft. Obviously there is not a checklist for *every* imaginable problem that might occur. Checklists do not fly the aircraft.

Summary

The use of checklists:

- Assists in checking or verifying that the aircraft and equipment are in the correct configuration.
- Initiates and directs communication and related activities.
- Provides a list of items or procedures designed to guard against failures of the human memory, particularly in times of stress and divided attention.

The concepts outlined here apply regardless of the size or technical complexity of the aircraft, the type of checklist used, or the composition of the flight crew.

We *can* train to be safe, and we *can* develop both our cockpit management skills and our situational awareness. But no matter what the situation, the best safety device in any aircraft is a well-trained crew. Safety does not just happen – you make it happen.

Chapter 2

The Facts You Need to Know About Asymmetric Flight

There is no mystery about asymmetric flight, or the aerodynamic and performance problems associated with it. However, in my experience as an instructor and check pilot, many professional pilots I have tested do not have an adequate general proficiency level, or understanding of the factors associated with single-engine operations.

The only way to develop skill in handling single-engine emergencies is by *continued* practice. An annual or biannual review of all the procedures is not enough. In professional flying even a six-monthly revision is hardly adequate to maintain the flying sharpness required. This is particularly important in STOL operations, where a high level of pilot proficiency and skill is a major factor in surviving an engine-out emergency from a really short airstrip with an obstacle climb-out procedure. The margin for error in airspeed and aircraft controllability is so narrow that only a really sharp pilot will cope efficiently with an actual emergency in these circumstances.

Competent pilots will therefore plan their *immediate* actions if one engine fails during or after take-off. They will be completely familiar with the aircraft performance and limitations (including accelerate-stop distance versus take-off distance available) covered in the STOL section of this book, with an explanation of associated factors.

General Considerations

The general techniques used for flight on asymmetric power are common to jet, turboprop and piston aircraft, and vary only in engine handling procedures, which can be found in individual aircraft Flight Manuals. We are looking only at the general principles of asymmetric flight in this book, with more detail on those aspects of vital importance in STOL flying.

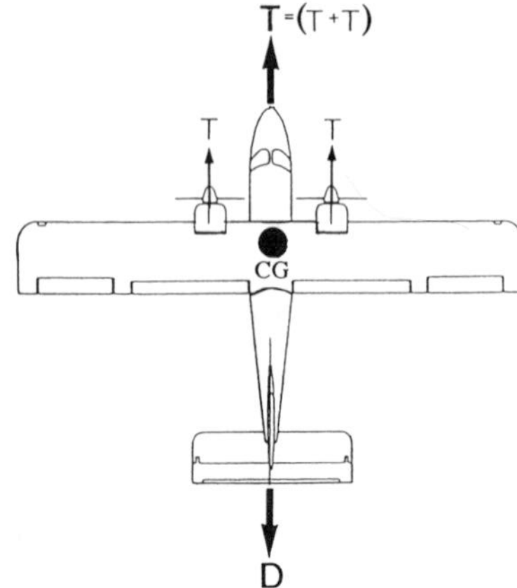

Figure 2.1 Balanced Thrust

The Basic Problem

In normal flight as seen in Figure 2.1, the thrust of both engines (**T**), is the combined total of the thrust from both engines (T) acting along the fuselage centreline. The forces are balanced and no yawing tendency exists.

In multi-engine aircraft with engines mounted on the wings, any imbalance of thrust about the NORMAL AXIS causes YAW see Figure 2.2. Therefore when an engine fails, the thrust is reduced compared to that of the live engine and is displaced to act through the position of the live engine (also refer to later paragraph on the critical engine) through the moment arm (x) and drag (D) via moment arm (y). The aircraft yaws towards the failed engine.

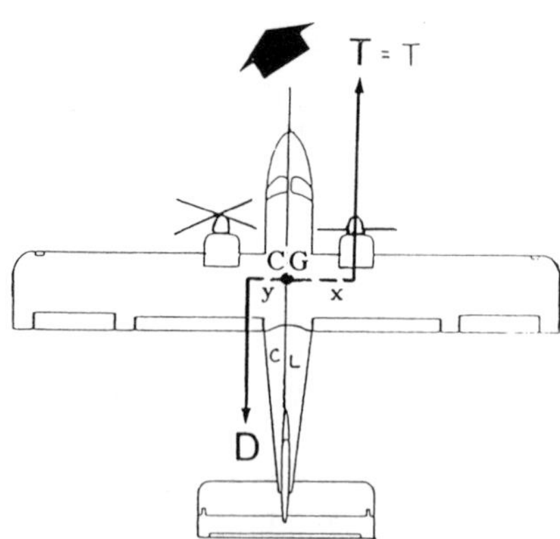

Figure 2.2 Yaw

A rolling moment is then generated in the same direction because of a reduction in slipstream velocity and lift over the wing with the failed engine.

If no corrective action is taken the aircraft would spiral into the ground.

Summary

When an engine fails the aircraft:

- Will YAW towards the failed engine.
- Will ROLL and SIDESLIP towards the failed engine. (Aircraft behaviour will subsequently depend upon its lateral and directional stability characteristics.)
- Nose will PITCH DOWNWARDS and enter a spiral dive.

Corrective Actions

The yawing moment is the real problem and the answer is the *immediate* and *positive* use of the RUDDER.

Any move to counteract the roll with aileron must be resisted, as it is at the stall or in an incipient spin. Drag generated by the down-going aileron (on the wing with the failed engine) could accelerate the yaw.

In the same way, pulling back on the ELEVATOR to try and stop the nose falling is the wrong action, for two reasons:

- Any consequent reduction of IAS amplifies the asymmetric thrust (YAW) effect of the live engine.
- With a developing spiral dive, use of the elevator will simply wind it up further.

The severity of the yaw will depend on:

- The amount of thrust being delivered by the live engine.
- The thrust moment arm (critical engine).
- The amount of offset drag (windmilling or feathered propeller).
- The indicated airspeed.

THE EFFECTIVENESS OF THE RUDDER IS OF PRIME IMPORTANCE TO THE PREVENTION AND CONTROL OF YAW.

During single-engine flight the large rudder deflection necessary to counteract the asymmetric thrust results in a *lateral lift* force on the vertical tail fin. This lateral *lift* represents an unbalanced side force on the aircraft, which must be overcome by allowing the aircraft to accelerate sideways (sideslipping), until the lateral drag caused by the sideslip equals the rudder lift force.

Figure 2.3 shows that the yawing moment due to thrust (Tx) has been

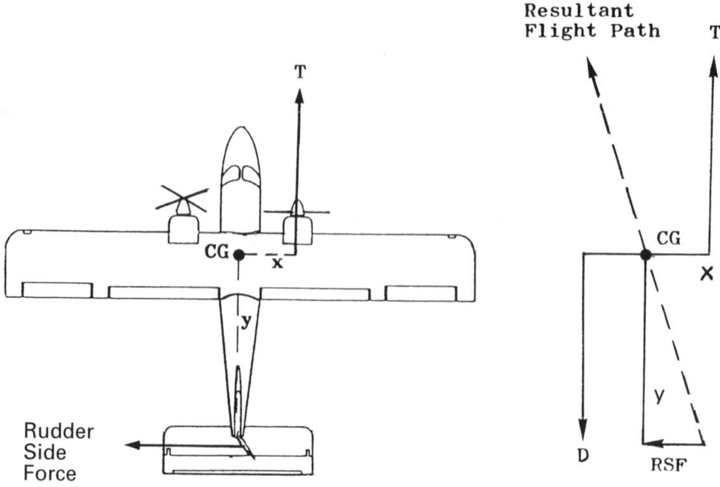

Figure 2.3 Rudder Side Force

balanced by the rudder side force (RSF) acting through arm (y). The aircraft yawing moments are therefore balanced and the aircraft under control with further yaw prevented, i.e. slip-ball centred, wings level, but there is a constant sideslip as shown in Figure 2.4.

It must be emphasised that this angle of sideslip is very small, around 2°–4°, but the 'sideslipping method' of dealing with an engine-out situation has several major disadvantages, both aerodynamic and practical.

- The relative wind blowing on the inoperative engine side of the vertical tail fin tends to increase the asymmetric moment caused by the engine failure.
- The resulting sideslip severely degrades stall characteristics.
- The greater rudder deflection required to balance the extra moment and sideslip drag, cause a significant reduction in single-engine climb capability (by as much as 300 FPM). It also reduces the aircraft acceleration capability.

Figure 2.5 shows the final balance of forces.

By considering all the factors, we can now conclude that asymmetric flight controlled by the 'sideslipping' method – wings level and slip-ball centred, is certainly not the best way to fly. Although from the pilot's point of view it is certainly easier. So what is the alternative?

After regaining control of the aircraft by use of rudder and aileron, with the

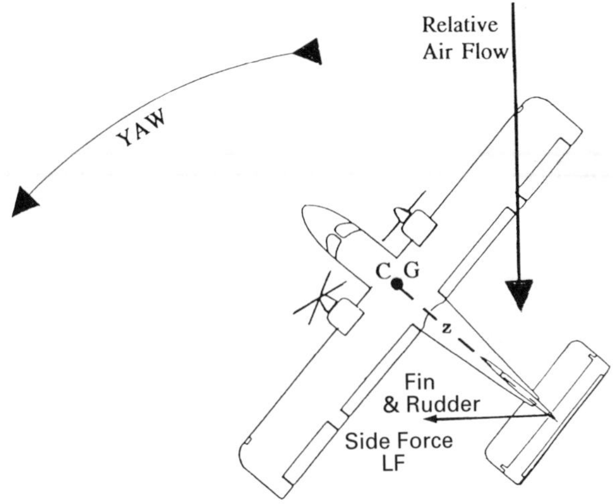

Figure 2.4 Effect of CG Location on Yaw

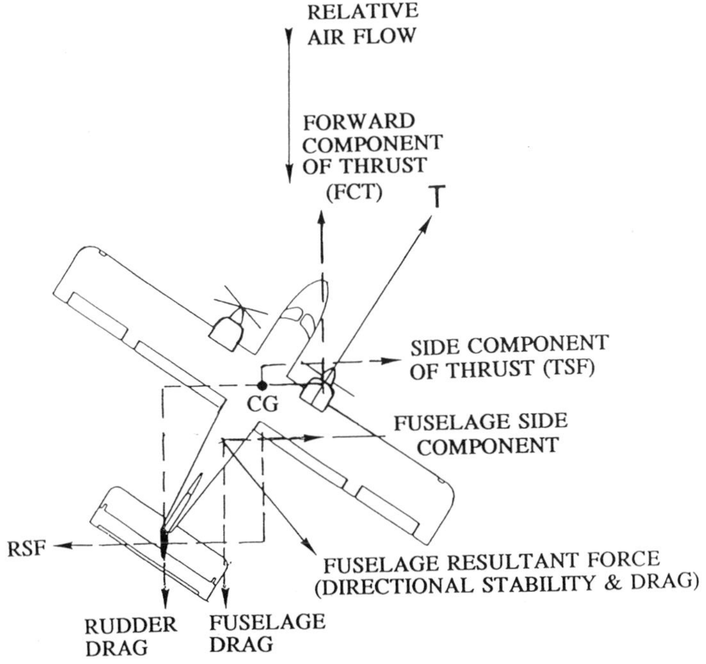

Figure 2.5 Summary of Forces

slip ball centralised, apply up to 5° of bank towards the live engine. (see Figure 2.6)

A lift side force is produced which acts towards the live engine and balances the rudder side force. By holding the angle of bank as accurately as possible the horizontal forces will be balanced, as in Figure 2.7, and the *slip-ball* will be around one ball diameter towards the lower side of the tube and the *live engine*.

Plenty of asymmetric practice using this method is required to obtain the desired accuracy.

Remember that the bank required is inversely proportional to the aircraft weight, and therefore varies.

If anything other than very small angles of bank are applied, the angle of attack must be increased to maintain the value of the vertical component

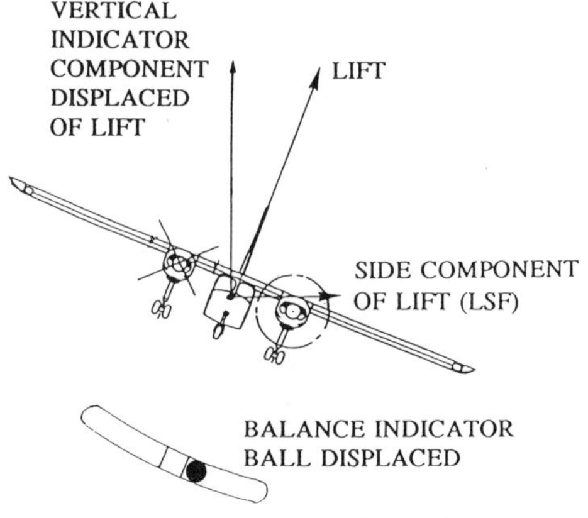

Figure 2.6 Producing a lift side force

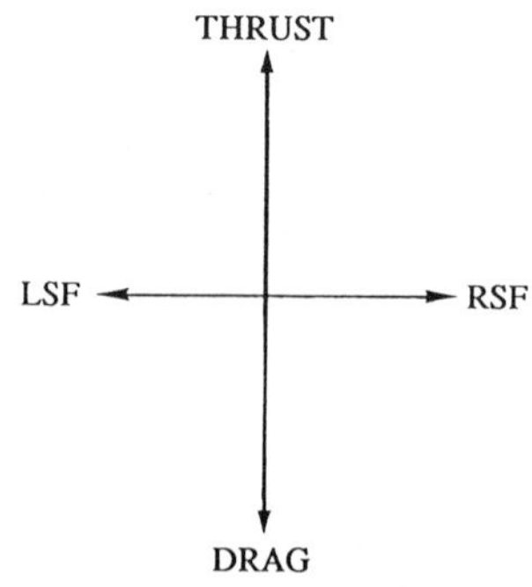

Figure 2.7 Horizontal Forces

of lift equal to the aircraft weight. This means more drag and a proportional increase in thrust to overcome it. This will obviously make the asymmetric situation worse.

At each angle of bank the pilot must judge the correct deflection of the slip ball which gives balanced flight.

With too much or too little bank applied, the aircraft will sideslip towards or away from the live engine.

Rudder Effectiveness

As we know, the rudder is the main control to counteract the yaw produced in an engine-out situation, and rudder effectiveness is therefore very important and depends on several factors:

- The indicated airspeed.
- The angle of deflection of the rudder.
- The rudder moment arm (distance of rudder from the CG).
- The size of the rudder, and the combined lift characteristics of the fin and rudder.

In an asymmetric situation at a constant power setting, a certain rudder deflection is required to counteract the yawing moment. So if the IAS is progressively reduced, the rudder deflection must be increased to produce the required rudder side force, as in Figure 2.3.

If the thrust or power of the live engine is increased, more rudder deflection must be used to overcome the increased yawing moment.

The required rudder deflection is therefore directly proportional to the thrust or power of the live engine, and inversely proportional to the IAS.

Use of the Rudder Trimmer

Like all trim devices, the rudder trimmer can easily balance out any rudder foot loads for the pilot in normal circumstances, but it does have limitations in an asymmetric situation.

This is because the normal rudder trim tab acts *by being deflected in the opposite direction to the rudder*, and thus *decreases the rudder effectiveness.*

In the case where a pilot is able to apply full rudder, and then uses the *rudder trimmer* to alleviate the foot load, a rudder trim tab will make the situation worse, i.e. by *slightly increasing the critical speed.*

Critical Speed

Definition: Critical speed is the lowest indicated airspeed on a multi-engined aircraft at which, at a constant asymmetric power setting and aircraft configuration, an individual pilot is able to maintain directional control. Note: *Critical speed* is not to be confused with V_{mc} (minimum single-engine control speed), which is covered later in this chapter.

Factors Affecting Critical Speed

The factors which affect critical speed are:

- The power output of the live engine.
- Which engine has failed (the critical engine).
- Loading. The position of the centre of gravity.
  Note: This is very important in STOL flying. The yawing moments act around the CG, so if it is moved forward *the CG – rudder moment arm will be increased and the rudder will be more effective*. Every bit helps in the event of an engine failure out of a STOL airstrip. However, it is not desirable to have the CG, and therefore the weight, too far forward, as the aircraft will not unstick as readily in a STOL take-off. Overall controllability will also be adversely affected. (See Figure 2.9 V_{MC} explanation).
- Drag. The position of the undercarriage and flaps.
- Asymmetric Drag. The propeller of the failed engine feathered or windmilling. On certain aircraft, asymmetric drag can be increased by aileron drag.
- Bank. Towards the live engine (5° max.).
- Slipstream Effect of Propellers. The slipstreams from the two propellers strike the fin and rudder at two different angles. One propeller tends to produce a sideforce from the fin which acts to assist the rudder side force needed to counteract the yawing moment. The other propeller produces a fin side force which acts in opposition to the rudder side force. It is apparent from this that failure of the first engine would result in a more critical situation than failure of the second. *Result: A higher critical speed.*
- Asymmetric Blade Effect of Propellers. At high angles of attack associated with low IAS, the propeller disc is tilted in relation to the airflow and the downgoing blade will produce more thrust than the upgoing blade.
  Note: This is fully explained in The Critical Engine – 'P-factor', which follows this section.
- Strength, Leg Length and Skill of the Pilot. The foot loads required to fly an aircraft at high asymmetric power or thrust, particularly at a low IAS, are high. So the physical strength and leg length of the pilot determines whether or not full rudder can be applied. If not, the situation will be serious, resulting in a higher critical speed.
  Seat position is also important and the skilful pilot will be better able

to directly control the aircraft than a less experienced one, who may be distracted by other events or actions both inside and outside the cockpit. (See section on Practical Cockpit Management – Situational Awareness in chapter 1). Therefore I stress once more, frequent asymmetric practice is essential to maintain personal flight proficiency.

The Critical Engine and the 'P-Factor'

When viewed from behind, most multi-engine aircraft propellers rotate clockwise. So the point through which the total thrust that each propeller acts will be displaced to the *right*, (see Figure 2.8). Because of this the starboard engine will produce a greater yawing moment than the port. In this case the *port engine* is referred to as the *Critical Engine.*

The 'P-factor' is caused by the dissimilar thrust of the rotating propeller blades in certain flight conditions. It is the result of the downward-moving blade having a greater angle of attack than the upward-moving blade – when the relative wind striking the blades is offset from the thrust line (as in a high angle of attack).

At low airspeed and high power, the downward-moving propeller blade of each engine develops more thrust than the upward-moving blade. This asymmetric propeller thrust, or *'P-factor'*, results in a centre of thrust at the right side of each engine as shown by lines P1 and P2 in Figure 2.8.

The turning, or yawing force of the right engine is greater than the left engine, because the centre of thrust (P2) is much further away from the centreline (CL) of the fuselage, as it has a longer lever arm.

So when the right engine is operative and the left inoperative, the turning, or yawing force is greater than in the opposite situation.

When the *critical engine* fails directional control is more difficult.

V_{MC} (Minimum Single-Engine Control Speed)

Definition: V_{MC} is that speed at which, in the event of sudden engine failure on a multi-engine aircraft, the pilot can stop the turn which results within 20 degrees of the original heading and, after recovery, hold a straight heading with no more than 5° of bank towards the live engine and full rudder.

Light to medium twin-engine aircraft have their particular single-engine minimum control speed given in the approved aircraft Flight Manual. This is determined during the manufacturer's type certification flights.

How to Establish and Maintain V_{MC}

In an engine-out situation, once the aircraft has been brought under control (wings level and slip-ball in the centre), bank the wings 5° towards the live

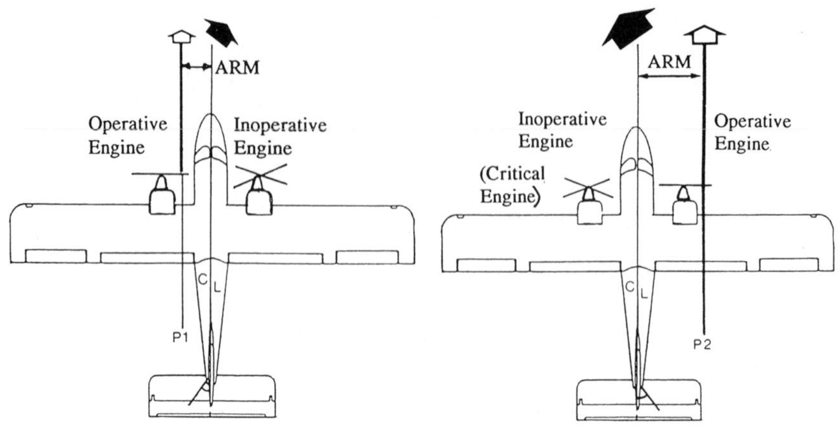

Figure 2.8 Forces Created During Single-Engine Operation

engine. This will place the slip-ball one diameter out on the same side as the live engine. Banking into the operative engine therefore reduces the V_{MC}. Note: For those curious aviators who might be wondering what happens if you bank *away* from the operative engine, the answer is – it *increases* V_{MC} at around 3 knots per degree of bank angle.

It is also worth remembering that holding the ball of the turn and slip indicator in the centre, while maintaining heading *with wings level*, can drastically increase V_{MC} up to 20 knots in some aircraft.

Be vigilant – guard against losing control of the aircraft. This can easily happen at a critical moment, particularly for the unwary or inexperienced pilot who suddenly finds he cannot control further yaw with rudder. The rudder is probably already at full deflection and the yaw is made worse by a decreasing airspeed. If he tries to pick up the dropping wing with aileron, the downgoing aileron on the wrong side will cause a sudden increase in (aileron) drag.

If an asymmetric stall should occur in this condition and no action is taken, there will be a violent roll towards the dead engine and the aircraft could easily spin. Any such situation can be avoided by keeping the airspeed above V_{MC} at all times during simulated or actual single-engine operation, and the aircraft will then always be controllable.

V_{MC} versus Altitude

For an aircraft with unsupercharged engines, V_{MC} decreases as altitude is increased. Therefore directional control can be maintained at a *lower* airspeed than at sea level. The reason is that since power decreases with altitude, the thrust moment of the live engine decreases, thus lessening the need for the rudder's yawing force.

Since V_{MC} is a function of power, it is possible for the aircraft to reach a stalling speed prior to loss of directional control. (Covered in the section on V_{MC} demonstrations later in this chapter).

There is a certain density altitude above which the stalling speed is greater than the single-engine minimum control speed. If the density altitude happens to be at or near ground level, because of elevation or ambient temperature, an effective V_{MC} flight demonstration will not be possible. Indeed, one should not even be attempted. Flight instructors and check pilots are advised to give a verbal briefing on the significance of V_{MC}, emphasising the dangers of trying to attempt flying below this speed in an engine-out situation.

How to recognise an imminent loss of control and the recovery techniques are covered in the section on V_{MC} demonstrations.

Effect of CG Position on V_{MC}

When the centre of gravity is on the rearmost limit, V_{MC} is higher. We know that the aircraft rotates around its CG, and the moments are measured using the CG as a reference datum.

A rearward CG would not affect the thrust moment, but it would shorten the moment arm to the centre of the rudder's horizontal 'lift'. This would mean that a higher airspeed would be required to counteract the single-engine yaw. An exaggerated plan view of the effect of a rearward CG is shown in Figure 2.9.

In light twins the CG range is short therefore the effect on V_{MC} is comparatively minor, although it should not be ignored. I have questioned pilots about this, and many only consider the rear CG in relation to pitch stability. They

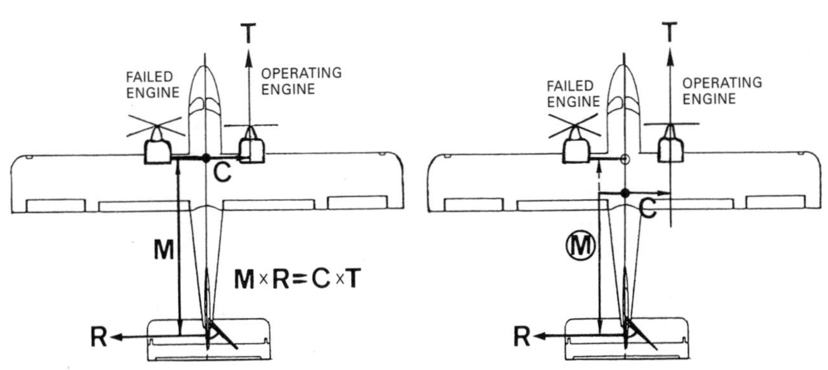

Figure 2.9 Effect of CG Location on Yaw

seemed unaware it could affect the aircraft *controllability* in a single-engine situation.

For STOL operations in aircraft such as the DH Caribou, DHC 6 Twin Otter and Short's Skyvan, it's an entirely different story. The CG position is of vital importance when considering all the other factors.

V_{MC} Demonstrations

Extreme V_{MC} demonstrations are not normally included in pilot training and flight tests, as they are at the very lower edge of the aircraft flight envelope and occur only in the most adverse circumstances.

Prior to any pilot checkout on a type where V_{MC} is given in the Flight Manual, it is essential that a thorough review of the factors affecting the minimum single-engine control speed is covered.

Being able to control the aircraft close to V_{MC} is essential in STOL operations, as it could save your life. This is why I am covering this in some detail here.

It is advisable that all V_{MC} demonstrations take place at a reasonable altitude above the ground, so that a safe recovery can be made if there is a loss of control. (Completion of pre-aerobatic – pre-stall HASELL checks is a normal routine precaution).

Two demonstrations are essential to show that there is a clear cut difference in V_{MC} between the two 'engine-out' aircraft configurations. The first with the wings level, the ball centred and sideslip. The second by banking 5° towards the live engine to eliminate the sideslip. This will show the minimum single-engine control speed for the prevailing conditions and emphasise beyond doubt the lower V_{MC} by banking into the live engine.

I stress at this point that all initial V_{MC} demonstrations should be flown dual under the supervision of a flight instructor, with no attempt to match the V_{MC} limits established during manufacturer type demonstrations.

So how do we do it?

- Set the propellers to max (fully fine) RPM, with landing gear retracted and flaps at the take-off setting. Then place the aircraft into a normal climbing attitude, speed at V_2 and rated take-off power on both engines.
- Reduce the power on the *critical engine* to idle and let it windmill; do not shut it down. Maintain heading, accept the asymmetric foot loading and ignore the rudder trimmer.
- Use the elevators to help reduce the speed, but avoid too high a nose attitude.
- At the exact point where you cannot maintain directional control, note the IAS. This is your V_{MC} for the critical engine.
- Reduce power on the live engine and lower the nose to regain directional

control. Then repeat the exercise but use 5° bank towards the live engine. Note the lower IAS at the moment you start to lose directional control.

- Recover to normal climb and repeat as required for practice, using the 5° of bank into the live engine method.
  WARNING: If you experience any indications of a stall prior to reaching the point where you cannot maintain directional control, immediate and positive recovery action must be taken. In this event, a minimum single-engine control speed demonstration is not possible under the existing conditions.

As well as being able to control the aircraft in a steady climb attitude close to V_{MC}, it is essential for the pilot to practise control of the aircraft following a sudden simulated engine failure, at or close to the published single-engine minimum control speed. Initially, this can be practised at a safe altitude in a training area, then during take-off on a long runway. In this way confidence and proficiency will be developed. Flight training in STOL operations includes intensive work on this exercise.

CHAPTER 3
WEIGHT AND BALANCE

Is your aircraft correctly loaded and safe to fly?

An overweight aircraft, or one with the centre of gravity outside its limits, is a potential accident looking for somewhere to happen. Flying a DC-3 in Central Africa some years ago, I discovered exactly what could happen when both those parameters were grossly exceeded! Except I was lucky.

The Dak was on charter to a major oil company to carry personnel, supplies and spare parts to a drilling rig in a remote area of Chad. An experienced dispatcher supervised the loading of the aircraft and brought me the completed load sheet for signature. It passed muster, no problem – or so I thought.

Finally I checked the security of the cargo, especially the straps holding a large diesel generator in place. Everything seemed okay, but I had missed one important item. Another error that would compound the chain of events to follow.

When I taxied out I remarked to my French copilot that the aircraft felt unusually heavy, requiring more power than normal to get it rolling. The real problem arose when we attempted to take off. Even at METO power we only started to move sluggishly down the runway. Within seconds I realised beyond any doubt we were not going to get airborne. And the high density altitude caused by an ambient temperature of 36°C had nothing to do with it, because the tailwheel would hardly rise even with considerable forward pressure on the control yoke. I aborted the take-off and taxied back to the ramp knowing something was very wrong.

On investigation I discovered we were grossly overloaded. Added to that the large generator had moved, gradually inching its way aft along the smooth steel freight floor of the cabin (sloping tail wheel aircraft) slipping the tie-downs as we started to move. It was certainly enough to make a considerable difference to the centre of gravity and thus the handling characteristics of the aircraft. Unfortunately there were no passengers on that particular flight who might have warned us of the danger.

The diesel generator, which was the major item of cargo, had been listed on the load sheet by the dispatcher as weighing 2000 lbs (our load sheets were made out in pounds). However, the generator was French and the plaque on the side stated *2,000 kilos – 4,400 lbs!*

What was a glaringly simple error by an experienced dispatcher (familiarity breeds complacency syndrome, see chapter 1 Practical Cockpit Management), could have turned into a nasty accident. Added to that the generator had not been suitably chocked at the aft end as a routine precaution against slippage (that was what I had missed). The type of straps securing the generator, although suitable for the weight listed on the load sheet, were totally inadequate for an item *over twice as heavy*.

For a long time after that, I broke into a cold sweat every time I thought about what could have happened had we actually managed to get airborne!

A salutary lesson was learnt by all.

Conditions for Controlled Flight

Having seen what can go wrong when an aircraft is incorrectly loaded, let us now consider the conditions that must exist for *controlled* flight at a given speed:

- The aircraft must be properly balanced within its centre of gravity limits, not exceeding the weight limitations, and stable.
- The overall pitching moment caused by wing, lift, drag, thrust, weight and tailplane lift, must be zero. (This can be obtained by variations in angle of attack, elevator angle and airspeed).
  The centre of gravity has a FORWARD and AFT limit, so the aircraft can be operated safely at a CG anywhere within these limits. It is when the aircraft is flown outside those limits that a whole range of problems occur.

The Effects of Improper Loading (see Figure 3.1)

The CG too far forward causes:

- Nose heaviness which must be corrected by application of elevator control.
- A tendency to nose in after take-off, and difficulty in getting the tail down on landing.
- An increase in drag, since elevator trim is required, and therefore more power is needed for a given speed.
- An increase in fuel consumption.
- A decrease in range.
- A lack of controllability if the movement of the Centre of Pressure materially alters the lift/weight couple.

Lateral imbalance will cause wing heaviness

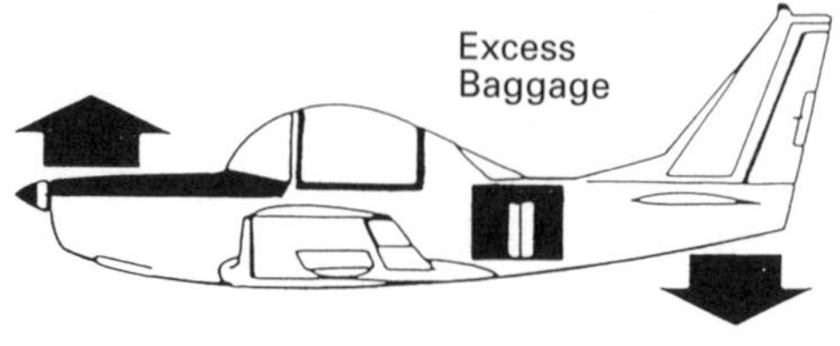

Longitudinal imbalance will cause nose or tail heaviness

Figure 3.1 Lateral or Longitudinal Imbalance

The CG too far aft causes:

- Tail heaviness, which must be corrected by application of elevator control.
- A tendency for the tail to stay down on take-off, or drop on landing.
- A tendency to stall, because tailplane moment has been reduced.
- An increase in drag since elevator trim is required, and therefore more power is needed for a given speed.
- An increase in fuel consumption.
- A decrease in range.

An out of balance condition for any STOL operation can lead to severe control problems that are extremely hazardous.

The Effects of Overloading

Excessive weight reduces the performance of an aircraft in almost every area. The most important deficiencies of the overweight aircraft are:

- Higher take-off speed.
- Longer take-off run.
- Reduced rate and angle of climb.
- Less manoeuvrability.

- Higher stalling speed.
- Increased possibility of the airframe structural limits being exceeded.
- Lower service ceiling.
- Shorter range with increased fuel consumption.
- Reduced cruising speed.
- Higher landing speed.
- Longer landing roll.
- Increased wear and tear on brakes and tyres.

Weight and Balance Definitions

Every pilot needs to be thoroughly familiar with the terminology relating to all aspects of aircraft loading. These terms are reasonably well standardised throughout the aviation industry, although some terms relating to general aviation do not apply to airlines operating heavy aircraft.

Centre of Gravity (CG or C of G).
The point from which an aircraft would balance if suspended. This is the theoretical point at which the entire weight of the aircraft is assumed to be concentrated. Its distance from the CG datum point is found by dividing the Total Unbalanced Moment by the Gross Weight of the aircraft. This may be expressed in inches from the reference datum, or as a percentage of MAC (mean aerodynamic chord) for larger aircraft.

Centre of Gravity Limits.
The specified FORWARD and AFT, or lateral points for the centre of gravity. These limits must not be exceeded during the entire duration of any flight, and are laid down in the aircraft Flight Manual and weight and balance records. They conform to the requirements of the civil aviation regulatory authorities in the aircraft's country of registry.

Centre of Gravity Range.
The distance between the forward and aft CG limits laid down in the aircraft Flight Manual and on other appropriate official aircraft specifications.

Arm (Moment Arm).
The horizontal distance in inches from the reference datum line, to the centre of gravity of a specified aircraft station, i.e. seat position, cargo or baggage hold. The algebraic is PLUS (+) if measured AFT of the datum, and MINUS (-) if measured FORWARD of the datum.

Datum or Reference Datum.

This is an imaginary vertical plane or line from which all measurements of arm are taken. This datum is established by the manufacturer. Once this datum is set, all MOMENT ARMS and the location of the permissible CG range must be calculated with reference to that point.

Delta.

A Greek letter expressed by the symbol Δ. It is used to denote a change of values. For example, Δ CG shows a change, or movement, of the CG.

Moment

The result of the WEIGHT of an item multiplied by its ARM. Moments are expressed in INCHES-POUNDS (IN-LBS), or POUNDS-INCHES (LBS-IN). TOTAL MOMENT is the aircraft WEIGHT multiplied by the DISTANCE between the datum and the CG. (see Figure 3.2)

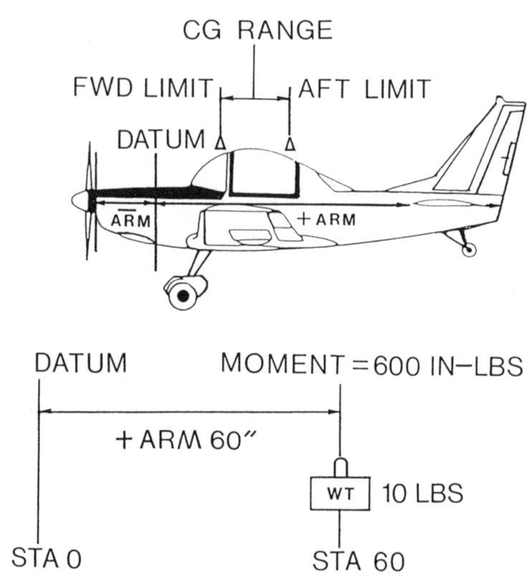

Figure 3.2 Moment

Moment Index, or Index.

A moment divided by a constant such as 100, 1,000 or 10,000. The reason for using a moment index is to simplify weight and balance calculations of large aircraft, where heavy items (such as palletised cargo and baggage) and long moment arms produce large unmanageable numbers.

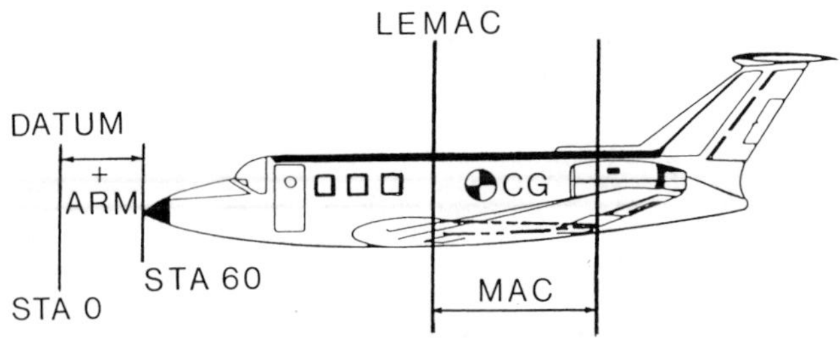

Figure 3.3

Mean Aerodynamic Chord (MAC)

The average distance from the leading edge to the trailing edge of the wing. The MAC is specified for the aircraft by determining the average chord of an imaginary wing which has the same aerodynamic characteristics as the actual wing.

LEMAC

The leading edge of the mean aerodynamic chord.

Reduction Factor

A constant which, when divided into a moment, results in an INDEX. Reduction factors of 100, 1,000, or 10,000 are used to simplify the actual process of weight and balance calculations.

Basic Weight (sometimes called the Tare Weight)

The weight of the aircraft and all its basic equipment and that of the declared quantity of unusable fuel and oil. In the case of turbine engined aircraft and aircraft of 12500 lbs (5700kg) maximum all up weight or less, it may include the weight of usable oil. (See Figure 3.4)

Basic Equipment.

This includes the weight of crew and baggage plus removable units and other equipment, the carriage of which depends upon the role for which the operator intends to use the aircraft.

Disposable Load.

The weight of all persons and items of load including fuel and other consumable fluids, carried in the aircraft other than the basic equipment and variable load. (See Figure 3.4)

Operating, or Aircraft Prepared for Service (APS) Weight.
The sum of the basic weight and the total variable load required for the particular role for which the aircraft is to be used.

Maximum All-Up Weight.
The maximum permitted total weight of the aircraft and its contents in accordance with the Certificate of Airworthiness in force.

Maximum Ramp or Taxi Weight
The maximum take-off gross weight, plus fuel to be burned during taxi and run-up.

All-Up Weight on Take-Off.
The actual total weight for a particular take-off. (see Figure 3.4)

Regulated Take-off Weight.
The maximum weight at which the aircraft can take off under the regulations considering the ambient conditions and the runway in use.

Maximum Landing Weight.
The maximum weight at which the aircraft may normally be landed. (See also Regulated Landing Weight).

Regulated Landing Weight.
The maximum weight at which the aircraft can land under the regulations considering the ambient conditions and the runway in use.

Empty Tank Weight or Zero Fuel Weight.
The total weight of an aircraft ready for take-off including crew, passengers, freight, etc, but excluding fuel. (see Figure 3.4)

Fuel Load.
The expendable part of the aircraft load. It includes only usable fuel; not that which is stated to be unusable and remains in the tank sumps or fuel lines to the engines.

Standard Weights.
These have been established for a whole range of items involved in weight and balance computations. It is stressed that the weights are not used for every flight, or in lieu of available actual weights.

In particular, standard passenger weights should not be used in computing the weight and balance of charter flights. Also, other special services which

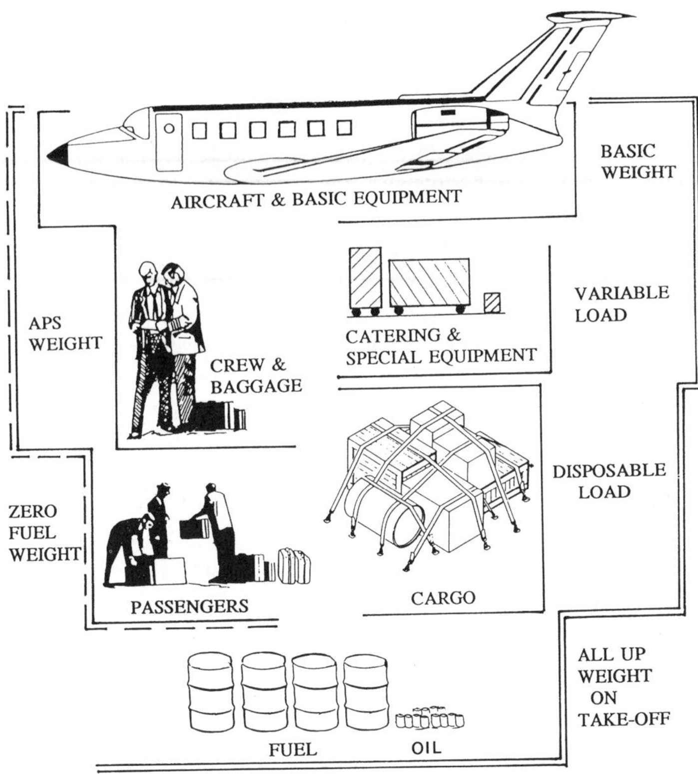

Figure 3.4 Load and Weight Definitions

involve sporting groups, or passengers originating from countries having a population who are generally small in stature.

All cargo and baggage *must* be weighed, and the total of these ACTUAL weights entered on the aircraft load sheet.

No attempt is made to include a list of standard weights here, as they do vary slightly from country to country. For example, some airlines add a set amount of kilos onto the passenger weight to allow for hand baggage.

Legislation

The weighing and calculation of an aircraft's CG is a matter which vitally affects the safety of the aircraft. All aspects of it are therefore covered by legislation which may be summarised as follows:

- The aircraft shall be weighed and copies of the Weight and Centre of

Gravity schedule and, where appropriate, the Weight and Balance Report shall be provided.

- The Weight and Centre of Gravity Schedule shall be signed by a representative of an approved organisation or a person suitably qualified and acceptable to the aviation authority. A statement shall be included indicating that the Schedule supersedes all earlier issues.
- According to the nature of a modification, the Weight and Centre of Gravity Schedule shall be amended or replaced by a revised Schedule.
- The commander of an aircraft shall satisfy himself or herself, before the aircraft takes off, that the load carried by the aircraft is of such weight and is so distributed that it may safely be carried on the intended flight.

Balance, Stability and Centre of Gravity

In STOL flying it is even more important for us to know *how* our aircraft behaves under all conditions.

BALANCE refers to the location of the CG of an aircraft. It is of prime importance to the stability and safety in flight. Pilots should never fly an aircraft if they are not *personally* satisfied with its loading and the resulting weight and balance condition.

The CG is the point about which an aircraft would balance if it were possible to support the aircraft at that point. The CG is therefore sometimes referred to as the 'pivotal point', or mass centre of the aircraft and is referred to officially as the CG DATUM. It is the theoretical point at which the entire aircraft weight is assumed to be concentrated.

An aircraft cannot be loaded and balanced on one point, as the CG is continually changing in flight as fuel and oil are consumed. So safe forward and aft limits are set by the manufacturer to take care of these variations. The limits for each aircraft are contained in the Pilot's Operating Handbook, Flight Manual or Weight and Balance (CG) Schedule.

Any attempt at flying outside the CG limits, means you would be operating in an area where the aircraft's handling has not been investigated. This could vary from unsatisfactory to just plain dangerous, *so don't do it.*

Note: You can also invalidate your insurance.

FAA and CAA regulations require that all aircraft have a valid Certificate of Airworthiness (C of A) or Permit to Fly. These documents either directly, or as stated in a Flight Manual/Pilots Operating Handbook, specify the limits within which the aircraft must be operated. If these limitations are not observed the pilot-in-command is failing to comply with a legal condition for the operation of the aircraft. Insurers could reject any claim in the event of an accident (caused by the pilot) which violates the CG-LOADING limitations, claiming that the C of A has been invalidated.

In order to calculate the aircraft state of balance, the *CG reference datum* (a fixed point) is used. The distances of all load items are then measured from this datum.

The combination of the *weight* of each load item and its *distance* from the CG datum give a measure of its 'turning' effect expressed as '*moments*'. When the *Total Unbalanced Moment* about the *CG Datum* is divided by the *Total Weight* of the aircraft, the resulting *lever arm* is the distance from the datum to the *Centre of Gravity*. If the CG lever arm falls within the forward and aft limits of the CG, the LOADING OF THE AIRCRAFT IS SATISFACTORY. But if the lever arm places the CG outside the limits, the aircraft load must be adjusted so that it falls within the limits.

Stability

In addition to balance (CG) the other vital and inter-related area is STABILITY. As the name implies, stability concerns an aircraft's ability to return to its normal in-flight position after a disturbance, *without any control correction.*

Stability is measured about the three axes of the aircraft as shown in Figure 3.5 and may be of three types.

- Positive – the body returns to original position.
- Neutral – the body adopts a new and constant position relative to the original.
- Negative – the body continues to diverge from original position.

If after a disturbance the aircraft moves back to its original position, it is considered *statically stable*. If the deviation (disturbance) from original position tends to die out with time, the aircraft is *dynamically stable*, and vice versa. So if any oscillation tends to remain constant the aircraft is *dynamically neutral*. Note that in roll, aircraft are *statically (neutrally) stable* and there is a damping effect in roll with increased altitude.

Let us consider the stability that most affects the centre of gravity.

Longitudinal Static Stability (Stability in PITCH)

In static stability it is assumed that no control corrections are made to correct any deviation from the flight path. This is called 'stick fix' stability. Longitudinal stability is achieved by the tailplane and for this reason it is often called the HORIZONTAL STABILISER.

Figures 3.6 shows the variations of stability with variable positions of the centre of pressure (CP) and centre of gravity (CG).

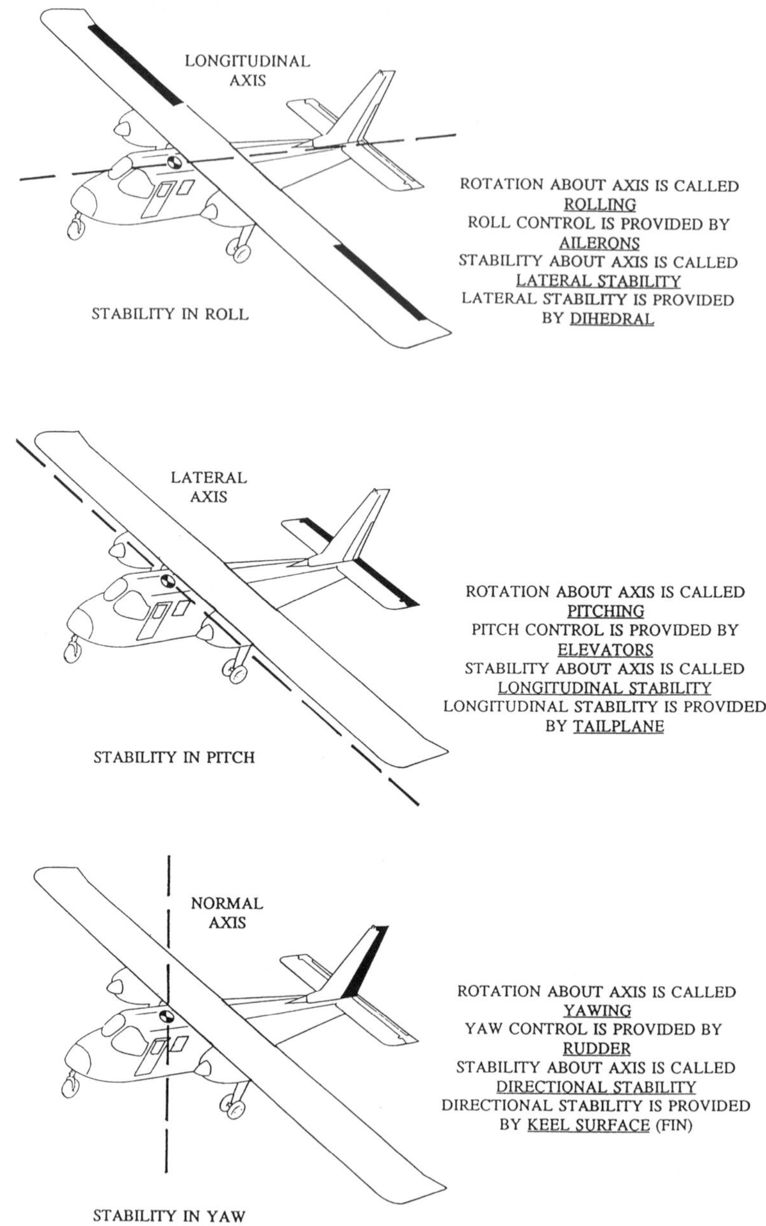

Figure 3.5 Measurement of Stability

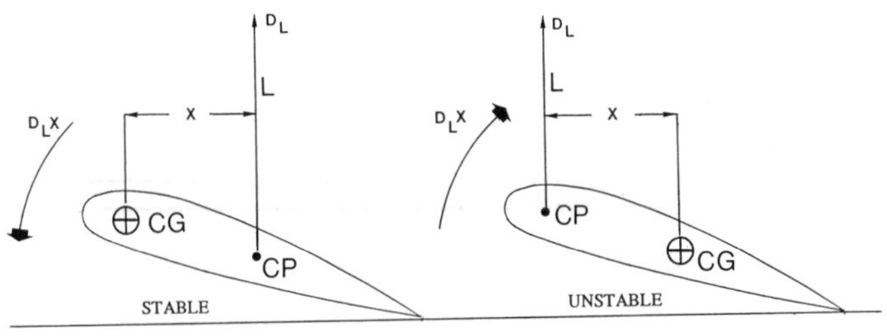

Figure 3.6 Longitudinal Static Stability Figure 3.7

In Figure 3.7 the CP is forward of the CG by distance X. Nose up displacement will increase the angle of attack, thereby increasing lift (L) by D_L, and increase the pitching moment by D_LX. The result is to increase the nose-up displacement – *an unstable effect.*

It is therefore apparent from Figure 3.6 that a similar displacement with CP and CG positions reversed will have a stabilising effect.

The pitching moment is also affected by movement of CP(L) with angle of attack. Therefore the relative positions of CP and CG will determine the stability of the wing. In the worst case the wing may be unstable, therefore the tail or horizontal stabiliser must be designed to overcome the instability.

Summary

The position of the CG affects the degree of stability; forward movement *increases* positive stability; aft movement *decreases* positive stability.

- LONGITUDINAL stability is about the *lateral axis – stability in PITCH.*
- LATERAL stability is about the *longitudinal axis – stability in roll.*
- DIRECTIONAL stability is about the *normal axis – stability in yaw.*

Therefore the CG position will affect the handling characteristics in pitch.

Lateral Stability

Lateral stability is often referred to as *dihedral effect*, although there are other important contributions. DIHEDRAL ANGLE is the upward inclination of the wing to the plane through the *lateral axis.*

Different parts of the aircraft structure contribute to the overall value of *lateral static stability*. These contributions will vary in accordance with flight conditions and aircraft configuration. They may be positive or negative, but the overall value should be positive.

Positive contributions include:

- Wing dihedral.
- Wing sweep angle.

(These two factors cause the dihedral effect which is pendulous on large aircraft – LATERAL (STATIC) STABILITY.)

- Wing/Fuselage interference effect, depending on wing position.
- Fuselage and fin keel surface effect.
- Pendular stability due to the relative positions of CG and the lift vector, depending on wing position.

Negative contributions include:

- Undercarriage position (makes lateral stability less positive).
- Flap settings make the aircraft laterally less stable. (With flap down the centre of pressure (CP) moves inwards along the wing towards the fuselage. This reduces the moment about the longitudinal axis, although design of the flaps can be used to control the contribution).

Knowing what happens to the flight characteristics of your aircraft will make you a better and *safer* pilot. It will also help you in your overall proficiency for STOL operations.

You can test your knowledge by completing the stability quiz at the rear of the book.

The Centre of Gravity

Aircraft operating manuals will always give the permitted range of movement of the CG. The FORWARD position is determined mainly by manoeuvre capabilities; of greater importance though is the aft limit. If the CG is moved sufficiently AFT, a position will be reached where wing moment (increasing) is equal to tail moments (decreasing). At this point the restoring moment is zero, the aircraft being neutrally stable. This position of *zero restoring moment* is known as the *neutral point*. The AFT limit of CG, as quoted in aircraft manuals, is *forward* of the neutral point.

The distance through which the CG can be moved aft (from a quoted datum) to the neutral point, is known as the *static* or *CG margin*. This is an indication of longitudinal stability, i.e. the greater the margin the greater the stability. Figure 3.8 shows the static margin relative to the CG limits and the neutral point. The bigger the static margin the more stable the aircraft is.

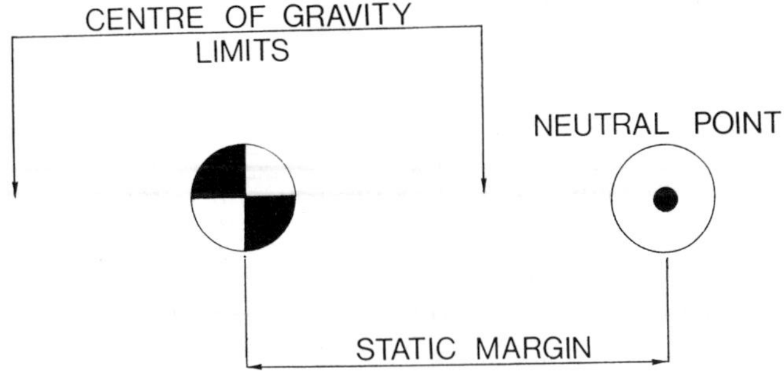

Figure 3.8

Forward Centre of Gravity

Loading in a nose-heavy direction causes problems in controlling and raising the nose. This can be particularly critical during take-off and landing.

It certainly may be possible to maintain stable *cruising* flight ahead of the manufacturer's forward limit. But as landing is one of the most critical phases of flight, the forward CG limit is often set at a location determined by the landing characteristics of the aircraft and is placed further aft to avoid the possibility of damaging the aircraft when landing.

Having a restricted forward CG limit ensures that the pilot has sufficient elevator movement (deflection) available at *minimum airspeed*, such as in the 'landing flare'.

When aircraft structural limitations – or large stick forces – are not a limiting factor to the forward CG position, it is located at the position where *full* UP elevator is required to obtain the relatively high angle of attack necessary during landing.

If the elevator has to produce a down load balancing force, this effectively increases the aircraft weight. So to maintain level flight at the same speed, the angle of attack must be increased to maintain lift. The increase in drag is known as TRIM DRAG.

Summary

The forward CG is limited to ensure full controllability with the elevators during landing. However a forward CG will mean that:

- Control deflections to manoeuvre will be greater.
- Stick forces will be greater.
- The stalling speed is higher.
- A great deal of *trim drag* will be created.

- The aircraft is TOO STABLE, although safe to fly.
- The wing lift needs to be greater than the weight, when the CG is fully forward.

Aft Centre of Gravity

An aft CG limit is the most rearward position at which the CG can be located for the most critical manoeuvre or operation. As the CG moves aft, a less stable condition occurs, which degrades the aircraft's ability to return to its original flight path after manoeuvring or after displacement by turbulence. Therefore having an aft CG, or loading in a tail-heavy direction, has a very serious effect on *longitudinal stability*. It can even escalate to the point of preventing recovery from stalls and spins.

Summary

An aft CG leads to:

- *Longitudinal instability*.
- Extreme tail heaviness which can prevent recovery from stalls and spins.
- A reduction in the elevator angles (control deflections).
- A reduction in stick forces.
- A lower stalling speed.
- Less trim drag.
- Wing lift less than the weight.

(Note: Outside the aft limit the aircraft is Neutrally Statically Stable until the Neutral Point. Beyond this it is Unstable.)

The *forward* and *aft* CG limits and the permitted range of movement are primarily based on the effectiveness of the elevators (or horizontal stabiliser), to control the aircraft in pitch at the point of stall – the lowest speed.

Calculation of Centre of Gravity

Having already considered many important aspects of weight and balance, it is essential to understand the basic principles and calculation of the aircraft CG. After all, this is the lynchpin and culmination of the whole exercise.

With an actual load sheet you are merely adding and subtracting numbers in a formulated pattern. The final result is an interpolation of an index graph to ensure the CG falls within the CG envelope, or a simple mathematical exercise which results in an actual CG. The understanding of where the basic weight and balance data originates is often not properly understood. It is common practice for private and commercial pilot students to be taught merely to pass the examination, not to have any really adequate knowledge of the subject. Weight and balance is not merely the calculation of the aircraft CG, it is a far more complex subject and mistakes can easily prove fatal.

In fact during oral examinations of pilots, I have found a significant percentage actually have an inadequate knowledge of basic CG calculations. So even *with* a load sheet, a standard problem like a last minute load shift posed a real problem.

When the basic aircraft weight, lever arms and moments have been calculated, it is straightforward to work out the effect of adding fuel, cargo, etc. This is done by adding the weights of these items to the *aircraft basic weight*. The moment of the additional items can then be added to the *aircraft basic moment*. Dividing the resultant moment by the total weight gives the CG of the loaded aircraft.

The final answer can be resolved by simple arithmetic, a loading graph and centre of gravity envelope. Figures 3.9 to 3.11 show the process involved in calculating the weight and balance for a light single-engine aircraft.

SAMPLE LOADING CALCULATION

		WEIGHT (Kg)	MOMENT (Kg.m)
1	Empty weight (includes unusable fuel, full oil and other fluids) as well as extra equipment and navaids	662	663
2	Fuel 139 litres at 0.72 kg/litre (standard tanks)	100	*120*
3	Pilot and front passenger	150	*140*
4	Rear passenger	80	*150*
5	Baggage or child's seat (54 kg max)	40	*100*
	TOTAL WEIGHT AND MOMENT	1032	*1173*

* The Moments are obtained by applying the known weights to the loading graph in Figure 3.10.

Figure 3.9

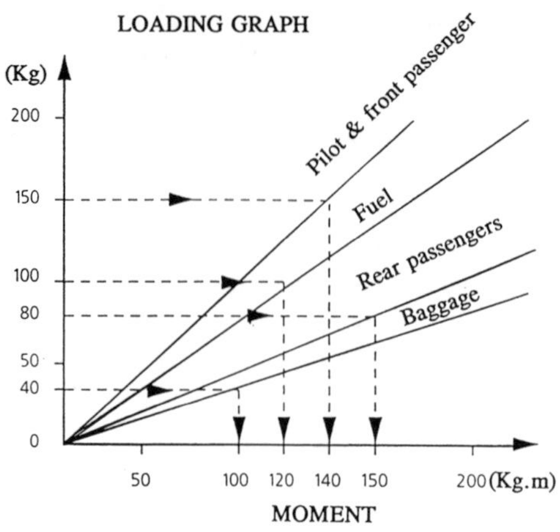

Figure 3.10

A CG can also be calculated using a standard load sheet as in Figure 3.12 for the SC7 SKYVAN. Here the moment arms are given for the passenger seat (or cargo) compartments. Again the CG is computed by arithmetic.

Figure 3.13 is a variation in the load sheet for a TWIN OTTER SERIES 300, FREIGHT CONFIGURATION. This is called the 'drop-line' format. The pilot starts at the top and works logically downwards until reaching the CG envelope. Any point inside the shaded perimeter is within the acceptable CG limit. This type of load sheet is widely used by airlines, high-density seating commuter operators and for STOL aircraft.

The third example (Fig. 3.14) shows the load sheet for the 30 passenger seat SHORT's SD3-30. This load sheet is in actual airline service and is easy to use. The final calculation within the CG envelope – bottom right-hand corner – only requires interpolation of passengers versus loaded index (LI), having first worked through the various compilation of weights. The point at which the actual CG intersects the continuous and dotted lines (showing numbers 1-9 on each), represents the maximum and minimum number of passengers that can be carried in Section A of the cabin. *This is towards the rear and therefore affects the AFT CG, a sensitive area as we have proved earlier.*

Some companies make up their own load sheets to cater for particular types of operation, but they are merely variations on a theme. More, or less, information might be presented, but they all arrive at the same conclusion – the ACTUAL CG OF THE AIRCRAFT.

Some heavy transport aircraft have the facility for the crew to observe an instantaneous CG read-out on a CG position indicator. This type of instrument expresses the CG in terms of percentage of Mean Aerodynamic Chord.

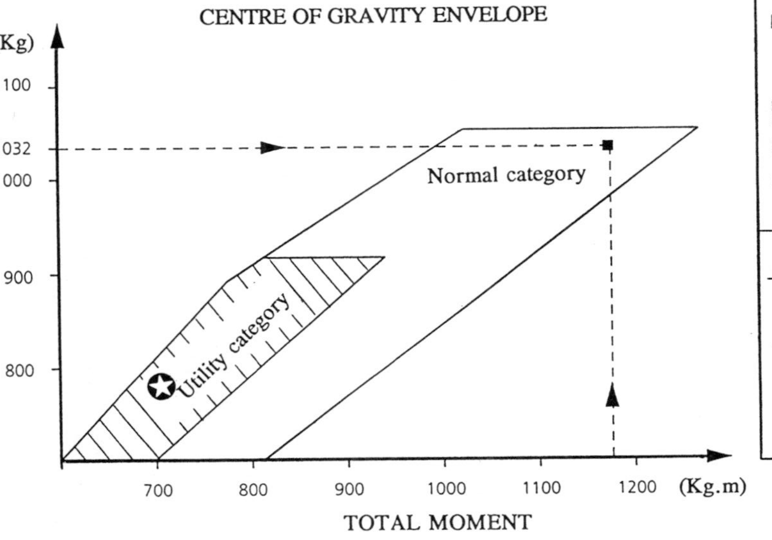

WEIGHT LIMITATIONS

Normal category

Maximum weight for take-off	1043 kg
Maximum weight for landing	1043 kg
Maximum weight for baggage or optional child seat	54 kg

Utility category

Maximum weight for take-off	907 kg
Maximum weight for landing	907 kg

FUEL CAPACITIES

2 Standard tanks of	81.5 litres	(21.5 US gallons)
Total fuel	163 litres	(43 US gallons)
Total usable fuel	152 litres	(40 US gallons)
Unusable fuel	11 litres	(3 US gallons)

✪ Restricted envelope for aerobatics (if permitted), spinning and other manoeuvres which may include steep turns.

Figure 3.11 In this example it can be seen that the weight is below the maximum allowed and the CG is within limits

LOAD SHEET

SKYVAN SC7

DATE .... CHARTERER ....

REGISTRATION .... FROM .... TO ....

CAPTAIN: ....

FIRST OFFICER: ....

			WEIGHT IN POUNDS	NEGATIVE MOMENT 1000/LBS/FT	POSITIVE MOMENT 1000/LBS/FT
AIRCRAFT Basic weight		WEIGHT & MOMENT	9400		16351.33
		MAX WEIGHT			
COMP'T A 2 (pilots)	(X 5.667)	1300 LBS	300	1700.10	
COMP'T B 3 PASSENGERS	(x 3.625)	1900 LBS	150	543.75	
COMP'T C 3 PASSENGERS	(x 1.208)	1900 LBS			
COMP'T D 3 PASSENGERS	(x 1.208)	1900 LBS	935		1129.48
COMP'T E 3 PASSENGERS	(x 3.625)	1900 LBS	935		3389.37
COMP'T F 3 PASSENGERS	(x 6.042)	1900 LBS			
COMP'T G 3 PASSENGERS	(x 8.458)	950 LBS			
COMP'T H 2 PASSENGERS	(x 10.896)	950 LBS			
ZERO FUEL WEIGHT			11720	2243.85	20870.18
FUEL IMP GALLS X .8 (1600 lbs x 0.03)	(x 0.03)	LBS	1600	NEGATIVE MOMENT 1000/LBS/FT	+48.00 20918.18 −2243.85
TAXI A.U.W.			13320	RESULTANT	18674.33

$$\text{C OF G} = \frac{\text{RESULTANT MOMENT}}{\text{ALL UP WEIGHT}} = \frac{18674.33}{13320} = 1.401 \text{ FT}$$

C OF G LIMITS + 0.833 TO + 2.083 FT

hereby certify that the aircraft has been loaded in accordance with the written loading instructions contained on the Loading Chart.

Signed: ....

Figure 3.12 Load Sheet

SERIES 300 TWIN OTTER FREIGHT VERSION

GROSS WEIGHT COMPUTATION					
BASIC WEIGHT					
CREW					
CREWS BAGGAGE					
EXTRA EQUIPMENT					
OPERATIONAL WT EMPTY▽					
FREIGHT					
WEIGHT LESS FUEL					
FUEL					
TAKE OFF GROSS WEIGHT					
FUEL USED					
LANDING WEIGHT					

INDEX FORMULA

$$10 + \frac{\text{BASIC WT(H.ARM} - 210)}{10\,000}$$

$$\text{INDEX} = 10 + \frac{(\qquad - 210)}{10\,000} =$$

BASIC INDEX 2 4 6 8 10 12 14 16 18

	Location	WT - LB	Scale
	NOSE		100
	CREW		100
	C - 1		100
	C - 2		100
	C - 3		100
	C - 4		200
	C - 5		300
	C - 6		500
	C - 7		200
	C - 8		100
	C - 9		100
	C - 10		100
	C - 11		100
	Baggage		100
	SHELF		100
* FUEL	FWD		100
* FUEL	REAR		100
* FUEL	Uniform Distr		300

* FOR WING TANK FUEL USE UNIFORM FUEL DISTRIBUTION COLUMN

AIRCRAFT REGISTRATION:		DATE:
FLIGHT NO:	FROM:	TO:
CAPTAIN:		FIRST OFFICER:

% M.A.C.
20 22 24 26 28 30 32 34 36

GROSS WEIGHT
12500LB
12300LB
11600LB
10500LB
9500LB
8500LB
7500LB

PERMISSIBLE WEIGHT & C. G. LIMITS
LANDPLANE
WHEEL - SKIPLANE

BASIC INDEX 2 4 6 8 10 12 14 16 18

Figure 3.13

SHORT SD3-30/100

LOADSHEET and LOADMESSAGE

All weights in kilos

Dest.	No. of pass. Adults M	F	Ch	Inf	Cabin Bagg.	WEIGHTS - KGS TOTAL	Distribution Compts FWD		AFT		Remarks
						Tr					
						B					
						C					
						M					
					CB	T	F		A		TW
						Tr					
						B					
						C					
						M					
					CB	T	F		A		TW
						Tr					
						B					
						C					
						M					
					CB	T	F		A		TW
						Tr					
						B					
						C					
						M					
					CB	T	F		A		TW
TOTAL											Load Weight ←

Passenger Weight ——→ +

Total Traffic Load =

Dry Operating Weight +

Zero Fuel Weight =

Take-off Fuel +

Take-off Weight =

Max.

Trip Fuel -

Landing Weight =

Max.

Last Minute Changes

Dest.	Specification	Cpt	+/-	Weight
	LMC Total			

ALTN A	—
Min. Ramp Fuel Leg II B	
Arr. Fuel C	
EET D	

FUELING ORDER

TANK	REQUIRED LBS	US.G	ACTUAL ACC. TO FUEL GAUGES LBS
FWD			
AFT			
TOTAL FUEL			
		KGS	
TIME		REFUELED LITRES	

From	Originator	Address	Flight	A/C Reg.
Version	Crew	Prepared by	Approved by	

Date

FORWARD BAGGAGE COMPT

AFT BAGGAGE COMPT

1 2 3 4 5 6 7 8 9 10

Sect. A

FWD CARGO COMP. Weight	Index
0 - 11	0
12 - 33	-0.5
34 - 55	-1.0
56 - 78	-1.5
79 - 100	-2.0
101 - 122	-2.5
123 - 144	-3.0
145 - 167	-3.5
168 - 189	-4.0
190 - 211	-4.5
212 - 227	-5.0

FUEL Weight	Index
0 - 71	0
72 - 214	+0.5
215 - 357	+1.0
358 - 500	+1.5
501 - 642	+2.0
643 - 785	+2.5
786 - 928	+3.0
929 - 1071	+3.5
1072 - 1214	+4.0
1215 - 1357	+4.5
1358 - 1500	+5.0
1501 - 1642	+5.5
1643 - 1745	+6.0

AFT CARGO COMP. Weight	Index
0 - 10	0
11 - 27	+0.5
28 - 45	+1.0
46 - 64	+1.5
65 - 82	+2.0
83 - 101	+2.5
102 - 119	+3.0
120 - 137	+3.5
138 - 156	+4.0
157 - 174	+4.5
175 - 193	+5.0
194 - 211	+5.5
212 - 229	+6.0
230 - 248	+6.5
249 - 266	+7.0
267 - 272	+7.5

PASS. ON ROW 1 No. of PASS.	I corr.
1	-0.8
2	-1.6
3	-2.4

		INDEX -	+
TOTAL No. OF PASS.			
No. OF PASS. ON ROW 1			
No. OF PASS. BEHIND ROW 1			
LOAD IN FWD CARGO COMP.			
LOAD IN AFT CARGO COMP.			
FUEL			
DRY OPERATING INDEX (DOI)			
		=	=

LOADING LIMITATIONS	
Max. In Sect. A	
Min. In Sect. A	

L.I.

LOADED INDEX (L.I.)

15 20 25 30 35

No. of PASS. behind ROW 1

0 5 10 15 20 25

MIN. IN SECT. A

MAX. IN SECT. A

9 8 7 6 5 4 3 2 1 0

Figure 3.14

Multi-role Aircraft

In STOL flying, particularly where aircraft such as the Twin Otter are being used to operate into difficult and often remote areas, the role (configuration) of the aircraft can change from day to day. Passenger, passenger-cargo or all cargo.

The Twin Otter is regularly fitted with high-density seating for up to twenty passengers; a large number of seats in relation to the fuselage size. The loading problems are therefore more difficult. So it is even more important that the weight and balance limits for high-density seating aircraft are accurate.

In my own experience, the load carried can vary considerably from flight to flight. Some high-density seating aircraft have special weight and balance problems because they have been modified from older aircraft with a lesser seating capacity. I found that South America and Africa have many of these modified aircraft, which are sensitive towards the rear limit of the CG.

All pilots of high-density seating aircraft are well advised to make themselves thoroughly aware of the effect of passenger and cargo locations on the CG limits. I have always stressed that they must have a *personal* knowledge of how to recognise and correct out-of-limit conditions.

In remote locations there is often no-one to assist the pilot with loading problems – the command pilot also acts as loadmaster and dispatcher. Add to that heat (high density altitude), possibly monsoon weather, perhaps dealing with a foreign language, plus the general chaos of trying to sort out thirty or forty people all trying to board a high-density twenty-seat aircraft and you end up with a situation that should not be faced by an inexperienced, or *unaware* pilot.

In any commuter or air taxi operation, particularly in the STOL environment, pilots are involved with the problem of frequent trips and varying loads (passenger and cargo). They need to have a positive, *accurate* and fast method to compute the weight and balance (CG) data. This includes an *up-to-date aircraft basic empty weight* – not one made out ten or fifteen years previously at some obscure maintenance facility. Aircraft (like humans) tend to increase in weight with age!

Weight and Balance Restrictions

Every pilot, from private to airline transport, is obliged to follow each particular aircraft's weight and balance restrictions. The loading conditions and basic empty weight of an individual aircraft almost certainly differs from the one given in the aircraft manual, due to modifications or equipment changes since manufacture. Sample loading problems given in the manual (using the manufacturer's basic weight) are useful only as a guide. Each aircraft of the same type must be treated individually for weight and balance.

From experience we know that although an aircraft is certified for a specified maximum gross weight, it cannot safely take off at that maximum weight under all conditions.

It must also be realised that with most aircraft, it is not possible to fill all the passenger seats and to use the maximum baggage/cargo allowance at the same time, or to fill all fuel tanks *and* remain within the approved weight and centre of gravity limits.

Technical Knowledge Boosts Flying Skills

Knowing your aircraft and how it handles within the CG limits, can dramatically increase your ability to extract the maximum performance from your aircraft. My own knowledge was to prove invaluable during an emergency rescue take-off from broken, moving pack-ice of the Arctic Ocean near the North Pole.

I was the pilot to the all-French women's North Pole Expedition (see Figure 3.15). The aircraft was a ski-equipped, Twin Otter we had named the 'Pink Panther'. Our Norwegian engineer had stuck linoleum on the under surface of the skis. This was to give us better manoeuvrability on the snow-covered surface and to stop the skis freezing to the ice in the extreme sub-zero temperatures of –30°C.

The four women had put out an emergency radio call to say they were trapped on a drifting ice-floe approximately 300 metres (980 feet) long. It was situated in a large area of dangerous, broken, drifting ice piled into jagged ridges after a blizzard.

The rescue flight from our Norwegian island base of Svarlbard (Spitzbergen), stretched the range (and overload capacity) of the Twin Otter, even at higher military approved MAUW. Our extra range fuel supplies were carried in three 44 gallon drums, plumbed into the fuel system inside the cabin.

We found the women's camp on the ice-floe by using a combination of GPS and Mark 1 eyeball. The floating ice moves at the rate of about seven miles a day. There were already red dye markers out to highlight the tiny landing area, which was surrounded by a mosaic of broken ice and several open water leads (See Figure 3.16).

The STOL landing on the ice was bad enough, then the sudden, blinding flurry of powdered snow churned up by maximum reverse on the props. We stopped one aircraft length from the edge of the ice-floe.

Our Norwegian Air Force engineer/loadmaster and my copilot helped the four women as they scrambled into the aircraft. All their equipment had to be abandoned on the ice. Then we jettisoned everything we could, leaving only our survival kit. We wanted to be as light as possible because every kilo of weight decrease counted if we were to take off from the ice-floe. Our engineer

Figure 3.15
One of two de Havilland Twin Otters used on the French North Pole expedition. The wheel-skis are strong enough to withstand the battering of rough landings on the open pack-ice of the Arctic Ocean. Here parked on an emergency airstrip beside a frozen fjord in Svarlbard (Spitsbergen). The airstrip was used by the German Luftwaffe in WWII as a base for raids on the Allied sea convoys to Russia.

Although the expedition was French, the support personnel was truly multi-national. The statistics read as follows:

Twin Otter Captain (self)	British/Australian
Second pilot	Canadian
Crew Chief/engineer	Norwegian
Air Force Arctic survival expert	Norwegian
Second engineer	Greenlander (local)
Expedition members: (all women)	
Four	France (Metropolitan)
Two	French-Canadian
Primary Twin Otter	Norwegian
Standby Twin Otter	Danish

As the expedition members were ski-walking to the North Pole, all necessary equipment (including survival gear) had to be hauled on specially designed and constructed lightweight sledges. They took *rehydrated* packaged meals. This was the only option because of limited drinking water (the frozen Arctic Ocean is frozen salt water – remember!)

even managed to dump two of the fuel drums which were already empty.

I had mentally planned the take-off and had everyone move to the rear of the cabin (AFT CG). With the additional drag of the large skis, I needed to get the nosewheel (ski) off the ice as soon as possible and the aircraft into the air. After that we could fly in the 'ground effect' and accelerate. There were

Figure 3.16
Bad light and the cracked pack-ice of the Arctic Ocean at 0300 hours on the way to pick up the expedition members. Open water leads and disintegrating ice-floes are a dangerous combination to land on. Every landing and take-off feels like a real emergency.

no obstructions except ridges of broken ice some way ahead. And no worries about engine temperatures in –30°C, only torque limitations.

The plan paid off but it was close, the aircraft getting airborne only feet from the edge of the ice-floe. Apart from the actual STOL technique, I firmly believe that knowing and using the plus factors of an AFT CG in those circumstances gave us the performance edge. Riding the 'ground effect' is a two-edged sword and this subject is covered in the STOL TECHNIQUES section. But whatever else can be argued, a good technical knowledge of all the pertinent factors, plus constant practice, is the only way to improve your proficiency – especially in STOL flying.

Now I suggest you read through the summary about an AFT CG. It will help to put things into a practical perspective.

The weight for altitude and temperature (WAT FACTOR) often affects take-off and climb performance, requiring operation at a reduced weight. The *density altitude* is a key part of any calculation (see PERFORMANCE SECTION).

Other factors to consider, of course, are runway length and type of surface, slope, surface wind and any significant obstacles. This is also covered in more pertinent detail in the PERFORMANCE SECTION.

RULE OF THUMB: If in doubt – reduce the load.

Load Distribution

When an aircraft is issued with a flight manual, the following limitations and data are included:

- The maximum permitted weight.
- The empty basic weight and CG location.
- The useful load.
- The composition of the useful load, including the total weight of fuel and oil with full tanks.

If the available loading space is adequately placarded, or arranged so that no reasonable distribution of the useful load will result in the CG falling outside the stated limits, the flight manual will probably not include any information other than the actual CG limits. In other cases, the flight manual includes enough loading data combinations to ensure the CG falls within the correct limits.

Of course care should be taken in all aircraft loading, because most aircraft can be loaded in such a way that will place the CG outside the proper limits. Proper completion of an aircraft trim/load sheet for the particular type is the only way of making sure the aircraft is correctly balanced for flight.

Dangers of Loose Cargo

Following my own frightening experience in Africa recounted earlier, I consider it appropriate to cover basic principles and precautions for securing cargo. The unexpected movement of cargo or baggage during flight can lead to a dangerous out of balance condition. For instance, if the aircraft CG is already near the forward or aft limit, a significant LONGITUDINAL cargo shift could make control difficult or even impossible. This dangerous condition is most likely to happen when cargo has been poorly secured in the aircraft cabin. Great care must be taken to firmly restrain such items with *proper tie-down devices*.

Figures 3.17 and 3.18 show two standard methods of securing heavy cargo in the cabin of the aircraft. Figure 3.19 gives a suitable way of strapping cargo onto a passenger seat. The graph of Cargo Load versus Lashing Angle (illustrated at Figure 3.20) provides a quick and accurate reference to ensure the load is safely tied down.

The breaking strain of the ropes must be of suitable strength in direct relation to the weight of the cargo. *Any old length of rope found lying in the corner of the hangar will not do.* A box of cargo weighing 300 kilos breaking loose during turbulence, then hitting you on the back of the head while you are flying the aircraft, can give you more than a nasty headache!

Landing, and/or taking-off from a STOL airstrip imposes high stress

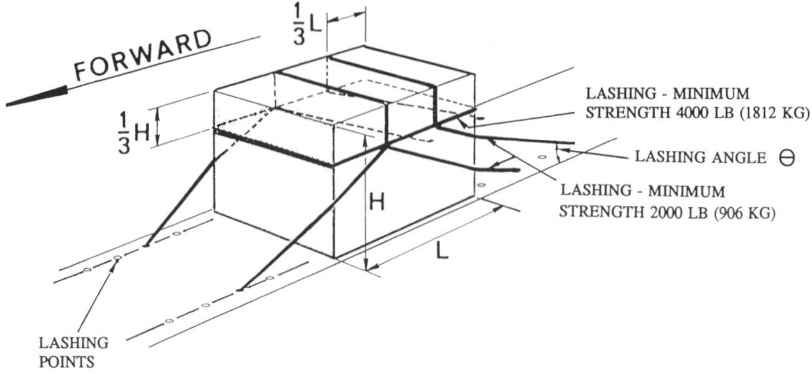

Figure 3.17 Cargo Restraint (1)

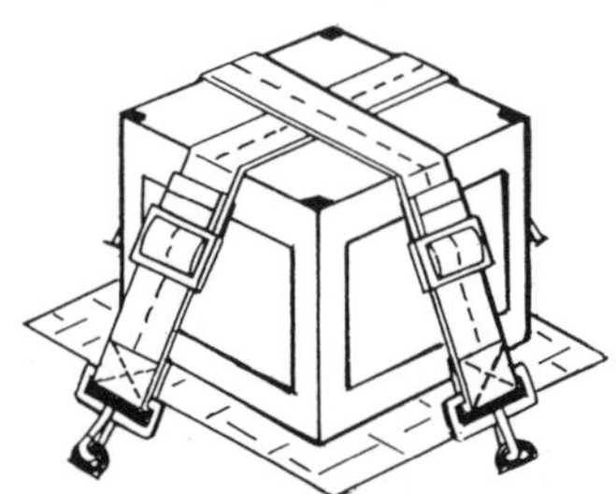

All heavy cargo should be firmly secured to the floor, using load spreader boards as required.

Figure 3.18 Cargo Restraint (2)

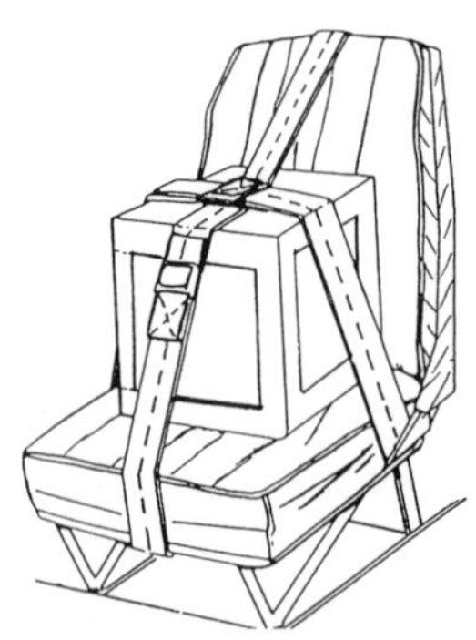

Cargo secured in passenger seat. Care should be taken not to exceed normal seat loading.

Figure 3.19 Cargo Restraint (3)

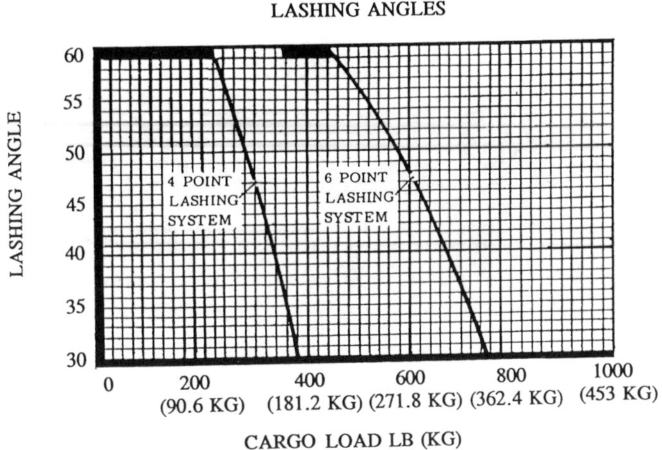

Figure 3.20 Cargo Restraint Details

factors on tie-down ropes and straps. Anything which is frayed or suspect must be rejected as unserviceable – your life may depend on it!

Also, if heavy concentrated loads are to be carried, it is prudent to check that the maximum floor loading of the aircraft is not being exceeded. If it is, load spreader boards will be required. The floor loading is published in the WEIGHT AND BALANCE section of the aircraft Flight Manual.

Weighing the Aircraft

In order to obtain the gross weight of a loaded aircraft it is first necessary to establish the BASIC EMPTY WEIGHT.

This can be accomplished by weighing the aircraft with accurately calibrated scales, the only sure method of obtaining a precise empty weight and CG location (a maintenance facility job). The type of equipment used varies with the size of the aircraft. Larger, multi-engine types are usually weighed with electronic weighing sets as shown in Figure 3.21, after the aircraft has been placed on suitable jacks.

As the aircraft ages, what is known as 'service weight pick-up' occurs. This will cause the basic weight and CG data to alter and become inaccurate. There always seems to be a 'weight pick-up', never the opposite. Re-weighing is particularly advisable in the case of older aircraft, or aircraft converted to high-density seating for commuter operators. A significant percentage of these types are used to fly into smaller airfields with restricted field lengths, or for STOL operations, so any unknown hidden kilos and a shift in balance, can

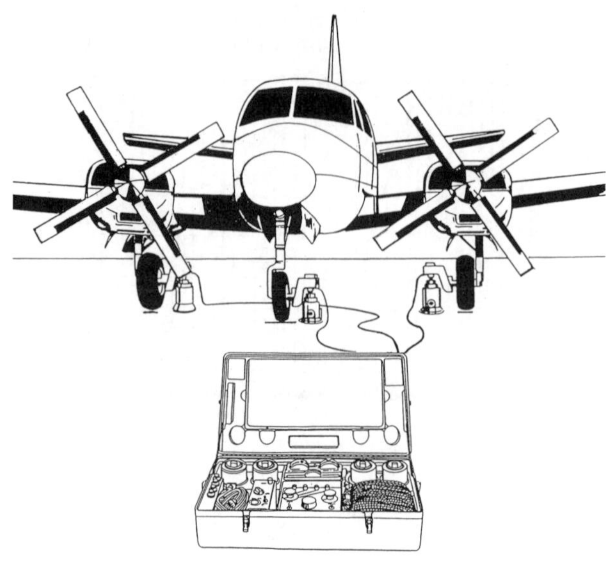

Figure 3.21 Electronic Weighing Kit

have a noticeably adverse effect on performance in an engine-out situation at or near maximum all-up weight.

The pilot or operator may never be directly involved in the weighing of an aircraft, but it is a good idea to be aware of how, but more importantly, *when* it should be done.

Quick Reference – Useful Loading-Weight & Balance Data

WEIGHT X ARM	=	MOMENT
MOMENT – WEIGHT	=	ARM
MOMENT ÷ ARM	=	WEIGHT
CG	=	TOTAL MOMENT / TOTAL WEIGHT

AIRCRAFT EMPTY WEIGHT X CG ARM	=	MOMENT
OIL WEIGHT X ARM	=	MOMENT
PILOT AND PASSENGER WEIGHT X SEAT (ARM)	=	MOMENT
PASSENGERS WEIGHT X SEAT (ARM)	=	MOMENT
BAGGAGE WEIGHT X COMPARTMENT (ARM)	=	MOMENT

FUEL WEIGHT X TANK (ARM)	=	MOMENT
AUX. FUEL WEIGHT X (ARM)	=	MOMENT

To Find:

- LOAD VARIATION
- TRANSFER OF LOAD
- WEIGHT TO MOVE
- OR MOVE CG

SHORT METHOD:
DIFFERENCE IN ACTUAL AND REQUIRED CG ARMS X TOTAL WEIGHT
DIFFERENCE IN HOLD ARMS

To Find New Location of CG

a) TOTAL WEIGHT X ARM
b) PLUS ADDITIONAL WEIGHT X ARM
c) ADD a AND b
d) CALCULATE NEW TOTAL WEIGHT
e) CALCULATE NEW CG

Load Removed

a) FIND CG (+MOM –MOM)
b) SUBTRACT LOAD (WEIGHT & MOMENT)
c) CALCULATE NEW WEIGHT
d) CALCULATE NEW CG

Added Load

a) MULTIPLY TOTAL WEIGHT X ARM
b) ADD ADDITIONAL WEIGHT X ARM
c) ADD a AND b
d) CALCULATE NEW TOTAL WEIGHT & CG

Conversion Table:

1 kg	=	2.205 lb	1 lb	=	0.454 kg
1 inch	=	2.5 cm	1 cm	=	0.394 inches
1 ft	=	0.305 m	1 m	=	3.28 ft
1 Imp gall	=	4.546 litres	1 litre	=	0.22 Imp gall
1 US gall	=	3.785 litres	1 litre	=	0.264 US gall
1 Imp gall	=	1.205 US gall	1 US gall	=	0.83 Imp gall

I carry a copy of all this data in my flight bag to cover any eventuality.

Calculation of CG Position

Consider a weightless beam resting on a central fulcrum point, the beam has a length of 10 units and a weight of 10 units is positioned at each end (see Figure 3.22).

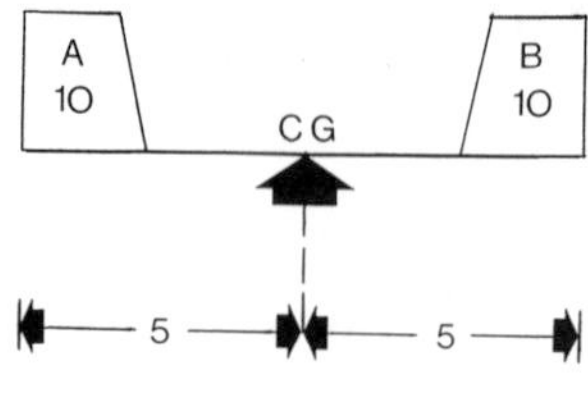

Figure 3.22

The CG is in the centre of the bar and the moments at either extremity are equal.

Weight A (10 units) x lever (5 units) = 50 (moment units)
Weight B (10 units x lever (5 units) = 50 (moment units)

If the position of the CG was unknown we could find it by taking moments from A and finding the total weight involved.

Weight (B) 10 x lever 10 = 100 (moment units)
Weight (A) 10 x Weight (B) 10 = 20 units.

$$\text{Arm of C of G} = \frac{\text{Total Moment}}{\text{Total Weight}}$$

$$= \frac{100}{20}$$

$$= 5 \text{ units of distance}$$

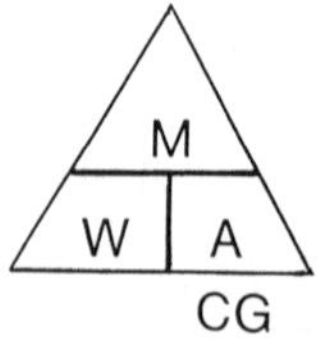

Figure 3.23

If arm = $\frac{\text{moment}}{\text{weight}}$

Then weight = $\frac{\text{moment}}{\text{arm}}$

And moment = Arm x Weight

Note that the total moment figure is always divided by something and never multiplied.

If we draw an aircraft around our simple beam we can use the same method to calculate the CG (see Figure 3.24 and 3.25). The nose wheel, or the nose of the aircraft, is used as a datum for the calculation, just as the end of the simple beam was used.

To find the CG from the nose wheel, we must know the total moments and the total weight.

Weight at nose wheel = 10 units of weight

Weight at main wheels = 10 units of weight

Total weight = 20 units of weight

Total moment = Weight x arm =

Weight at main wheels (10 units) x arm (10 units)

= 100 (moment units)

CG = $\frac{\text{Total moment}}{\text{Total weight}}$ = $\frac{100}{20}$

= 5 units of distance from the nose wheel

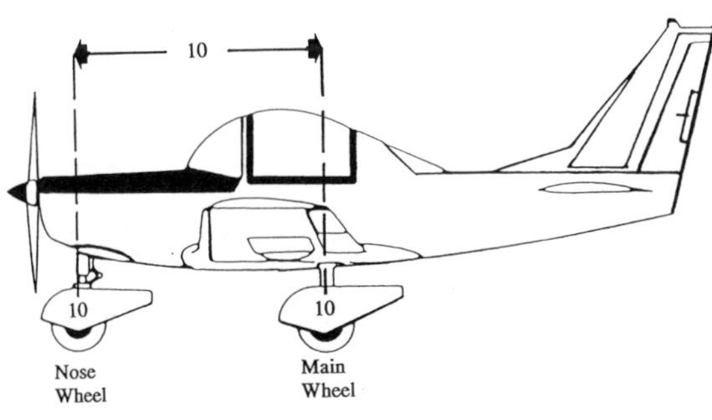

Figure 3.24

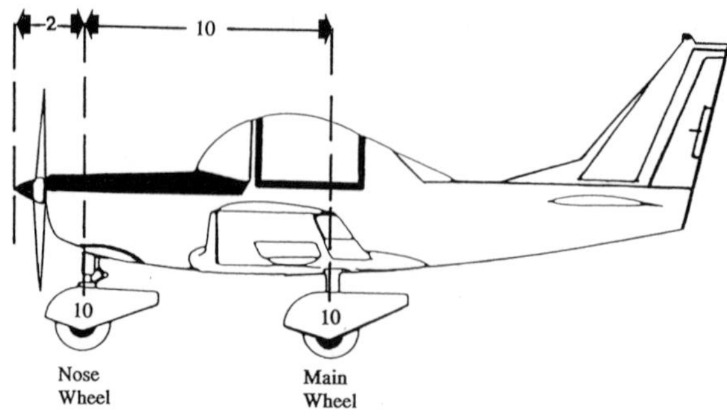

Figure 3.25

To find the CG from the nose of the aircraft, 2 units of distance ahead of the main wheels:

Once again we require $\frac{\text{Total moment}}{\text{Total weight}}$

Weight remains unchanged 10 + 10 = 20 units of weight

Taking moments from nose datum

Weight at nose wheel (10) x arm from datum (2) = 20 (moment units)

Weight at main wheels (10) x arm from datum (12) = 120 (moment units)

Total Moment = 140 (moment units)

$$\text{Arm of CG} = \frac{\text{Total moment}}{\text{Total weight}}$$

$$= \frac{140}{20}$$

= 7 units of distance from the nose datum

The CG position thus determined is exactly the same as that obtained by the previous method.

We know that the CG range of movement for an aircraft may be quoted in terms of distance from a CG Datum Point, which has been defined as a reference point from which all arms, or distances, are calculated. To find the CG position with respect to a CG datum, we still require to calculate the Total Weight and Total Moment.

Since we are calculating moments around a datum it is conventional to consider that all weights positioned aft of the datum give rise to POSITIVE moments and would cause our aircraft to pitch NOSE UP. Weights positioned ahead of the datum give NEGATIVE moments and would cause the aircraft to pitch NOSE DOWN. (See Figure 3.26)

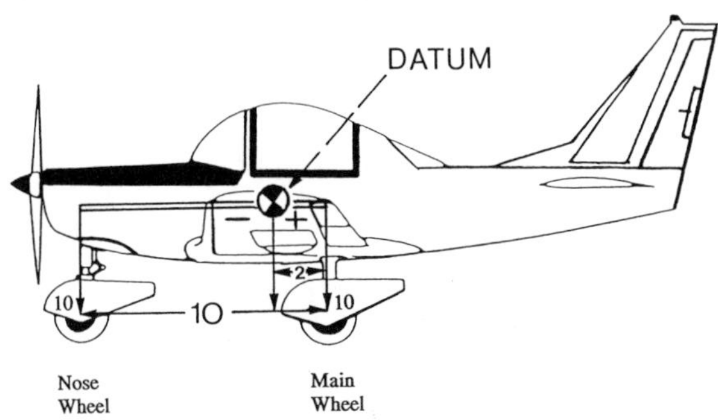

Figure 3.26

Datum Point = 2 units of distance ahead of the main wheels

Total Weight remains unchanged = 10 + 10 = 20 units of weight

Total Moment = (10 x (–8)) + (10 x (2)) = –80 + 20
= –60

$$CG = \frac{\text{Total moment}}{\text{Total weight}} = \frac{-60}{20}$$

= –3 units(3 units of distance ahead of datum)

Again the CG arm obtained is in precisely the same position as hitherto, although the method of calculation has changed.

Calculation of CG of a Loaded Aircraft

In order to calculate the CG of a loaded aircraft the basic weight and basic CG must be determined, but now the weightless beam has become an aircraft. First, the aircraft must be weighed and the required arms calculated.

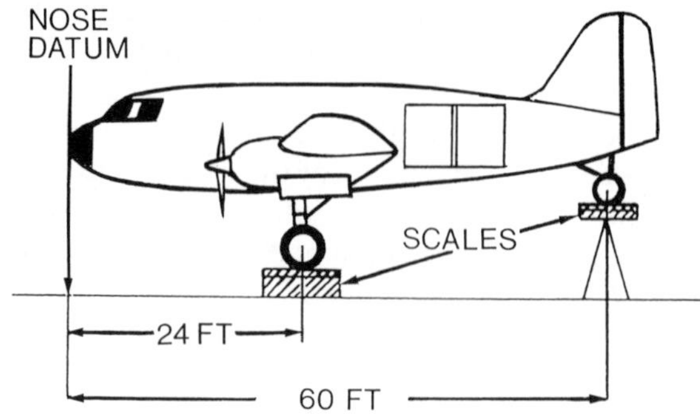

Figure 3.27 Basic Weight and CG Calculation (1)

To find the basic weight and CG from the nose datum point make out a load sheet. (See Figure 3.27)

Item	Weight lb	– Arm + ft		– Moment + lb/ft	
Weight on port wheel	20 000		24		480 000
Weight on stbd wheel	20 000		24		480 000
Weight on tail wheel	1 000		60		60 000
Totals	41 000				1020 000

$$\text{C of G} = \frac{\text{Total Moment}}{\text{Total Weight}} \quad \frac{+1020\,000}{41\,000\text{ lb}} = 24.88\text{ft aft of datum}$$

Basic Weight	=	41 000 lb
Basic Moment	=	1020 000 lb/ft
Arm of Basic CG	=	24.88 ft Aft of Datum

Note that all the arms used in our calculations were positive and all the moments were positive. This makes the problem simple since we are dealing with only positive quantities. Unfortunately the size and weight of modern aircraft are such that the quantities involved may well run into millions.

Using a CG reference datum point which falls within the pre-calculated CG range makes the figures less unwieldy. Assuming that the datum point is fixed

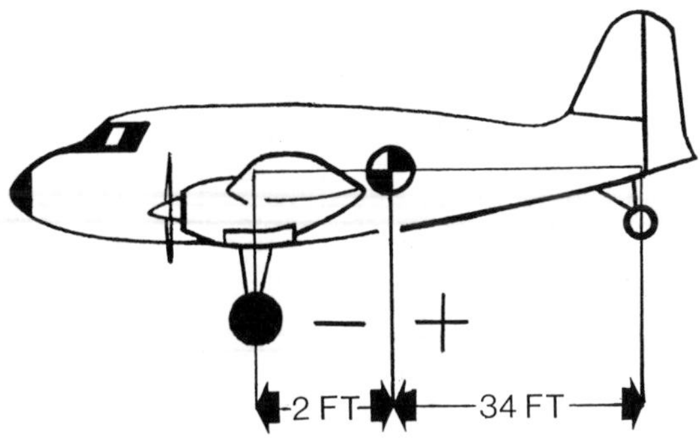

Figure 3.28 Basic Weight and CG Calculation (2)

at 2 feet behind the main wheels, let us work out the same problem again. (See Figure 3.28)

Item	Weight lb	– Arm + ft		– Moment + lb/ft	
Weight on port main wheel	20 000	2		40 000	
Weight on stbd main wheel	20 000	2		40 000	
Weight on tail wheel	1 000		34		34 000
	41 000			80 000	34 000
				– 46 000	

$$\text{CG} \quad \frac{\text{Total Movement}}{\text{Total Weight}} = \frac{-46000}{41000}$$

$$= -1.12 \text{ ft}$$

$$= 1.12\text{ft forward of datum}$$

The result is exactly the same as the result arrived at by using the Nose Datum point calculation, only the method has changed. We can now add the weights, arms and moments of the crew, fuel and cargo to our trim sheet.

Item	Weight lb	– Arm ft	+ Arm ft	– Moment lb/ft	+ Moment lb/ft
Basic Weight	41 000	1.12		46 000	480 000
Crew 2 at 150	300	6		1 800	480 000
Fuel	10 000	1		10 000	
Cargo	600		20		60 000
	51 900			57 800	1020 000
				–45 800	

CG = Total Moment lb/ft / Total Weight lb = –45800 / 51900
= .88 ft
= .88 feet ahead of datum

The effect of using fuel and oil, or off-loading or on-loading cargo, may be calculated by adjusting the basic trim sheet.

So consider fuel burn-off or off-loading freight as a 'minus' weight. Uplift of fuel or oil or water must be considered as a 'plus' weight.

Thus we can easily find the zero fuel CG for our aircraft:

Item	– Weight lb	+ Weight lb	– Arm ft	+ Arm ft	– Moment lb/ft	+ Moment lb/ft
Take-off weight		51 900			57 800	12 000
Fuel burn-off	10 000		1			10 000
Weight after burn-off		41 900			57 800	22 000
			Adjusted moment		–35 800	

Total Weight = 41 900 lbs

∴ Zero Fuel CG = –35800 / 41900

= .85 feet ahead of datum

A 'minus' weight multiplied by a 'minus' arm results in a *positive moment* ('two minuses make a plus'). Similarly a 'minus' weight multiplied by a 'plus' arm results in a *negative moment*.

When working out problems of this type, make sure that no loading or aircraft limitations have been exceeded. In other words, our aircraft will have:

- A maximum all up weight.
- A maximum zero fuel weight.
- A range of CG movement.

Your answers must all be within such limits.

If the CG limits were quoted as '3 feet ahead to 3 feet aft of the datum', then our loaded and zero fuel CG positions are obviously within limits. If we find that the CG with MAXIMUM FUEL, and the centre of gravity with ZERO FUEL fall within the stated limits, then the CG at any stage of the proposed flight would also be within limits.

Remember the golden rule:

CG always moves towards the point where weight is added.
CG always moves away from the point where weight is removed.

Thus, when weight is shifted from one location to another, the total weight of the aircraft is unchanged. However, the total moments do change in relation and proportion to the direction and distance the weight is moved. When weight is moved FORWARD, the TOTAL MOMENTS DECREASE. When weight is moved AFT, TOTAL MOMENTS INCREASE. So the moment change is proportional to the amount of weight moved.

Since the majority of aircraft have forward and aft baggage compartments, weight may be shifted from one to the other to change the CG. If we start with a known aircraft weight, CG and total moments, we can calculate the new CG (after the weight shift) by dividing the new total moments by the total aircraft weight.

An aircraft weight and balance quiz is included at the rear of the book so that you can test your knowledge if you wish.

CHAPTER 4

THE WHY AND HOW OF STOL

I can quickly answer why, but how is going to take much longer.

General Background

Short take-off and landing operations have been described as the ultimate challenge in aviation operations. Whether that is true or not, I'm not going to dispute it. What we can say is that it involves flying and controlling the aircraft at the extreme lower end of the flight envelope, often for operations in difficult terrain and adverse weather conditions. In this section we will also be considering the more important factors which make life difficult for the STOL pilot.

In many parts of the world, thick jungles, rain forests and mountains make overland travel to remote areas either lengthy and difficult, or just plain impossible.

I flew for some time in Papua New Guinea where the only realistic way to reach the highland areas was by air, with airstrips only usable by STOL aircraft such as the BN Islander or DH Twin Otter. The majority of the airstrips were clear areas hacked from virgin jungle and tropical forest. When you combine these factors with mountainous terrain and high ambient temperatures, it results in high density altitudes – altogether the worst combination for STOL operations. But without STOL aircraft these areas would have remained remote and inaccessible.

At the other end of the STOL spectrum, the STOLPORT was born; purpose-built airports with a single short runway within rapid transit distance of business and commercial centres in major cities. The time-consuming transfer of passengers from international airports built many miles from the city could, in part, be avoided.

However, this posed two sets of problems for aircraft operators and civil aviation authorities; environmental (the responsibility of the politicians) and safety-operational (looked after by the manufacturers, civil aviation authorities and aircraft operators, together with their training organisations).

It meant high-angle (around 6°) obstacle-clearing, noise acceptable, precision instrument landing system approaches (ILS) which involved special pilot training. Also, in many instances, complicated *Standard Instrument Departure Procedures* (SIDS) to fit in with nearby international airports. And naturally, the aircraft performance capability to maintain a positive and (CAA) acceptable nett gradient of climb in an engine-out situation. The DH DASH-7 was one aircraft designed specifically for regular airline STOLPORT operations.

All these STOL problems have, to a significant degree, been resolved. However, the average length of STOLPORT runways are much longer (and have far better surface pavements) than the rough jungle/mountain airstrips of places like the Papua New Guinea highlands. (LONDON, CITY (STOLPORT) runway is 3,934 feet (1199 metres) long – plus 'starter extensions' at each end. The ILS and visual PAPI angle is 5.5°).

Purpose-built aircraft with a whole new generation of specially designed wings and associated high lift devices such as modified flaps, plus slats and slots to maintain airflow over the wings near the stall, have been manufactured. Propeller design has been improved and made more efficient. In some cases additional blades have been added. The reversing pitch propeller (as fitted to the PT6 engine on the Twin Otter – even the negative BETA mode) has given a whole new meaning to the phrase, '*short stopping distance*' although technically it cannot be taken into consideration for *landing performance* purposes. However, I'm sure there isn't one STOL pilot who hasn't ignored this from operational necessity. On one occasion I am certain reversing-pitch props saved me, the aircraft, and the passengers I was carrying, in very unusual circumstances. It certainly had absolutely nothing to do with landing performance.

I had flown a group of tourists from Nairobi, down to a bush airstrip in a game park as part of a photo-safari. I circled once around the airstrip in the Twin Otter (standard drill) to make certain the runway was free of wildlife, as well as alerting the nearby safari camp so that they would send transport. Then I landed. The runway was not particularly short, so I had no need to make the passengers any more nervous (or excited) than they already were by using reverse thrust. However, when we stopped it was not far short of the other end.

It was at this moment that the drama started. One massive and *very angry* bull elephant suddenly appeared out of the nearby tree line, throwing his head and trunk about and looking as if he was going to charge us! Thank goodness I couldn't hear the loud trumpeting sound it was making over the engine noise, otherwise I would probably have jumped out of the aircraft and run back down the airstrip immediately.

'Do something!', screamed the Danish courier who was (unofficially) occupying the copilot seat as it was her first trip.

I can cope with an aircraft emergency as there is a predictable checklist to follow – but this was different. Except it was still an aircraft emergency whichever way you looked at it.

'Slowly backing away from an animal was one way of telling it you didn't want a confrontation, wasn't it?' I thought. Therefore back up the aircraft with reverse thrust. No hesitation on my part at that point.

When we had reversed about fifty yards with me struggling to stay on the narrow runway, the elephant made one short 'authority-establishing' charge and stopped. For one ridiculously wild moment I wondered if the Twin Otter was capable of taking off backwards! The patriarch of the herd tossed his head and trunk one last time, obviously satisfied with his efforts, then turned and disappeared between the trees with his ears flapping. He *knew* he was the boss, and I certainly wasn't going to argue about that.

Each time I flew to that same airstrip from then on I circled it three times before landing.

Length and Gradient

However restricted the available landing take-off distance, it must have sufficient length to enable an aircraft operator to fly in and out with a viable payload for a reasonable percentage of the time. A steep gradient can create a problem for a pilot flying in because a false impression is gained of the aircraft's position on the approach (see Figures 4.1 and 4.2).

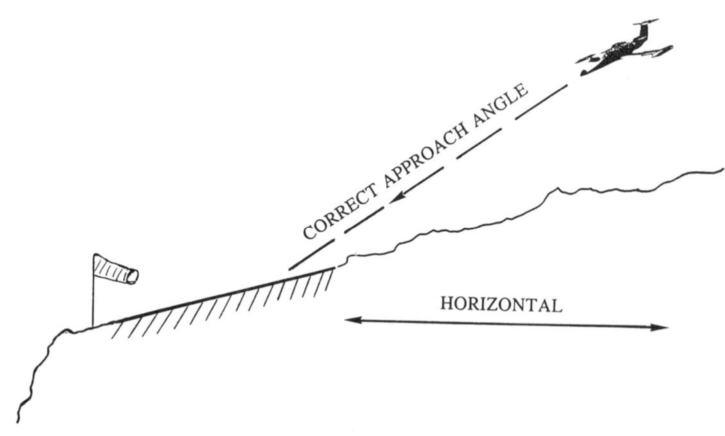

Figure 4.1 A Downward Slope on the Runway gives the Pilot the Illusion of being *Too Low*.

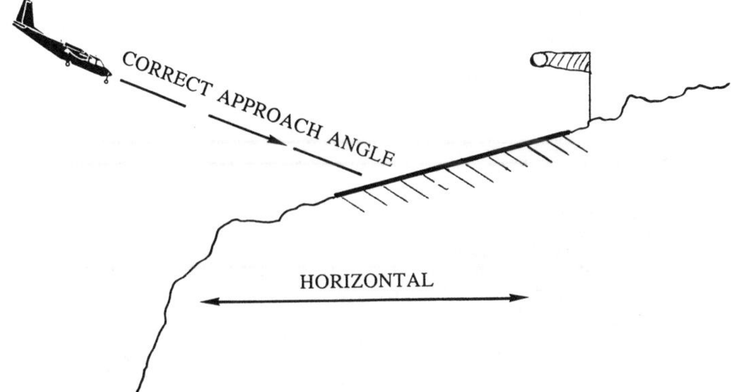

Figure 4.2 An Upward Slope in the Runway gives the Pilot the Illusion of being *Too High.*

Also, a steep gradient will often determine whether it is classified as one-way, i.e. always landing uphill and taking off down the slope. A prime example of this problem is LUKLA in Nepal, (see Figures 4.3 to 4.8). In this instance the runway faces directly into the side of a high mountain, making it operationally impossible to consider anything else.

Some airstrips may have a gradient but no obstructions at either end. In this case we have to assess the actual wind conditions.

Take-off Rule of Thumb.

If the wind is 15 knots or less, *take off downhill.* A 1% down-slope is equivalent to a 10% increase in runway length depending of course on the type and condition of the surface.

If the wind is more than 15 knots *take off uphill.* There is every probability it will take a greater amount of time to get airborne, but overall, the total distance will be shorter.

As a final guide, place an easily distinguishable marker at the side of the runway half-way along the available take-off distance. *If you have reached at least three-quarters of your V_R/V_2 speed by this point, there is sufficient runway remaining to take-off.* (On the type of aircraft we are looking at, V_R and V_2 are very close together.)

Slow Flight

Slow flight can be defined as flight in the speed range from below the ENDURANCE SPEED to just above the STALLING SPEED. In all STOL flying the pilot must have the ability to control the aircraft at very low airspeeds – and to do this SAFELY.

Long finals at Lukla. A one-way landing across the gorge can be turbulent. Caution at all times.
Figure 4.3

The approach by air to Lukla is breathtaking, and can be unacceptably turbulent other than in the early morning or late afternoon. The steep uphill gradient of the one-way airstrip gives the pilot the illusion of being too high.
Figure 4.4

Figure 4.5 Short finals

Figure 4.6 Then the landing (arrival!) After touchdown it takes almost full power to taxi up the slope to the parking area.

Figure 4.7 The downhill take-off at Lukla, straight out over the deep Dudh Kosi river gorge.

Figure 4.8 The Air Route to Lukla from Kathmandu

The primary objective when training for slow flight is to strengthen the pilot's sense of awareness that the aircraft is being flown close to the stall. Slow flight should be practised on each STOL aircraft type you plan to fly. This will develop *control feel*, and an appreciation of the rate and amount of control movement that can be expected when flying in this lower airspeed range. It also trains the senses of vision, hearing and feel, to recognise an impending stall situation immediately.

Characteristics and Forces in Slow Flight

The moment of lift and the control of an aircraft in flight depend upon the maintenance of a minimum airspeed. This speed will vary with the all-up weight, manoeuvring loads, aircraft configuration and density altitude. Therefore the closer the *actual airspeed* to this minimum speed, the *greater the angle of attack*, which results in *less effective* flying controls. (The minimum speed below which it is impossible to maintain controlled flight is called the STALLING SPEED).

An increase in the angle of attack brings the CP and CG closer together (see Figure 4.9), and weakens the normal nose down tendency resulting from the LIFT/WEIGHT couple. At the same time, the *elevators* which depend upon

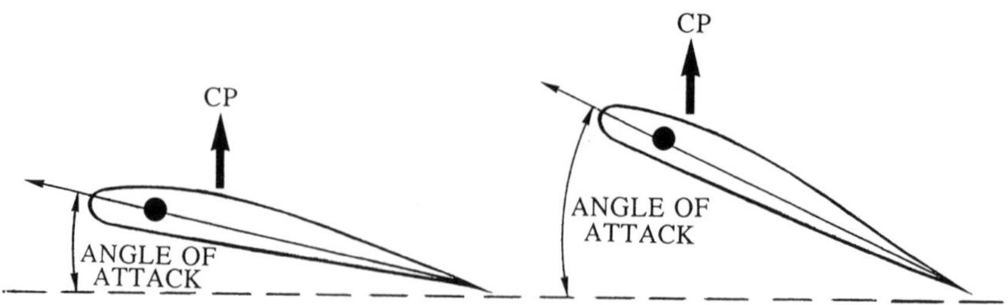

Figure 4.9 With an increase in angle of attack. The centre of pressure moves forwards

the speed of the airflow for their effectiveness, will become *less responsive* as the airspeed drops with increasing angle of attack.

The ailerons and rudder will also begin to lose their effectiveness as the airspeed decreases. Coarse movements of all controls will become necessary to control the aircraft in all three axes.

In a propeller driven aircraft, if the power is *increased*, the elevators and rudder will become *more effective* in direct relationship to the amount of power increase (within the area of slipstream effect). At slow flight airspeeds, the slipstream effect produces a very strong yawing moment. So a positive use of the rudder is necessary to maintain balanced flight. The further effect of using a larger rudder deflection, means a positive application of aileron will be needed to *keep the wings level.* This will result in having to fly the aircraft with 'crossed controls' to maintain balanced flight with the wings level.

The positive result of slow flight practice is the development of a pilot's ability to estimate the *margin of safety above the stalling speed.* This will also help in *controllability* during STOL take-offs and landings – the most critical phase.

The other advantage which results from being able to handle an aircraft proficiently and confidently in slow flight, is the increased skill that is developed for coping with *stall recovery* and the *incipient stages of a spin.* At very low airspeeds with power on, it is easy for the aircraft to enter an unbalanced flight condition. It can drop a wing very rapidly, which can progress into a spin.

Note: A spin is more likely to occur when the aircraft's *centre of gravity* is in an aft position, although still within limits.

If a pilot can safely control an aircraft whilst flying at preselected slow airspeeds (speed control), altitudes and headings, with the aircraft in balance, then more confidence will be gained for:

- STOL pattern flying around an airstrip, including take-offs and landings.
- Controlling the aircraft during a slow STOL final approach.
- Handling the aircraft in a 'go-around' situation.
- Controlling the aircraft close to the stall, and recognising the early symptoms of a stall.
- Developing the ability to *safely* control the aircraft after a bad landing. (ballooning, bounce or excessive float, incorrect 'flare-out').

How to Set Up Slow Flight

Initially setting up for slow flight can be done from straight and level flight using two different speeds in stages.

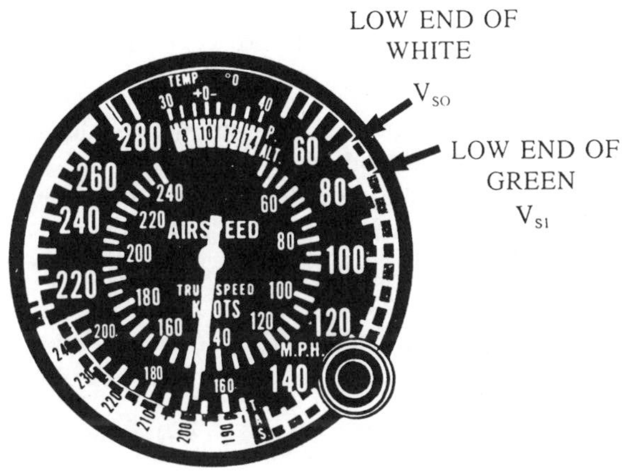

Figure 4.10 Slow Flight Airspeed Markings

Firstly at V_{S1} + 10 knots, meaning 10 knots higher than indicated on the ASI at the low end of the green arc (see Figure 4.10). After proficiency is gained, then practise at V_{S1} + 5 knots can be attempted. This is realistic for the speeds used in serious STOL approaches.

When setting up:

- The power should be gradually reduced and the nose (pitch) attitude raised to maintain a constant *altitude*.
- Maintain *lateral* balance and heading as the airspeed falls to the chosen figure.

The speeds of V_{S1} + 10 knots and 5 knots, are close enough to the stalling speed for the reduced effectiveness (sluggishness) of the controls to be felt and

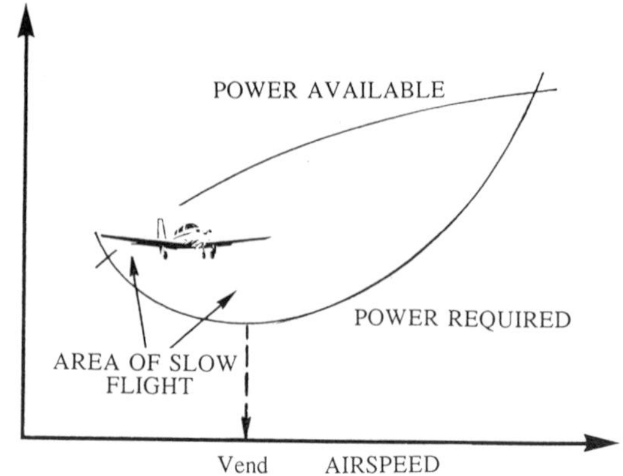

Figure 4.11 Power Available within Slow Flight Limits

appreciated, and for all practice manoeuvring. In this situation the aircraft will be flying at the lower end of the 'power curves' shown in Figure 4.11. Within this area there will be minimal climb performance.

Any attempt to regain lost altitude by raising the nose will rapidly increase the induced drag. Without an increase in power the airspeed will decrease. *No altitude will be gained, and if this is allowed to continue altitude will be lost and the aircraft will quickly reach the stall.* Note: Any attempt to regain altitude when flying at very low airspeed requires an increase in power as the nose is raised.

After practising slow flight in straight and level, medium level turns (up to 30° of bank) – without an increase in power – can be attempted.

The airspeed will *reduce rapidly* as the altitude is maintained. The speed loss is much greater and far more rapid than medium level turns at normal cruising speed.

Straight climbs and descents can then be tackled, followed by climbing and descending turns. During slow flight climbs, the performance will be poor due to the *increased induced drag*. This can be seen in Figure 4.11, where only a small margin of power is available between the *power available* and *power required* curves.

Descents at slow speed should be practised with and without power. When using power, the desired rate of descent can be achieved at the selected airspeed by:

- Reducing the power.
- Readjusting the nose attitude to a lower position, the same as for a descent during normal flight.

After some proficiency has been obtained in all these various attitudes of flight in the clean configuration, the same procedure can be started all over again With flaps lowered to the different stages. This will be at V_{S1} + 10 knots, progressing to V_{S1} + 5 knots.

Use of Full Power in the Landing Configuration

There will be occasions during the approach and landing phase which require a 'go-around' procedure to be undertaken. The key aspect of this situation, is when the aircraft has landing gear and flaps lowered and is trimmed for the approach.

THE APPLICATION OF FULL (TAKE-OFF) POWER CAN CAUSE A VERY PRONOUNCED PITCH CHANGE, REQUIRING RADICAL USE OF THE ELEVATOR TRIMMER TO OFFSET THE STRONG OUT OF BALANCE CONTROL PRESSURE.

Note: A similar change can occur when retracting flaps in the initial climb-out phase.

I would like to make the point here that the entire series of slow flight exercises should initially be practised with a qualified instructor/check pilot. They should also be undertaken at a safe altitude AGL, with the pre-stall HASELL checks being completed before commencing.

Flight sequences for Slow Flight. (Controlled flight at slow airspeed.)

AIRCRAFT ATTITUDE	FLIGHT SEQUENCE
From straight and level flight	Maintain a lookout whilst reducing power and maintaining altitude, heading and balance. Re-trim in stages and when V_{S1} + 10 knots is established, adjust power as necessary to maintain airspeed and altitude. Note the change in pitch attitude and reduced response from the flying controls. Correct altitude loss by use of the elevators together with increasing the power.

AIRCRAFT ATTITUDE	FLIGHT SEQUENCE
Climbing flight	From controlled straight and level flight V_{S1} + 10 knots. Nominate a particular climb rate. Lookout and gradually increase power whilst maintaining speed, heading and balance. Stabilise the power setting when the selected rate of climb has been achieved.
Turning flight	From level slow flight at V_{S1} + 10 knots, lookout and enter a medium level turn without increasing power. Note loss of speed when altitude is maintained. Re-enter a medium banked turn, increasing power and maintaining constant speed and altitude.
	Note the higher pitch attitude and the need to use elevators and power to correct any altitude loss.
Descending flight	From controlled straight and level flight at V_{S1} + 10 knots. Nominate a rate of descent. Lookout and check a clear area along the descent path. Gradually decrease power whilst maintaining speed, heading and balance. Stabilise the power setting when the selected rate of descent has been achieved. Return to straight and level slow flight by maintaining speed and increasing power until the descent rate is zero. Heading and balance should be maintained throughout.

Following the completion of this initial SLOW FLIGHT sequence, practise with flaps down at V_{S0} + 10 knots can be undertaken. Manoeuvres should include straight and level, level turns, straight climbs and descents, and climbing and descending turns.

AIRCRAFT ATTITUDE	FLIGHT SEQUENCE
From straight and level flight	Maintain a lookout whilst reducing power and maintaining altitude, heading and balance. Re-trim in stages and when V_{S1} + 5 knots is established, adjust power as necessary to maintain airspeed and altitude. Note the change in pitch attitude and reduced response from the flying controls. Correct altitude loss by use of the elevators together with increasing the power.
Climbing flight	From controlled straight and level flight at V_{S1} + 5 knots, nominate a specific rate of climb. Lookout and gradually increase power whilst maintaining airspeed, heading and balance. Stabilise the power setting.
Turning flight	From level slow flight at V_{S1} + 5 knots, lookout and enter a medium level turn without increasing power. Note how quickly the airspeed lowers when altitude is maintained in the turn. Return to straight slow flight. Lookout and re-enter a medium turn whilst increasing power to maintain airspeed and altitude.
Descending flight	From controlled straight and level flight at V_{S1} + 5 knots, nominate a rate of descent. Lookout and select a clear area along the descent path. Gradually decrease power whilst maintaining airspeed, heading and balance. Stabilise the power setting when the selected rate of descent has been achieved. Retrim.

Following the completion of this final set of flight sequences, practise with FLAPS DOWN at V_{SO} + 5 knots. Straight and level flight, level turns, straight climbs and descents, and climbing and descending turns. Note: At the end of this period, practise in recovery from the symptoms of the stall can be undertaken. (Buffet, audio and/or visual stall warner). Only a small forward movement of the yoke is necessary to recover into *controlled* slow flight.

CHAPTER 5

THE SHORT-FIELD (STOL) TAKE-OFF AND CONDITIONS WHICH AFFECT IT

The Short-field (STOL) Take-off (Tricycle Undercarriage Aircraft)

The short-field technique outlined here is applicable to all tricycle undercarriage aircraft types, or to lighter aircraft with more marginal performance.

It is assumed that on the majority of short-field (STOL) take-offs, you will be unable to make a 'rolling start' (reaching your take-off point already at taxying speed, then opening the throttle to METO power) mainly due to the constraints of the airstrip. Therefore, you will have to make a standing start (see Figure 5.1). Note: Caution must be used when taxying onto any runway

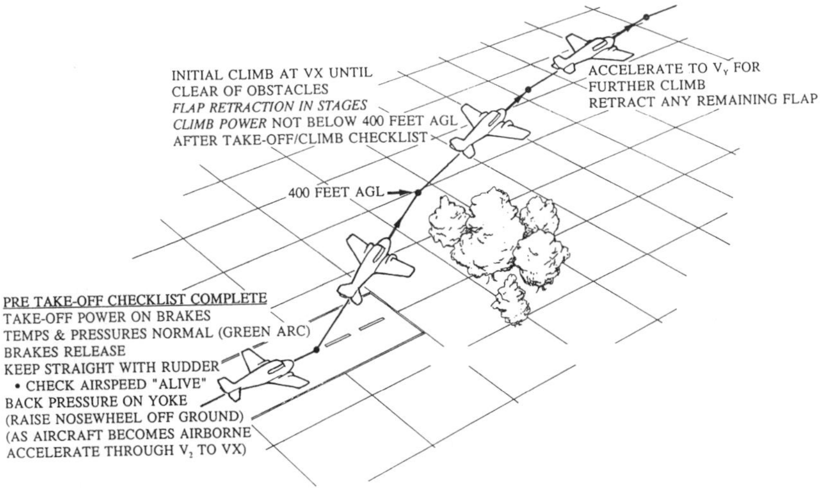

Figure 5.1 Short-Field (STOL) Take-off

for a rolling takeoff. Taxying speed must be kept reasonably low to avoid excessive side-loading on the undercarriage.

- Perform the pre-take-off checks and set flaps as recommended by the manufacturer in the Flight Manual.
- Line up in the centre of the airstrip.
- Holding the aircraft on the toe-brakes with firm back pressure on the yoke (rear of neutral), open up to max RPM (fixed or VP prop piston), to recommended METO power/manifold pressure (turbo-charged piston), or pre-calculated torque pressure (jet-prop).

  (Aerodynamically the propellers must have forward movement through the air before becoming efficient. We are merely checking that the engines are developing the correct power for take-off).
- Release brakes, check yaw with rudder (remember it will be more than a normal takeoff) and monitor engine instruments as you confirm the airspeed rising (airspeed indicator).
- As V_R/V_2 approaches, increase back pressure on the yoke to assist placing the aircraft in the correct attitude/climbing angle to achieve V_X (best angle of climb speed).
- When clear of obstacles accelerate to V_Y (best rate of climb speed), retract flap appropriate to type (this may be in stages), but not before 200 feet AMSL.

Additional Take-off Advice and Caution

Aircraft performance charts are all very well and I'm not advocating you should not use them, but for any *real STOL take-off*, there is a good back-up rule of thumb which you can use to make sure you will get airborne in the distance available.

During the take-off roll, if you have not reached a minimum of 70% of your V_R/V_2 speed at the half-way point down the runway – then abort the take-off. It's almost certain you won't make it.

Having said that, you are working on the dubious margins of performance. Although, if you follow this rule you will get airborne, it won't guarantee obstacle clearance in the immediate take-off path if required. So consider this factor carefully.

The following set of Performance Charts (see Figures 5.2 a to f) is from the SHORTS SKYVAN SERIES 3M twin turbo-prop aircraft. The charts relate directly to the SHORT FIELD (STOL) performance.

The main comparison I want to show from the example given at Figures 5.2, is the difference between the GROUND RUN and TAKE-OFF DISTANCE REQUIRED. Therefore:

SHORT FIELD TAKE-OFF GROUND RUN REQUIRED	780 FEET
SHORT FIELD TAKE-OFF DISTANCE REQUIRED TO 50 FEET SCREEN HEIGHT (1ST SEGMENT CLIMB)	2100 FEET
A difference of	1320 FEET

As you can see, if you have even minor obstacles to clear, this factor has to be taken into consideration.

The graphs for the EFFECTS OF A GRASS RUNWAY ON SHORT-FIELD TAKE-OFF PERFORMANCE are also included for the same example (see Figure 5.2f). They show the extent to which the TAKE-OFF DISTANCE REQUIRED is lengthened.

Naturally, if you are undertaking a short field (STOL) take-off on a *hard, flat desert* airstrip with no obstructions, as I have many times, then the GROUND RUN is all you have to worry about.

Know and use the aircraft performance charts on every occasion you have any doubt about the take-off performance. Then as a back-up you can use the rule of thumb procedure by marking the runway mid-point as an abandon/abort take-off point if the circumstances dictate.

When you are finally airborne and congratulating yourself on a fine STOL takeoff, remember that you must maintain accurate speed control at V_x (best angle of climb) if you are striving to climb over obstacles in your flight path.

SHORT-FIELD TAKE-OFF FIELD LENGTH DATA
INTRODUCTION

The short-field take-off performance in this sub-section has been established by calculation procedures which were subsequently proved by sample flight test demonstration of compliance, using the take-off speeds as defined.

The following definitions of field lengths apply:-

Short-field take-off run required	:	Distance from where the main wheels are static to where they just leave the ground
Short-field take-off distance required to 50 foot screen	:	Distance from where the main wheels are static to where they just clear a 50 foot obstacle

Figure 5.2a

SHORT-FIELD TAKE-OFF GROUND RUN REQUIRED

The short field take-off run required, achieved using SHORT FIELD TAKE-OFF (30° FLAP) techniques, for varying air temperatures, airfield altitudes, weights, reported wind components and uniform runway slopes.

ASSOCIATED CONDITIONS

Engines	:	Both operating at maximum take-off power.
Engine Anti-Icing	:	Off (but see Note (2))
Wing Flaps	:	SHORT-FIELD TAKE-OFF (30°)
Speeds	:	Rotation initiated at rotation speed V_R. After lift-off, the short-field take-off screen speed is achieved by 50 feet height. Refer to sub section 6.2 for Short Field Procedures and Speeds.
Runway	:	Hard, dry runway (see Note 3 below)

The example illustrated (Fig. 5.2c) by the arrowed broken lines shows that with an air temperature of 24°C (ISA + 17°C) at an airfield altitude of 2,000ft and a weight of 12,500 lb with a reported headwind component of 10 knots and uniform downhill runway slope of 2.5% the short-field take-off run is 780 feet.

NOTES:

(1) The wind correction grids have been factored by 50% for headwinds and 150% for tailwinds. Reported winds may therefore be used directly in the grids.

(2) To take account of engine anti-icing, the distances should be increased by 7% when EGT limited.

(3) When operating from grass runway surfaces, the take-off run obtained must be increased by an amount appropriate to the grass conditions. Allow for the effect of the grass runway surface on the take-off performance.

Figure 5.2b

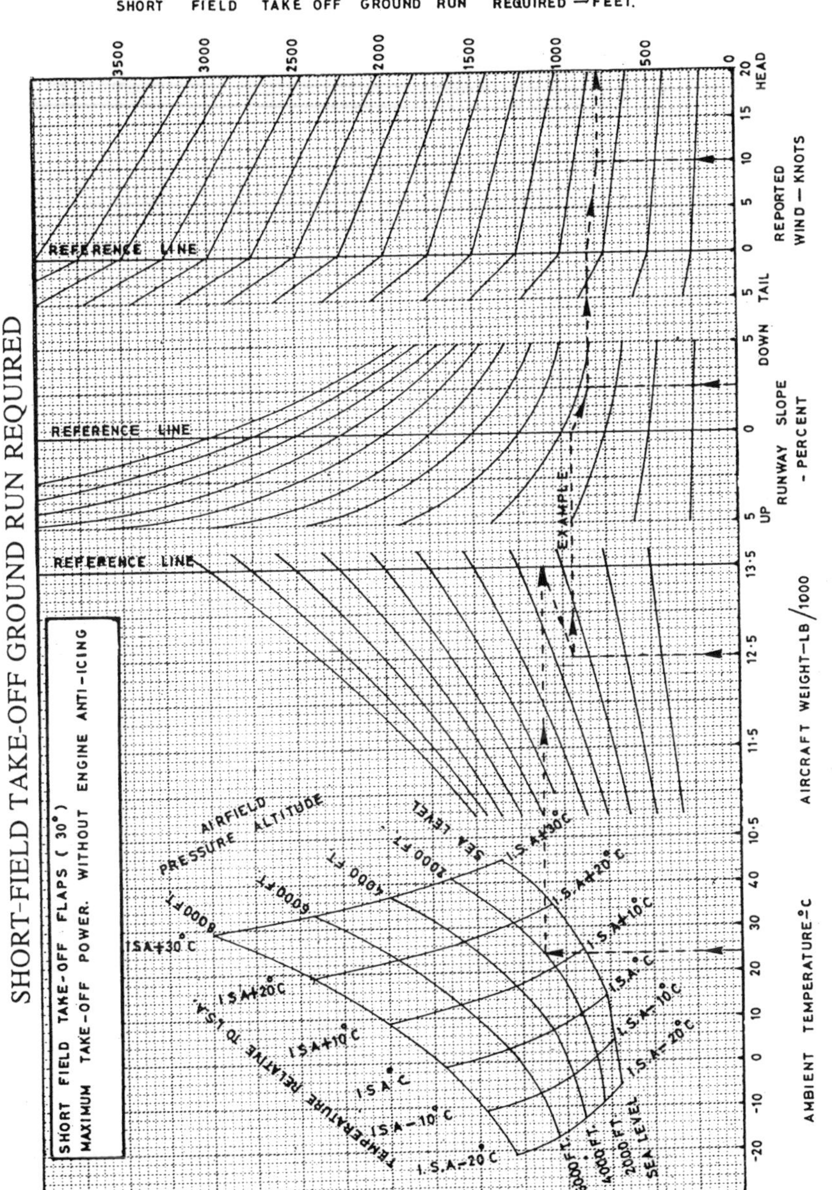

Figure 5.2 c Short-Field Take-off Ground Run Required

SHORT-FIELD TAKE-OFF DISTANCE REQUIRED TO 50 FOOT SCREEN

The short field take-off distance required, achieved using SHORT-FIELD TAKE-OFF (30° FLAP) screen is shown for varying air temperatures, airfield altitudes, weights, reported wind components and uniform runway slopes.

ASSOCIATED CONDITIONS

Engines	:	Both operating at maximum take-off power
Engine Anti-Icing	:	Off (but see Note (2))
Wing Flaps	:	SHORT FIELD TAKE-OFF (30°C)
Speeds	:	Rotation initiated at rotation speed V_R. After lift-off, the short-field take-off screen speed is achieved by 50 feet height. Refer to sub section 6.2 for Short-Field Procedures and Speeds.
Runway	:	Hard, dry runway (see Note 3 below).

The example illustrated (Fig 5.2E) by the arrowed broken lines shows that with an air temperature of 24°C (ISA + 17°C) at an airfield altitude of 4,000ft, a uniform uphill runway slope of 2% and an 11kts headwind, the short-field take-off distance required to 50 feet screen is 2,100 feet.

NOTES

(1) The wind correction grids have been factored by 50% for headwinds and 150% for tailwinds. Reported winds may therefore be used directly in the grids.

(2) To take account of engine anti-icing, the distances should be increased by 7% when EGT limited.

(3) When operating from grass runway surfaces, the take-off run obtained must be increased by an amount appropriate to the grass conditions. Use should be made of the data given in this sub-section to correctly allow for the effect of the grass runway surface on the take-off performance.

Figure 5.2d

SHORT-FIELD TAKE-OFF DISTANCE REQUIRED TO 50 FOOT SCREEN

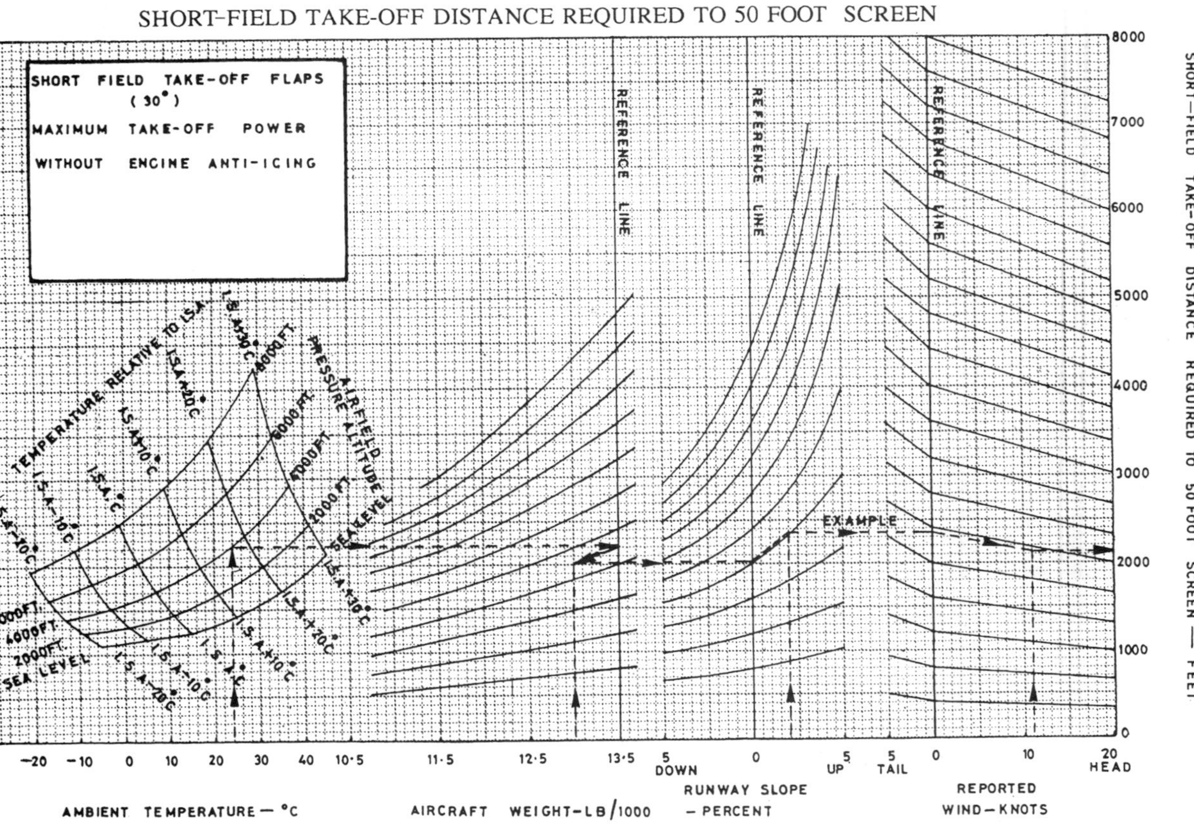

Figure 5.2e Short-Field Take-off Distance Required to 50ft Screen

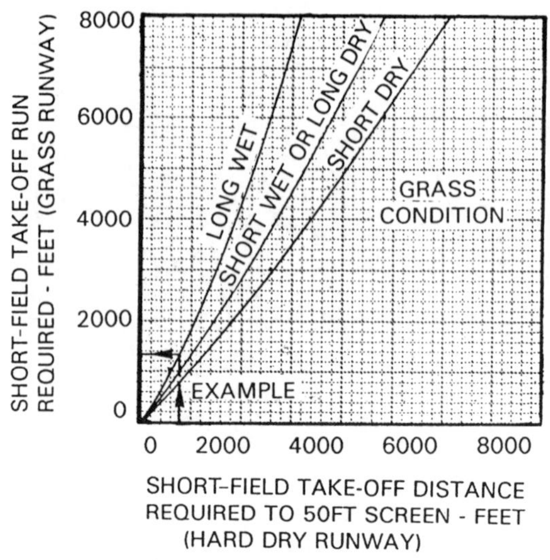

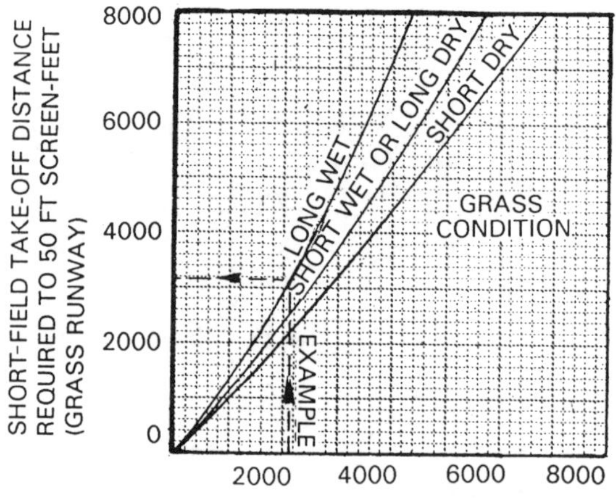

Figure 5.2f Effects of Grass Runway on Short-Field Take-Off Performance

Cumulus granitus is very hard indeed, and hitting it would spoil your whole day. Note the diagrammatic comparison of V_X and V_Y at figure 5.3.

Some instructors and quite experienced bush pilots operating out of short airstrips, advise using no flap at all for a short field (STOL) take-off until just before V_R/V_2. Their argument is that it reduces drag to a minimum and provides the MAX/LIFT FLAP boost at the right moment.

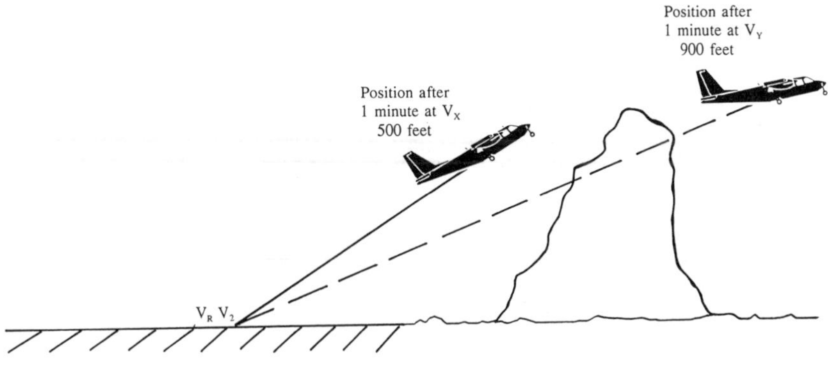

For any STOL obstacle climb-out procedure, you must maintain your V_x until clear of all obstacles. Be careful when retracting flaps, as the wrong aircraft handling technique could result in a marked (if temporary) decrease in the rate of climb, especially if a climbing turn is involved. You do not want radical trim changes in this critical phase of flight.

Figure 5.3 Comparison in Altitude Gain Between Best Angle and Best Rate of Climb

I would never recommend this method for the following reasons:

- If the manufacturer (Flight Manual) states that FLAP should be used for take-off then do it. The aircraft has been flight-tested as giving the best performance with flap – *but from the beginning of the take-off roll.*
- Flap lowers the stalling speed.
- You do not want to be fiddling about trying to lower the *correct amount of flap* at the most critical phase of the take-off. You need to be concentrating on the runway and keeping the aircraft straight, especially in a crosswind, not having unnecessary cockpit distractions.
- It is possible to get into a dangerous asymmetric flap situation if something malfunctions or breaks in the flap mechanism. Remember the pre-take-off check:

ITEM	ACTION
FLAPS	SET FOR TAKE-OFF. CHECK GAUGE AND VISUALLY.

- You need to get the aircraft off the ground as soon as possible (this is even more important in a soft-field take-off). Therefore you need flap, which gives extra lift, to do it. The best results can only be achieved by setting flap prior to the take-off.

The Soft-field (STOL) Take-off (Tricycle Undercarriage Aircraft)

A soft-field take-off means a take-off from an airstrip where the surface is unpaved, wet, loose sand, muddy or snow-covered, with the tendency for the aircraft wheels to sink into the top surface, or in long grass which also has a retarding effect causing increased drag.

The flap setting is the same as for a SHORT-FIELD take-off, but the object of the exercise now is to get the *nosewheel* off the ground as soon as possible. Therefore the yoke should be hard back on brakes release at the beginning of the take-off roll. This will give a high angle of attack to assist in lifting the nosewheel very early. As the nosewheel leaves the ground, release some back pressure on the yoke to reduce the angle of attack which will assist aircraft acceleration.

The aircraft will leave the ground at a very low airspeed (perhaps with the stall-warner going). There will be increased foot pressure needed to counteract the yaw (low speed, high power setting, with a momentary increase from the asymmetric blade effect of the propellers caused by the higher than normal angle of attack, especially at lift-off).

Once the aircraft is safely airborne, lower the nose and allow the aircraft to accelerate to V_X (best angle of climb speed) before transiting into the climb.

Flap retraction as before.

Short-field/Soft-Field Combination (Tricycle Undercarriage Aircraft)

A short-field/soft-field combination will mean that the aircraft will accelerate faster and cope more efficiently with surface 'friction drag' on the wheels, rather than the increased 'induced drag' of the wings at the normal high STOL angle of attack. Therefore the angle of attack must be reduced during the initial part of the take-off roll. The elevators can then be used in a delicate balancing act to 'feel' (with variable back pressure on the yoke) for the best lift angle.

At the earliest moment haul the aircraft off the ground, but remember the aircraft is very close to the stall. Therefore, lower the nose immediately to accelerate in *ground effect* to V_X.

In point of fact I seem to use this combination technique frequently because wilderness STOL strip surfaces vary so much.

Taildragger (STOL) Take-offs

I have flown a number of tailwheel STOL aircraft, from the single-engine Pilatus Porter, Helio Super Courier, even the old Cessna 185, which has a very acceptable short-field performance. I found the Dornier could also perform well, and would you believe the DC-3 can still get in and out of places other aircraft couldn't even consider. I love flying the Dak, it's one of my favourite aircraft. We have certainly had some adventures together. But back to the take-off technique for this type of aircraft.

Line up in the centre of the runway as normal, hold the aircraft on the toe brakes and have the yoke fully back as you increase power. There is every possibility full power cannot be used on brakes release, as the high engine torque will cause the aircraft to yaw dramatically. You may not be able to stop the swing, even with full rudder. This could result in an embarrassing uncontrolled ground-loop right on the end of the runway, or the aircraft veering off the runway into the bush with every possibility of damage. On my first STOL take-off in a Helio Super Courier I lost it completely. The aircraft ended up just a few metres along the runway facing in the opposite direction. Did I have a red face! Therefore, a progressive increase in power to allow 'yaw control' is essential.

As the aircraft rolls forward, exert a positive forward pressure on the yoke to raise the tail as early as possible into the flying attitude. (Be careful not to overdo it and hit the props on the ground, as the tail section has a tendency to rise suddenly without warning). Let the speed increase and haul the aircraft off the ground. Lower the nose and accelerate, then transit as normal into the climb at V_X.

With a taildragger there is minimal variation in technique for a short-field/soft-field combination. The object being to get the aircraft airborne at the earliest possible moment in the take-off roll and accelerate in *ground effect*.

Advice About Arctic Temperature Take-offs

Take-offs in extremely low temperatures pose their own particular set of problems. They also have considerable advantages as far as *lift* is concerned.

I have operated in the Arctic in surface temperatures as low as –40°C, with both turbo-prop and piston (recip) powered aircraft. So here are a few things to bear in mind.

- Remember that with multi-engine aircraft, V_{MC} (the minimum single-engine control speed) will be *higher* than stated in the Flight Manual. This is because it was set at sea level on a standard day.
- The danger is, if you do not use the *performance charts* to establish the correct *power setting*, the engine power output could easily exceed the rated power.

  With jet-prop engines the limiting factor is *torque pressure*, the ITT (internal turbine temperature) will not even get close to the maximum limit in very cold temperatures. The same thing will happen to turbo-charged piston engines with maximum permissible boost pressure.

- The problem with normally aspirated piston engines is that the power increases around 1% for each 10 degrees of temperature below ISA standard, so you must be aware of this. In fact in really subzero arctic temperatures, even though manifold pressure and RPM limits are not exceeded, an engine could develop up to 10% *more than rated power*.
- For extreme cold weather operation, it is advisable to have a *carburettor heat temperature gauge* fitted with piston engines. In some instances it is essential to use carburettor heat to vaporise the fuel.

  The problem with using carb heat in very low temperatures (where it is too cold for icing to occur), is the strong possibility the temperature could be raised to the point where carb icing will form (–10°C to +25°C).

Note: See CARBURETTOR ICING – SYMPTOMS, DANGERS AND PRECAUTIONS later in this chapter.

More About the Use of Flaps

From the various STOL take-off techniques we have been through in this chapter, we can see that flaps provide the additional lift the aircraft needs to achieve the shortest possible take-off for any particular set of conditions. But are we maximising the full potential of the flaps fitted to our aircraft? The answer in many cases is *no*.

I have already stated that you should use the flap recommended by the manufacturer in the Flight Manual. But some manufacturers make no recommendations at all. In that case, it could be to your advantage to conduct a series of safe flight tests to see how your aircraft performs at various flap settings (not full flap!).

Use a long runway with clear side markers. Runway lights are fine. (No farm airstrips of marginal length and dubious surface, though). Then, with a competent observer in the right-hand seat, find out the distance of your take-off roll by experimentation, using various flap settings. If you do this on a calm day it will give you a good basic indication of how your aircraft performs. I have done this with a Twin Otter using a variety of flap settings and came up with some startling results. This knowledge has got me in and out of some unbelievably short airstrips and restricted spaces around the world.

As a rule of thumb, to obtain the max lift-flap combination, sit in the cockpit and deflect the ailerons either full right or left. Then match the *flap setting* to the *down aileron*. (Obviously on some aircraft there are fixed flap settings with no possibility of any variation. In that case try out what you have.)

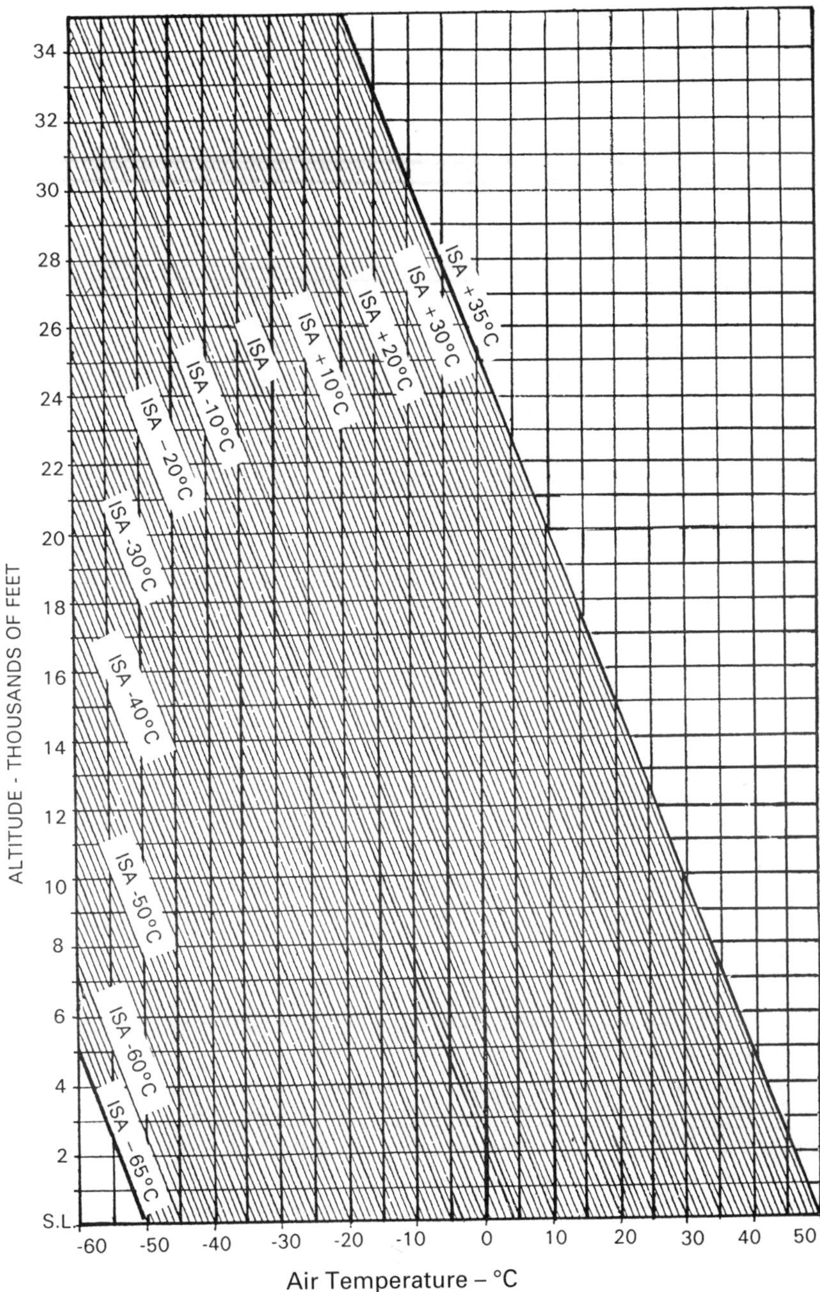

Figure 5.4 Determination of Temperature in Relation to ISA

Flap Retraction, Trim Changes and 'Sink'

Any use of flap will lead to a trim change. We know this from our early flying as student pilots. The greater the amount, the greater the change. Therefore we should be aware and ready to deal with this.

On a STOL take-off, if there is between 20-30 degrees of flap, as can easily be the case, *retract the flap by stages*, no more than 10 degrees at a time, letting the speed settle in between. This will give you time to cope with the attitude and trim changes, and avoid a marked loss in the rate of climb if all the flap was retracted in one go – not to mention a super excessive trim change.

At the same time, the flap retraction 'sink' can be avoided if there is sufficient speed. Just hold the nose up slightly with back pressure on the yoke/elevators as each particular stage of flap is retracting.

Cold Weather Operation – Effects on Landing Gear

Taking-off and landing from wilderness STOL airstrips which may be covered in icy water, slush, snow or mud, will inevitably result in the wheels and lower parts of the gear struts collecting some surface debris which will stick. With *retractable gear* aircraft this debris will be carried up into the wheel bays, fouling the mechanism and freezing the gear in the UP POSITION; a very undesirable situation.

To avoid this happening, lower and raise the gear two or three times after you are clear of all obstacles during the climb-out. Don't wait until you reach cruising altitude – the gear will almost certainly be frozen!

Ground Effect

Quite a number of general aviation accidents have been caused due to a lack of understanding of '*ground effect*'. In STOL take-offs, the use of ground effect makes an important contribution to the aircraft staying airborne whilst accelerating to V_X. It also has considerable effect during the landing.

It is possible to fly an aircraft *just clear of the surface* at a slower airspeed than that required for level flight at a higher altitude outside ground effect. The depth of this layer of air is around 25 feet. After that, the full impact of *induced drag* suddenly affects the aircraft. It can be devastating to a pilot struggling to control a sluggish aircraft just a few knots above the stall. In these circumstances coming out of ground effect *stalls* the aircraft, which then literally crashes onto the ground. (See Figure 5.5)

Research has given some interesting results about *ground effect* versus *induced drag*. It relates to the varying height of the wing above the ground and the *reduction* in induced drag:

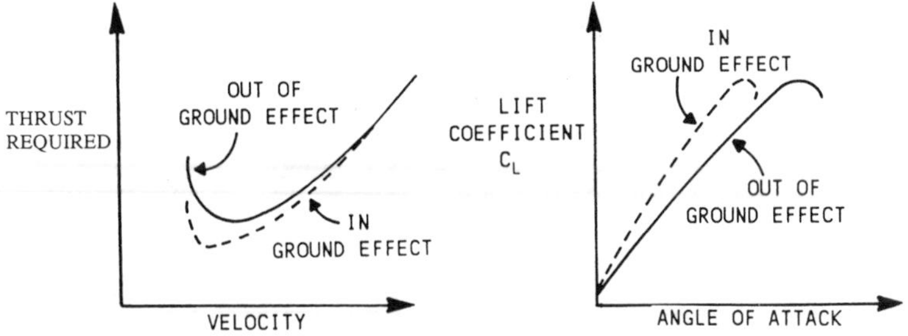

Figure 5.5 Ground Effect Changes Lift and Drag

One span width	1.4% reduction
One fourth the span	23.5% reduction
One tenth the span	47.6% reduction

Rule of Thumb about Ground Effect

When airborne just after a STOL take-off, hug the ground as close as possible when accelerating to Vx. To be safe, make sure you are no higher than 15 feet AGL. It is better to allow a good speed margin over and above your target speed, to fully compensate for the induced drag problems when leaving ground effect.

Airflow Patterns

Ground effect is caused by *ground interference* with the *airflow patterns* around an aircraft in flight. These patterns primarily change the aerodynamic characteristics of the wings, as well as across the tail surfaces and around the fuselage.

Principally, the *vertical component* of the airflow around the wing is restricted by the close proximity of the surface. It affects the three-dimensional flow pattern.

Ground Effect is not a 'Cushion of Air'

There is a mistaken belief among both private and professional aviators, that ground effect is a *cushion of air* between the bottom of the wing and the ground. This is not true. It works on wing *downwash* and wingtip vortices.

As the wing enters the narrow layer of ground effect, the wing's coefficient of lift remains constant. The consequence of this is a reduction in the *upwash, downwash* and *wingtip vortices.*

We know that induced drag varies with the wing's angle of attack. The higher the angle (as at low speed) the greater the induced drag. The wing lifts the aircraft by accelerating a mass of air downwards. It is also a fact that *reduced pressure* on top of an aerofoil provides the essential lift. But this is one of the elements that helps in the overall effect of pushing a mass of air downwards. So the greater the downwash, the harder the wing is pushing the air down.

However, the reduction of the wingtip vortices due to ground effect, alters the spanwise lift distribution and *reduces the induced angle of attack* and therefore the *induced drag*. This means the wing will require a lower angle of attack in ground effect to produce the same lift. Or if a constant angle of attack is maintained, there will be an increase in lift.

Ground effect will also alter *thrust* versus velocity (airspeed). Since induced drag is higher at low speeds, a reduction in induced drag (due to ground effect), will significantly reduce the thrust required (parasite plus induced drag) at low speeds. Having said that, there is no *direct* effect on parasite drag.

With the airflow changes around the aircraft already mentioned, there may be a change in *position* (installation) error of the airspeed system associated with ground effect. In the majority of cases this will cause an *increase in the local pressure* at the static source, thus a *lower indication* of airspeed and altitude. Which means that when you get airborne in ground effect your airspeed indicator under-reads. This is why I advised an adequate airspeed safety margin when accelerating to V_X in ground effect.

Ground Effect During Landing

Although this chapter is largely about take-off, it is worth referring here to ground effect during landing. When the aircraft enters the ground effect during the final landing phase of the approach the pilot is 'flaring out' (initially maintaining a constant angle of attack). Then 'floating' will occur due to an increase in lift and a reduction in power required.

Because of the reduced drag and power-off deceleration in ground effect, any excess speed at the point of flare can lead to an excessive 'float' distance. For STOL landings, this must be avoided at all costs. Hence the accurate control of *power* and *airspeed* is essential throughout the approach – and especially during the landing.

Carburettor Icing – Symptoms, Dangers and Precautions

'What went wrong?' asked the nervous pilot of the Cessna 172, who ended up having to make a forced landing on a disused airfield. There had been every indication of an imminent engine failure, with falling RPM and increasing rough running. Then he suddenly realised it was the old enemy – *carburettor icing*. In a panic he applied full carburettor heat and the engine cut out, but too late to clear the ice.

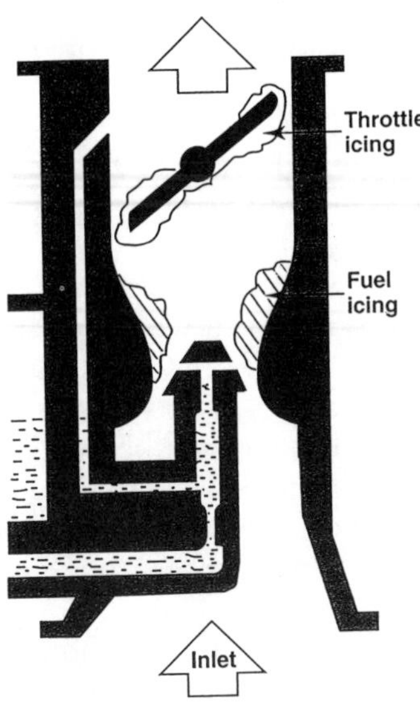

Figure 5.6 Carburettor Icing

The winter weather conditions consisted of a lowering cloud base and rain showers, with the freezing level at 3,000 feet, just 500 feet above the VFR cruising level used by the pilot of the Cessna. In fact, ideal conditions for carburettor icing. (See Figure 5.6)

Carburettor heat works best as an *anti-icing* measure. For *de-icing*, the general rule is to apply *full heat*. Therefore, by using carb heat at the right time – to *prevent* ice forming – the ensuing drama experienced by the Cessna pilot would never have happened. Steady application of hot air as required is a lot better than using maximum hot air on and off.

Application of full carburettor heat may take a short time to work (up to 90 seconds) and pilots might notice deterioration of engine performance, or even momentary cut-out, as a piece of ice is melted and some water or partially melted ice is ingested through the system.

If the aircraft is fitted with an induction air temperature gauge, partial heat may be used in accordance with the manufacturer's instructions. However, it can be dangerous to use partial heat without knowledge of the air temperature at the point of induction. *If the air is so cold that ice will not form, partial use of carburettor heat could bring the temperature up to a range which will actually promote icing.* In addition, applying partial heat can fail to arrest the reduction in power, and the consequent loss of exhaust heat will reduce the effectiveness of the carburettor heater.

When applying carburettor heat, *remember to readjust the mixture*, as the hotter – and therefore less dense – air will result in a richer mixture.

Causes of Carburettor Icing

Carburettor ice has been known to occur within the range of –10°C to + 25°C, especially if the relative humidity is high, and sometimes at even higher temperatures.

Carburettor ice forms as a result of the cooling effect of fuel vaporisation and the expansion of air as it goes through the carburettor. There can be a 15°–20°C, drop in temperature between the outside air intake and the coldest part of the carburettor.

Carburettor icing can form at any time of the year as long as the incoming air has sufficient moisture content. Rough running and loss of power are the key symptoms. For fixed pitch propellers, the loss of power is indicated by reduced RPM; for constant speed propellers, this is indicated by reduced manifold pressure.

During your analysis of the meteorological forecast and your route selection, always consider the possibility of carburettor icing – as well as airframe icing if IFR qualified. Even if you do not believe conditions are conducive to carburettor icing, check the operation of the carburettor heat control during the engine run-up (CHECKLIST ITEM!). It is better to discover that the system is not working on the ground than when you need it during flight. Further, if the carburettor heat control is not functioning, it must be rectified prior to flight.

Always use the carburettor heat in accordance with the aircraft manufacturer's instructions. Identical engines (that is, the same make and model) can react differently to the formation of carburettor icing in different airframes.

What to do if carburettor icing is a problem.

If carburettor heating is not effective, for whatever reason, change your altitude and/or your course to take your aircraft clear of icing areas as soon as possible. The options are:

- *Climb* – this can enable cruising on top of the cloud and clear of ice, or at a level that is so cold that ice will no longer form.
- *Descend* – descending may enable you to cruise at a level not so conducive to carb icing, but ensure that you keep above the lowest safe altitude.
- *Go back or divert* – if climbing or descending is not an option, then go back or divert to where conditions are less favourable to ice formation and re-plan from there.

Don't let the situation deteriorate to the extent that you cannot rectify the problem and end up like the Cessna pilot. *You* might not be so lucky.

Chapter 6

The Short-Field (STOL) Approach and Landing

Our review of STOL flying has shown that it is merely an extension and honing of existing skills, in which we need to carefully consider all the additional factors involved.

It is important to plan and execute a STOL approach and landing in a precise manner. One of the most important aspects is the close control of Rate of Descent (ROD) with power in addition, of course, to controlling airspeed with elevator.

The Drag Curve

A considerable number of landing accidents stem from the pilot's lack of understanding with the 'back side of the drag curve' – the area of reverse command. It is essential to have at least a basic understanding of DRAG during low-speed manoeuvring for STOL landings, in the same way that we have studied *ground effect*. Chapter 10 THE AERODYNAMICS OF HIGH-LIFT DEVICES will go into this in more detail, but I would like to cover a few points which directly relate to STOL approaches.

Drag is a combination of induced drag, and parasite drag.

Induced Drag is connected with *lift* (angle of attack), which reaches its maximum point just before the aircraft stalls. Therefore, drag results from the production of lift. *Induced drag varies inversely with the square of the airspeed.* So when the speed decreases by 50%, induced drag *quadruples* – just the opposite of the creation of *parasite drag*.

Parasite Drag is caused by *air friction* over the surface of the aircraft (FORM DRAG) dictated by the shape of the aircraft. Parasite drag increases with the *square of the speed.* At low speed parasite drag is low, but at high speed it has a marked influence on performance.

Skin Fraction Drag, incorporating *Interference* or *Disturbance Drag*, is the interference of the airflow between different parts of the aircraft. For instance, where the wings and tailplane meet with the main fuselage. The Robertson-STOL conversion (fitted to many general aviation aircraft), has vastly improved the 'fairings' and fitted other 'streamlining' additions to the airframe where this type of drag is highest.

Explanation of a Drag Curve

The total drag of an aircraft in flight is the combined sum of INDUCED and PARASITE drag and is shown in the Figure 6.1 a.

A. is the STALL SPEED of the aircraft.

The minimum speed for flight.
The maximum lift angle.
Any further increase in angle of attack and the aircraft will stall.

B. is the MINIMUM RATE OF DESCENT SPEED without power and also the MAXIMUM ENDURANCE SPEED WITH POWER as defined in the aircraft Flight Manual performance charts.

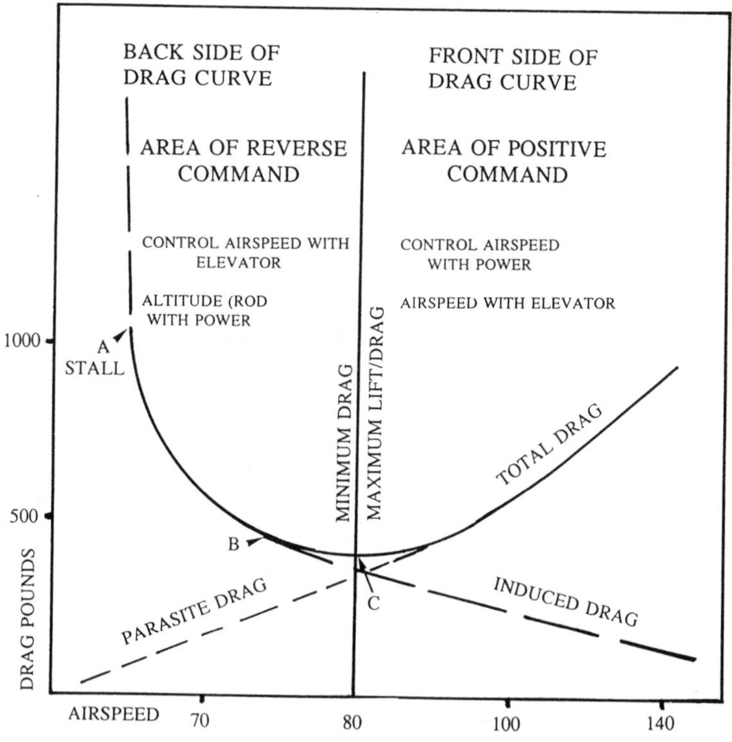

Figure 6.1a The Drag Curve

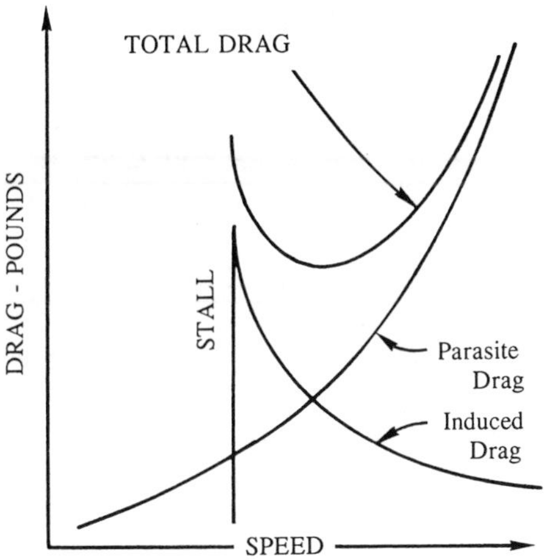

Figure 6.1b Drag Versus Speed

C. is the MINIMUM TOTAL DRAG SPEED. This provides the maximum range in nil wind. The aircraft is operating at Lift/Drag Max.

An aircraft can operate in the Front Side of the Drag Curve with safety. The aircraft flies efficiently as the design allows and it is Speed Stable. Should the airspeed fluctuate (turbulence), it will tend to return to the original airspeed, provided that the power setting/trim remain the same (level flight).

The back side of the drag curve poses a number of problems for the pilot, particularly during a STOL approach. Getting into a *low* and *slow* situation below the desired glide path is the worst scenario.

The pilot *must not* pull back on the yoke to ease the nose up. Any increase in angle of attack without adding power will:

- Lower the airspeed still further.
- Greatly increase the induced drag.
- Create an excessively high rate of descent.
- If unchecked, result in a disastrous stall at low altitude.

On the back side of the drag curve *elevator* controls *airspeed* and *power* controls *rate of descent.* There is no real problem about operating in this area, so long as there is an awareness of what can happen with low altitude, slow speed flight.

How to Accomplish a Short-field Approach and Landing

Anything to do with STOL and we are looking at using the maximum performance capabilities of the aircraft.

There are two types of STOL approach, one with an obstacle and one without. We'll be going through the procedures for both.

A good approach requires planning, a close familiarity with the aircraft type, sound technique and *exact* speed control. This is probably the most important aspect of the whole operation. A 10% increase in approach speed (seven knots for an average 75 knots approach) will mean a 20% increase in landing distance, not far short of a quarter of the runway. On a STOL airstrip, it would probably mean you would run out of runway. In the highlands of Papua New Guinea and many airstrips in difficult areas of South America, the aircraft could end up buried in thick jungle or hung up in tall rain forest trees on a steep slope!

I once had an alarming experience landing on a short bush airstrip in southern Tanzania, East Africa. The aircraft was a fully loaded Cessna 206. I had flown in there many times and until then there had been no problems. The surface was smooth laterite surrounded by tall elephant grass and thick shrub.

What I had failed to recognise on that particular day was that the laterite surface was soaking wet with recent rain. (The top inch or two soon turns to slick mud – braking action dubious to bad.) With the sun out the laterite appeared firm – familiarity breeds over-confidence syndrome – until I touched down in the usual place and things started to happen very fast.

The surface was like a skating rink and brakes were useless, with the end result that the aircraft slid off the far end of the runway and ploughed into tall elephant grass. The propeller promptly and efficiently chewed the grass into a shredded liquid green mass that totally covered the outside of the windscreen – and I was instantly IFR on the ground! I already had the engine stopped as we slithered to a surprisingly smooth halt, thankfully having hit nothing solid. I sat there gripping the controls trying not to show my intense nervous shock.

Then all the passengers applauded. They were foreign tourists of various nationalities, and thought the whole incident had been staged deliberately as part of what the brochure described as, *'a safari holiday of a lifetime packed with excitement!'* The manager and staff at the safari camp said nothing, much to my relief.

Good landings start with good approaches. That statement is certainly true. The approach commences when you enter the downwind leg (at the correct height and no excess airspeed). This is generally at 1000 feet AGL and slowed to 1.7 VSO (see Figure 6.2).

From this position you can mentally assess your approach and select a 'touchdown aiming point' on the runway. Then complete your approach/pre-

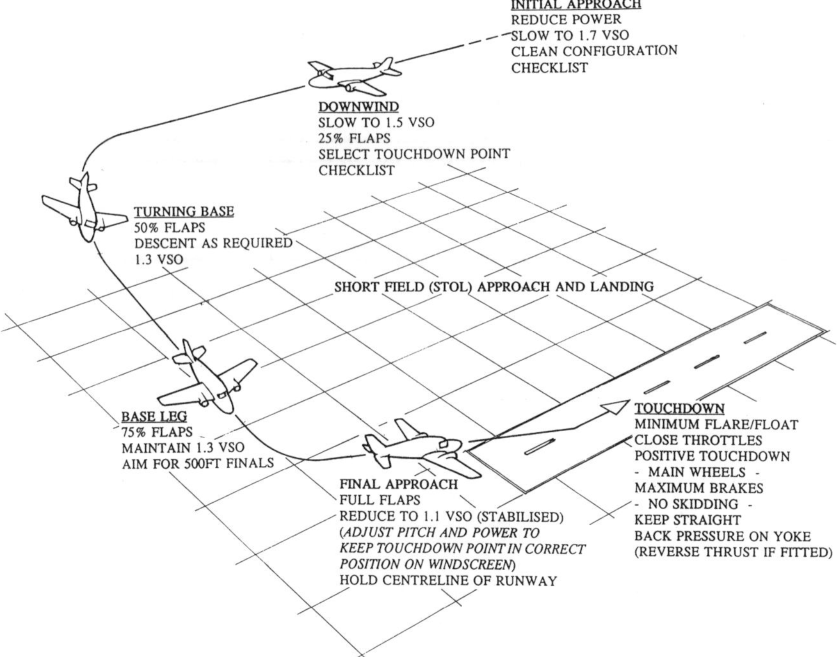

Figure 6.2 Short-Field (STOL) Approach Pattern

land checks as early as possible. *Don't do it in a hurry at the end of the downwind leg, there isn't time.* It is even more important if your aircraft has a retractable undercarriage. Get it down and locked as this will help to stabilise the speed to that required downwind.

Make sure the aircraft is correctly trimmed, with NO DRIFT to push you out of position. I have found that this a common fault among pilots. They concentrate so much on their selected touchdown point and speed control that they forget drift and maintaining an accurate height.

Remember the final downwind check:

DGI (HEADING) – HEIGHT – POSITION AND DRIFT.

Correct Base-leg Turn is Critical

If you make a judgement error on the base-leg turn, you can spoil your whole approach. When abeam the threshold of the runway (not your aiming point which should rarely be the threshold), continue the downwind leg until the threshold is at a 45 degree angle to your position. Alternatively, count to 25, this will place you in the same position.

Then make the base leg turn.

The base leg turning point is critical in the STOL approach procedure.

An *early* turn means you are too close with excessive height. Any attempt to correct this with a radical power reduction (maybe more drag flap too early) almost certainly leads to an *overshoot* of the selected touchdown point and speed above target. This could easily end with the aircraft running off the far end of the runway.

A *late* turn is the lesser of the two evils but invariably results in misjudgement of the *base leg descent,* then turning finals too low. This means you will be 'dragging' the aircraft in on a longer than normal finals, which adds to the associated problems of trying to control speed and ROD, while struggling to re-establish the correct approach profile at a very low airspeed.

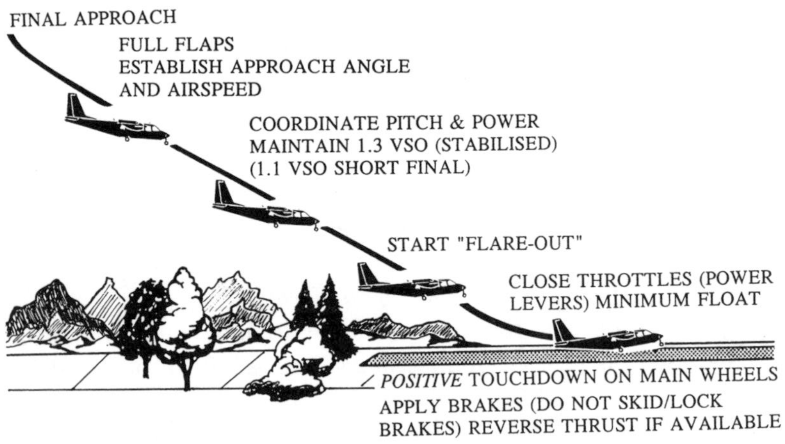

Figure 6.3 Short-Field (STOL) Approach and Landing (Side View)

Base Leg/Finals

Make a further speed-power reduction and increase drag flap to no more than 75%.

Turning onto final approach at 500 feet AGL is ideal to capture the correct *approach profile* glideslope.

From this point concentrate on 'fine-tuning' the approach (see Figure 6.3). Use a combination of pitch and power adjustments as required to keep the position of your touchdown point in the same position on the windscreen - about one-third of the way up from the bottom. (See Figures 6.4, 6.5 and 6.6)

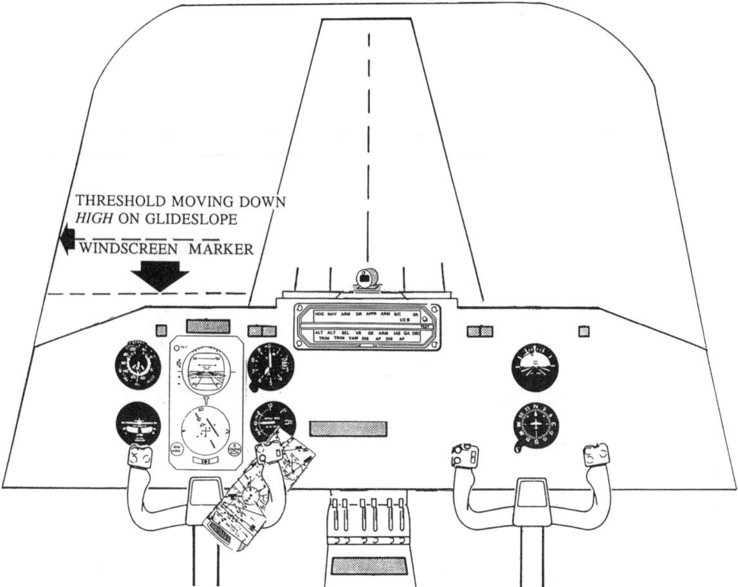

Figure 6.4

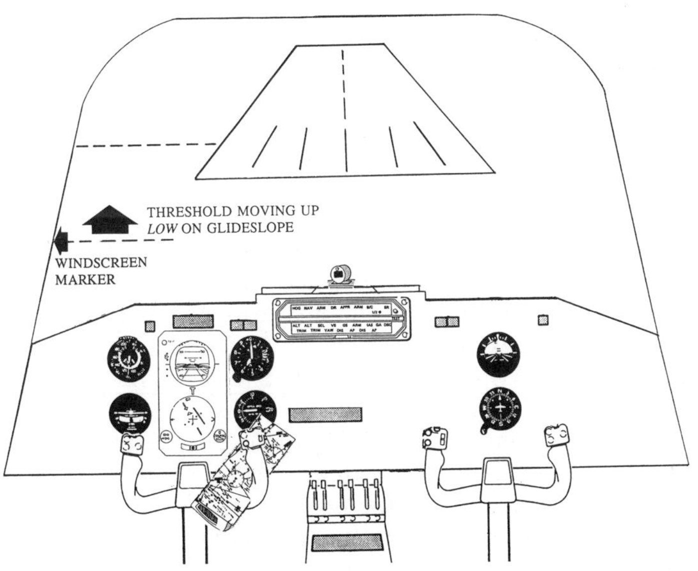

Figure 6.5

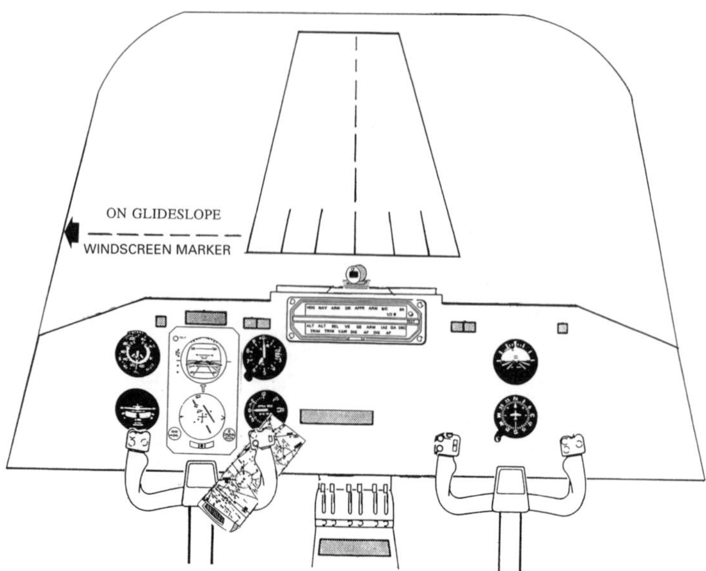

Figure 6.6 DIA

If this is done accurately, very little change in the aircraft pitch attitude will be necessary to adjust the angle of descent. Therefore only small changes are needed to control the airspeed.

CAUTIONARY NOTE: Be careful to avoid an excessively low airspeed. *This is particularly important at high altitude airstrips. Be aware you will not be able to land as short as you do at sea level. The indicated airspeed (IAS) remains the same, but the true airspeed (TAS) increases by about 2% per thousand feet AMSL.*

If the speed is allowed to drop too low, an increase in pitch and application of full power may only result in a further increased rate of descent. This occurs when the angle of attack is so great, and creating so much drag, that the maximum available power is not enough to overcome it. If we refer back to Figure 6.1a THE DRAG CURVE, we can see that this is operating way on the back side of the *power curve*, in the 'area of reverse command'.

Until you are really proficient in STOL work, you would be well advised to initially maintain 1.3 VSO to avoid getting into this situation. When you have gained more experience, that is the time to try the more extreme STOL airstrips (and the lowest speeds). Remember that just because you are flying a STOL aircraft, it doesn't mean you are *automatically* an expert STOL pilot – that takes dedicated practice.

In the final stages of the approach, only select FULL FLAP when you are committed to the landing. Your decision is going to be made earlier than on a NORMAL approach, but this should not be a problem if the correct Glidepath/Approach Profile is being maintained.

Judgement of the flareout (roundout) point must be accurate to literally avoid flying into the ground – or stalling prematurely with a sudden sink and excessively hard landing. The ideal situation is to arrive at the flare with minimum airspeed (1.1 VSO). There will be enough *elevator control* to make one 'checkback' on the yoke to transit to the landing attitude and hit the *impact point* on the runway. The short-field STOL landing technique is not one where you are supposed to 'grease it on'. A lack of 'float' during the flare, with the aircraft fully under control followed by a *positive* landing, confirms it was a good one.

As an additional guide, touchdown should occur with the aircraft in the approximate pitch attitude that would result in a power-off stall when the throttles are closed. Some STOL pilots I know leave a trickle of power on at the flare, saying they have more control over the landing. I'm not dismissing this technique, but it certainly isn't necessary if the landing is judged accurately. And it can *delay the touchdown* for a few critical metres – which could make all the difference in a max performance STOL landing at a tight airstrip.

After touchdown (for tricycle undercarriage – nosewheel aircraft) use temporary back pressure on the yoke with a positive nose-up pitch attitude for aerodynamic braking with the wings – as long as the elevators remain effective. Tailwheel types should be held firmly in the three-point attitude, using a combination of aerodynamic braking and wheel-brakes to stop the aircraft.

When the nosewheel is on the ground, use maximum braking but avoid skidding. (If fitted, anti-skid will take care of that.) At the same time reverse pitch on the props if the aircraft has the facility, or simply bring them back into BETA. Executed properly this combination will have the aircraft stopped *safely* in the *shortest possible distance*. If you lock the brakes it will:

- Wear flat spots on the tyres making them unserviceable.
- Take longer to stop, as skidding tyres have less resistance than they have while turning with hard braking action.

Short-Field Landing Over an Obstacle

Due to the location and position of many STOL airstrips, it is common to find an obstacle on the approach to the runway. This means that you may not be able to follow a standard circuit pattern. It can mean a restriction to the landing distance available and/or an adjustment in your approach procedure.

The final approach over an obstacle is made at a much steeper approach angle and close to the aircraft stalling speed not advisable in turbulent conditions or if wind shear is suspected. The choice of *touchdown point* must be such that you are able to maintain visual contact throughout the entire approach. In effect this means the base leg turning point will be closer in than for a normal short-field STOL circuit. Therefore, enter the normal downwind position at a slightly lower height, 800 feet AGL would be reasonable. Perform the approach/pre-land cockpit checks, lowering 50% flaps and airspeed 1.5 VSO.

When the trailing edge of the wing is abeam the end of the runway, turn onto base leg and commence a descent maintaining 1.3 VSO airspeed. Turn onto final approach not below 400 feet AGL, but clear of the obstacle, and complete a normal STOL approach and landing as previously described.

Cautionary Notes

- Do not be tempted to fly a normal STOL approach involving a sudden and radical reduction in power once the obstacle is cleared. This type of 'step-down' approach technique leads to considerable aircraft handling/control problems (trim changes), not to mention the possibility of a 'heavy landing' and/or running off the end of the runway due to drastically overshooting the selected threshold.
- Only a *constant* and *controlled* approach angle will ensure the aircraft reaches the target touchdown point in the most accurate and safe manner.
- If you *slightly* overshoot your touchdown point with excess speed and look like running out of runway – Retract the Flaps, this will kill the lift. But make sure you are close to the ground or you could damage the aircraft with what, in effect, is a heavy stalled landing. This is an emergency measure and does not necessarily ensure a safe outcome to the landing. If in doubt initiate a go-around early and try again.

Soft-Field Landing

The soft-field technique (see Figure 6.7) is used on runways which have a soft or rough surface, or even for landing on shallow snow or slush:

- Set up a normal approach and after turning finals select full flap.
- Control ROD with power and airspeed with elevator.
- Airspeed 1.3 VSO, then add 25-30% to the *full flap – power-off – indicated Flight Manual stalling speed.*
- Minimum float during the 'flare-out'. If there is noticeable float the airspeed is too high. A *short* application of power when entering the 'flare' will check the ROD and cushion the touchdown. No residual power should remain once the aircraft is on the ground.

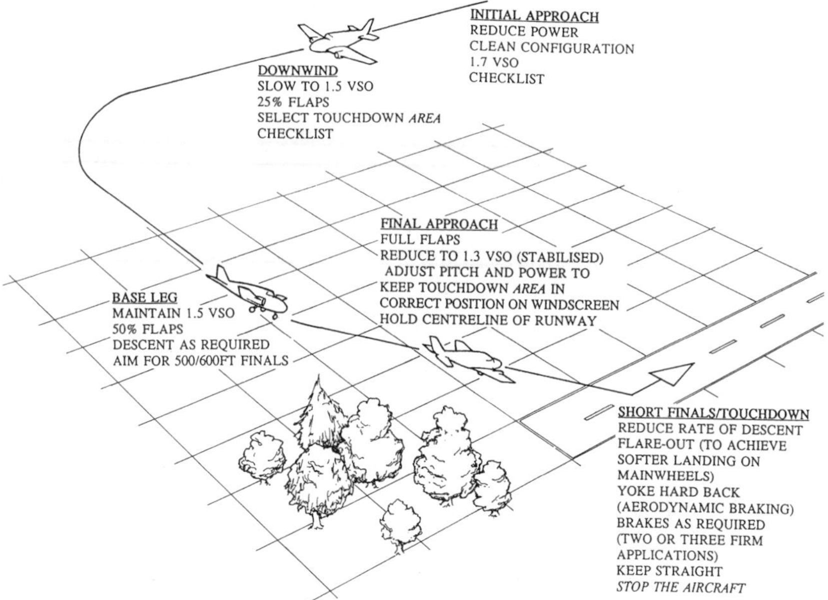

Figure 6.7 Soft-field Landing

- On the runway, hard back pressure on the yoke (aerodynamic braking) wheel brakes as necessary.
- Keep straight and stop the aircraft.

Retracting flap after touchdown will undoubtedly increase the weight on the undercarriage. But I advise caution as you are involved in a cockpit distraction at a critical phase of the landing. (No problem with a two-crew aircraft.)

How to Handle Steep Gradient Runways

Most STOL runways tend to be far narrower than normal, as they are usually laid out in relatively confined areas. Some have steep gradients, particularly in mountainous areas. These can present the unaware or inexperienced pilot with a visual illusion on the approach. In other words the *perspective* will be different.

Upwards Slope

When flying your normal approach profile an *upslope* will tend to look *longer*. This means you will have the illusion you are high on the glideslope when you are actually where you want to be. This phenomenon was mentioned briefly earlier and illustrated in Figures 4.3 and 4.4.

The natural reaction will be for you to descend (reduce power and increase ROD) to make a shallower approach. Therefore *knowing* that the runway has an upslope will automatically warn you to maintain your correct approach angle.

Downwards Slope

Approaching a *downwards* slope will make the length look *shorter*. The illusion in this case will indicate you are low, (undershooting) the glideslope, when in reality it is being flown accurately.

The illusion will be telling you to increase power and make a steeper approach, so once again you must resist believing the incorrect perspective.

Varying Size and Width Versus Illusion

STOL runway lengths vary considerably. One that is *larger* will give the illusion of being closer than it actually is. A *smaller* one will appear further away.

In the final stages of the approach a *wide* runway will cause the illusion of being too *low* (see Figure 6.9). Figures 6.10 and 6.11 show the approach to Jumla in Nepal, where the runway is wider than normal.

Moving on to the final part of the approach, the danger here is the tendency to flare out too high, which would result in a heavy landing if the pilot continued with the normal landing procedure.

The opposite example with a *narrow* runway will give the perspective of being too *high*. So there is a danger you could miss the normal flare-out and end up with a heavy landing.

Weather Conditions Affect Visual Perspective

Reduced visibility, heat haze, light rain, or any combination of these can also make you believe you are closer to the runway than you really are. The illusion will be the same as for a narrow runway – too high on the approach with the tendency to delay the flare-out. Result: heavy landing.

Knowledge and familiarity with the environment you are flying in and the STOL airstrips you are, or will be, operating from, is the key to safer flying.

Watch Out for Wind Shear

The Citation II was cruising at FL390 on a southerly track out of London heading for Lisbon.

Out over the Bay of Biscay it was a crystal clear night. A large area of

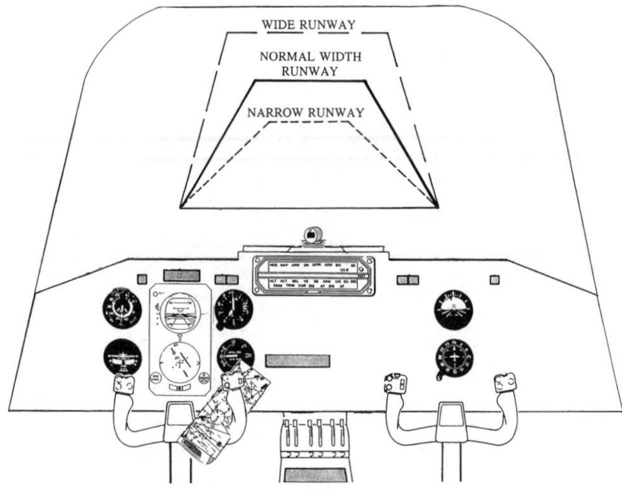

Figure 6.8 How Runways with *Varying Slopes* are seen from the cockpit on final approach giving a false impression to the Pilot

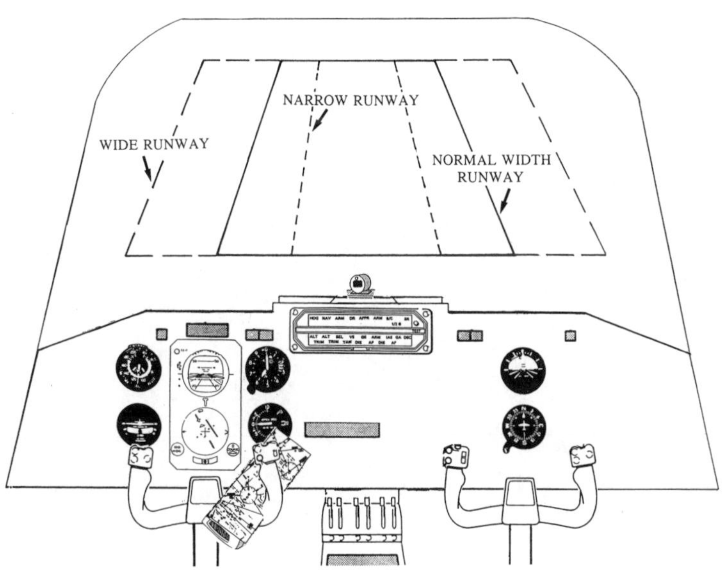

Figure 6.9 How Runways of *Varying Widths* are seen from the cockpit on final Approach giving a False Impression to the Pilot

Figure 6.10

Figure 6.11

The final approach to Jumla. This STOL airstrip is 7,700 feet AMSL and 2,200 feet (687 metres) long with a grass runway. The one feature is that the runway is very wide. This gives the pilot the illusion that he is too LOW, as depicted by the pictures above. The aircraft is on the correct glideslope.

western France and Northern Spain was spread out below in a brilliant patchwork of lights like a giant illuminated map. The cockpit instrument lights glowed dimly, and the four VIP passengers in the cabin were asleep. Overhead, it was the sort of sky you only see when flying high on a long ocean crossing, so dense with stars that there was difficulty picking out the famous constellations.

The British captain, who was chief pilot of his company's executive jet operation, especially enjoyed his job on such a smooth, clear night. Lisbon was a frequent destination so he was familiar with the approaches. The crew were relaxed and not expecting any weather problems.

Thirty minutes later the copilot called for descent towards Lisbon.

'Blazer 33, this is Lisbon, you are cleared to descend to FL100, report passing FL200.'

After further descent the Citation was radar-vectored with no delay for an ILS approach to runway 21. No problem there, smiled the captain to himself. The runway was 12,484 feet long, and easy after the short STOL airstrips he had been using during a Twin Otter operation in the Middle East only months before.

The captain knew how turbulent and difficult Lisbon could be in bad weather. Any strong wind caused turbulence and down-draughts as it forced its way over and between the hills around the airport. Nothing like that now though, and they would be on the ground in a few minutes. This was his only thought, as he concentrated on the approach.

The captain began the final descent towards the ILS outer marker, and soon intercepted both the localiser and glideslope at eight miles from touchdown. But even with the gear and first stage of flap extended he was having some trouble getting down to the glideslope.

'Blazer 32, you are above the glidepath on the centreline and cleared to land runway 21. The wind is 200 degrees 10 to 15 knots – six miles from touchdown!' Lisbon approach-radar were monitoring the final approach.

The captain could see the runway clearly, but an unanswered question was nagging at the back of his mind. For one thing the approach wasn't taking much thrust, even allowing for the fact there was a relatively light passenger load and they had burnt off more than 75% of the fuel load.

At two miles from touchdown he managed to capture the glideslope with the power levers well back towards flight-idle – a very unusual situation. With one mile to go and as the captain called for 'full flap', the VSI needle suddenly plunged downwards showing a terrifyingly rapid rate of descent. The high intensity approach lights seemed to leap towards them.

'What the ——!' the copilot started to say, but the captain was already pushing the power levers forward, hauling back on the controls and shouting for 'GEAR UP!'

For agonizing seconds both pilots were convinced the aircraft was going to plough through the long line of elevated approach lights. Then they were clear, climbing away from what could have been a disastrous crash.

The captain realised what had happened and reacted too late. You might ask how such an experienced command pilot, with Check and Training qualifications, could let the aircraft get so close to crashing straight into the ground on short finals on a clear night? Even the copilot, although relatively inexperienced, should have been aware something was going wrong. Of course it was a prime example of LOW LEVEL WIND SHEAR.

Only in recent years have aviation researchers become aware of wind shear and the dangers it presents. Now there are published civil aviation safety warnings and research papers readily available for every pilot to study. It is a complex problem, particularly in the context of minimum airspeed approaches at the ragged lower end of the flight envelope.

What is Wind Shear?

Wind shear can be described as a change in wind speed and/or direction over a short distance. It can occur either horizontally or vertically, and is most often associated with strong temperature inversions or density gradients. Wind shear can occur at both high and low altitude.

As we are concerned with STOL operations, I will concentrate purely on low altitude wind shear. There are four common sources:

- Frontal activity
- Thunderstorms
- Temperature inversions
- Surface obstructions

Frontal Wind Shear

Not all fronts have associated wind shear. In point of fact, shear is normally only a problem in those fronts with steep wind gradients. However, like so many things in weather there is no absolute rule, but here are two clues:

- The temperature difference across the front at the surface is 5°C or more.
- The front is moving at a speed of at least 30 knots.

You can obtain clues to the presence of wind shear from synoptic charts and personally from a weather forecaster. Because of the dangers connected with wind shear, air traffic controllers are always alert to warn of its possibility on the approach if the conditions seem right. Except there is no hard and fast rule, as with any weather phenomenon.

Thunderstorms

Wind shear is just one of the many unpleasant aspects of thunderstorms. The violence of these storms and their winds are well documented. However, the two worst problems, outside actual storm penetration, are *shear* related. These are:

- The 'first gust'.
- The 'downburst'.

Almost everyone has experienced and seen the rapid shift and increase in wind just before a thunderstorm hits. This is the *first gust* (see Figure 6.12). The gusty winds are associated with *mature* thunderstorms, and are the result of large down-draughts striking the ground and spreading out horizontally. These winds can change direction even up to 180 degrees very rapidly, as well as reaching speeds of 100 knots easily up to 10 miles or more ahead of the storm. The gust wind speed may increase as much as 50% between the surface and 1500 feet, with most of the increase occurring in the first 150 feet. The implication for a shear on the approach in such a case is obvious.

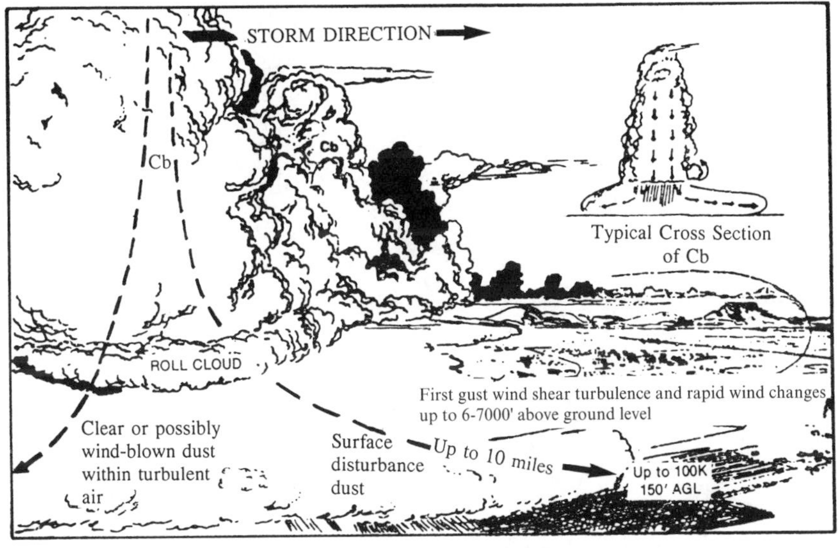

Figure 6.12 First gust hazards

On one occasion I had made a rapid high-speed descent to reach my destination airport ahead of a massive mature thunderstorm. I was cleared by ATC to report downwind for a particular runway with the surface wind already gusting up to 40 knots. Halfway along the downwind leg, the controller suddenly told me the landing runway had been changed *180 degrees in the opposite direction, with the wind gusting to 50 knots!* I estimated at that point the thunderstorm was a good 15nm away. The radical wind shift in this case had taken place within *one minute.*

The second wind problem I mentioned, the *downburst*, is also down-draught related. It is an extremely intense localised down-draught from a thunderstorm. This down-draught is often more than 700 feet per minute *(vertical velocity)* at 300 feet AGL. The power of the downburst can actually exceed aircraft climb capabilities. This does not relate just to light and general aviation aircraft, but even to high performance military jets.

The downburst is much closer to the thunderstorm than the first gust, but there is not a really reliable way to predict the occurrence. One pointer is the presence of dust or roll clouds and often intense rainfall. These are the areas to avoid.

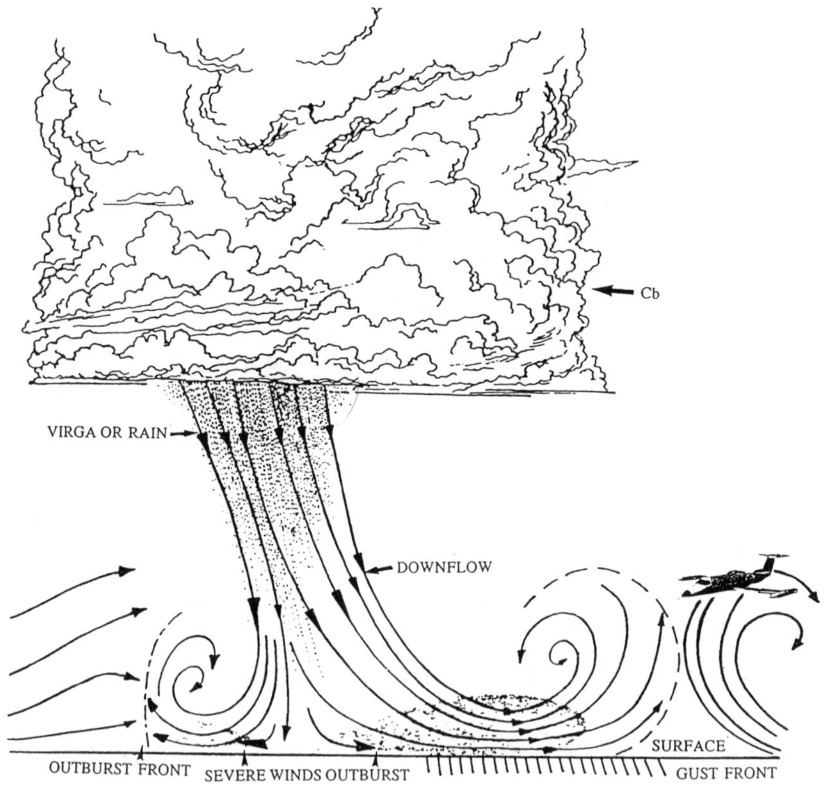

Figure 6.13 Wind Shear

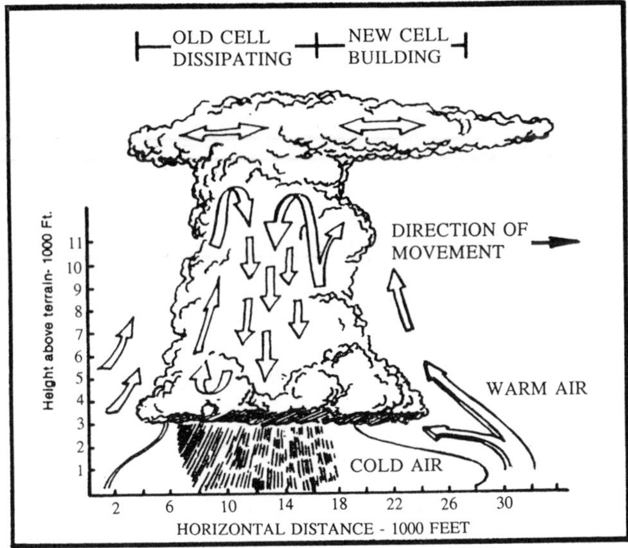

Strong down-draughts from a dissipating thunderstorm cell spread horizontally as they approach the ground. This wedge of cold air provides a lifting force on surrounding warm air which may be sufficient to initiate formation of new thunderstorm cells.

Figure 6.14

Temperature Inversions

Overnight cooling creates a temperature inversion several hundred feet above the ground. When this is coupled with high winds from what is known as the *low level jet*, it can produce significant wind shears close to the ground.

One particularly bothersome aspect of temperature inversion shears, is that as the inversion dissipates, the shear plane and gusty winds move *closer to the ground*. Making an approach in these circumstances could be very difficult.

Surface Obstructions

Surface obstructions are usually thought of in terms of hangars or other buildings near the runway. The sudden change in windspeed – especially in a crosswind – can seriously affect a landing.

There is another type of obstruction which affects some airfields close to high ground or mountain ranges – mountain passes close to the final approach paths. Strong surface winds funnelling through these passes can increase considerably with the *venturi effect*, which can cause serious localised wind shears during the approach.

The real problem with wind shear is that it is almost totally unpredictable in its magnitude of severity. A pilot can therefore expect such shears whenever strong surface winds are present.

Types of Wind Shear

Wind shear can be either *horizontal* or *vertical*. Although both components can affect an aircraft simultaneously, it is easier to discuss each one separately.

Horizontal Shear occurs when the flight path of an aircraft passes through a wind-shift plane. Fig. 6.15 shows how such a penetration would appear as an aircraft crosses a cold front.

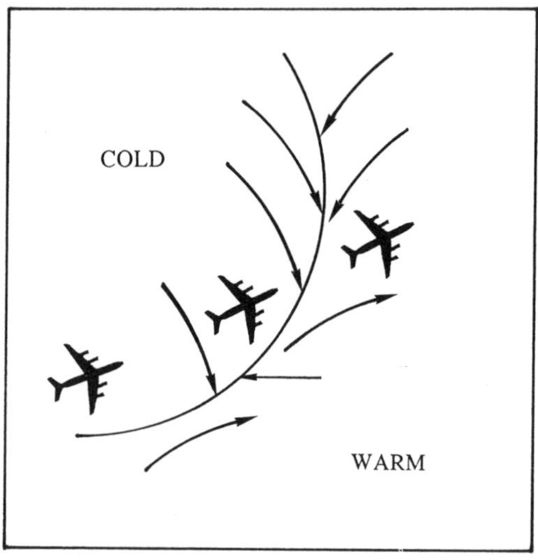

Figure 6.15

Vertical Shear is the one that is most often associated with a landing approach. The vertical shear is normal near the ground and can have the most serious effect on an aircraft. The change in velocity or direction can drastically alter lift and indicated airspeed (IAS), and the thrust requirements can exceed the pilot's capability to recover.

Summary

- Wind shear is an abrupt change in direction and/or velocity of wind.
- The shear can be horizontal or vertical.
- It is associated with frontal activity, thunderstorms, temperature inversions and surface obstructions.

As we have seen in the dramatic scenario at the beginning of this section, wind shear in its many forms can, *in a matter of seconds*, change a routine approach into an emergency recovery. The situation described highlights the very real dangers that can be encountered. Being aware of the warning symptoms can help to combat it. (By the way, the captain of the Citation II was the author of this book!)

The Effects of Wind Shear on an Aircraft

Now we have looked at the different kinds of wind shear and their sources, we can turn our attention to the effects of wind shear on an aircraft. This will include pilot techniques for coping with it.

An aircraft is affected by a change in wind direction and velocity, because the aircraft motion relative to the ground is also changed by the wind.

Let us take an aircraft that is stabilised on an instrument landing approach (ILS). The aircraft encounters a shear which results from a decreasing headwind. In this case there is a transient loss of airspeed and lift causing the aircraft to descend. So the pilot must compensate for this loss of lift. The critical factor is whether there is sufficient altitude to complete a recovery. In Figure 6.16, the shear occurs at an altitude high enough for the pilot to complete the recovery (just past the final approach fix, for example).

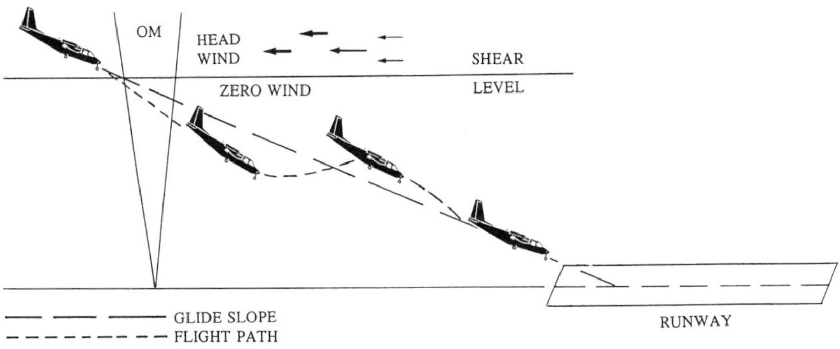

- Loss of indicated airspeed is equivalent to shear value.
- Lift is lost, aircraft pitches down, drops below glideslope.
- Pilot applies power to regain speed, pulls the nose up and climbs back to the glideslope.
- Probably overshoots the glideslope and target airspeed but recovers and lands without difficulty.

Figure 6.16 Moderate Shear – Altitude Sufficient to Effect Recovery (Example 1)

As the aircraft passes through the *shear level*, airspeed and lift are lost. The aircraft starts to sink and drops below the glidepath. The pilot sees this as a *deviation* and corrects with increased pitch and power. Very often the correction is too large and the aircraft overshoots the desired airspeed and glidepath. Since there is sufficient altitude to correct, the pilot is able to land safely.

Next we face the situation where the shear encounter is further down the glidepath. Of course reaction time is more critical. But the initial reaction of the aircraft to the shear and the pilot's correction are the same. If the pilot over-corrects and the aircraft goes above the glideslope and airspeed increases sufficiently, there is not enough altitude to recover. This means the aircraft may land long at a really excessive speed, (see Figure 6.17).

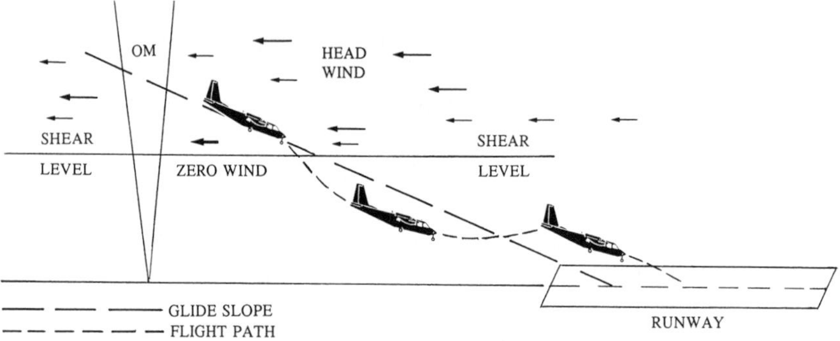

- Loss indicated airspeed is equivalent to shear value.
- Lift is lost, aircraft pitches down, drops below glideslope.
- Pilot applies power to regain speed, pulls the nose up to climb back to glideslope. Nose up trim may have been used.
- When airspeed is regained, thrust required is less than required for previously existing head wind.
- Thrust is not reduced as quickly as required, nose-up trim compounds the problem, airplane is climbed back above glideslope.
- Airplane lands long and fast.

Figure 6.17 Moderate Shear – Altitude Sufficient to Effect Recovery (Example 2)

The next case is more serious. When the altitude of the encounter is too low for recovery, or the shear itself is so strong it overcomes the aircraft performance, the aircraft lands short.

A decreasing tailwind has the opposite effect. When the aircraft crosses the shear plane and loses the tailwind, lift increases and the aircraft climbs above the glidepath. As in the headwind case the pilot's reaction can mean an over-correction.

The worst case here is the one similar to that shown in Figure 6.18. There

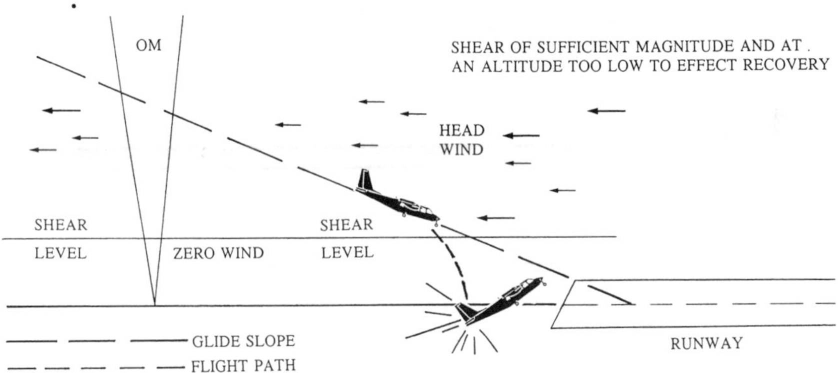

- Loss of airspeed is equivalent to shear value.
- Lift is lost, aircraft pitches down, drops below glideslope.
- Pilot applies the power to regain airspeed, pulls nose up to climb back to glideslope, engine spool-up requires time.
- Aircraft is in high drag configuration, altitude critical, increase in angle of attack produces only a slight or momentary increase in lift accompanied by a tremendous increase in drag as the maximum value of the lift/drag ratio is exceeded. The result is a momentary arrest of the descent with decreasing airspeed followed by a large increase in an already high descent rate.
- Pilot's only hope is to pull on the yokes and push on the throttles.
- Pilot action is too late, aircraft crashes short of the runway.

Figure 6.18

the over-correction leads to a transition and descent below the glidepath, but without enough altitude to correct. This is the classic high sink rate, hard landing scenario.

As we have seen from our study of thunderstorms, they generate the most hazardous form of wind shear there is. The severe, sudden changes of wind, can exceed the performance and airframe stress capabilities of many sophisticated aircraft. There have been numerous documented cases of aircraft mishaps directly related to thunderstorm wind shear.

The best way a pilot can cope with a shear is to:

- Know (or suspect if the conditions are right) that it is there.
- Know the magnitude of the change (deduced, or reported from the actual weather conditions).
- Be prepared to correct, or initiate a 'go-around' when shear symptoms appear.

High Altitude Airstrip – Indicated Airspeed

When operating at an airport with a high density altitude, the air is less dense than at sea level. This causes the aircraft to have a higher TAS stalling velocity. Many pilots therefore believe it is necessary to add anything between 10-15 knots onto the approach speed. But when they reach the flareout point, the aircraft continues to float down the runway well past their aiming point. With a short STOL strip this can lead to more than an embarrassment.

Whether you are at sea level or at a high altitude airstrip, always make your landing approach *at the same airspeed* (IAS) which you read straight off the airspeed indicator. The same applies to the climb out. It is easy to see why. The same air density that affects the lift characteristics of the aircraft also affects the airspeed indicator. The ASI pitot tube is generally mounted under the wing, or each side of the fuselage just forward of the cockpit.

The pitot tube is subjected to ram air pressure which the ASI converts into indicated airspeed. As the ASI measures the amount of ram air, it will therefore *indicate* a lower speed at a high elevation airstrip, compared to the same at sea level. This is the reason you can use the same IAS at higher density altitude airstrips. You are in fact going faster than the ASI reads, so this compensates for the decrease in aircraft performance and the increase in stall speed.

In general terms, you will find that for every thousand feet AMSL, the airspeed will be roughly 2% higher than the IAS. Therefore, you should *always use the normal IAS for take-off and approach to land, regardless of the density altitude or airstrip elevation. The ASI will automatically compensate for the conditions.*

The Dangers of Wake Turbulence

Quite frequently STOL (general aviation) aircraft use major airports as part of commuter link operations from rural and remote areas. This means integration with heavy jet traffic, often up to the size of a Boeing 747. Therefore the wake turbulence hazard to light aircraft (by this I mean up to 7000kg), is most likely at major airports where general aviation mixes with airline traffic.

In recent years there have been a number of fatal aircraft accidents directly attributable to wake turbulence. Also several serious incidents in the USA, the United Kingdom and Europe, where light aircraft have been severely affected by wake turbulence generated by much heavier aircraft.

All aircraft generate vortices at the wing tips as a consequence of producing lift. The heavier the aircraft and the slower it is flying, the stronger the vortex.

Among other factors, the size of the vortex is in proportion to the span of the aircraft which generates it. For example a Boeing 747, with a span of

Figure 6.19

65 metres (208 feet), trails a vortex with a diameter around 65 metres from each wingtip – *the same size as the entire wingspan* (See Figure 6.19). This is most severe when flaps are NOT being used.

Vortices generally persist for up to 80 seconds, but in conducive atmospheric conditions, they can last as long as two and a half minutes. They tend not to decay gradually, but come to a sudden end.

Basically, the lighter the aircraft you are flying, the greater the degree of upset will be caused if you encounter a wake vortex. At the extreme end of the scale, a microlight aircraft could easily be vulnerable to the vortices of all other aircraft, including many general aviation types.

Vortex Encounters

A light aircraft penetrating a vortex generated by a larger aircraft on the same trajectory and axis can be subjected to *severe rolling*. (See Figure 6.20). For most types it may be beyond the power of the ailerons to fully counteract the roll.

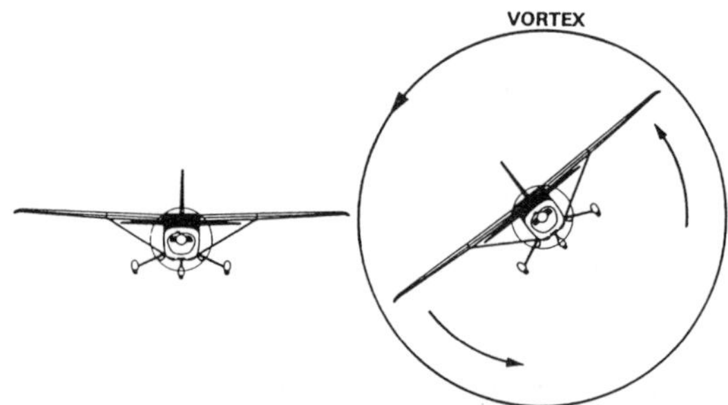

Figure 6.20 Same Trajectory Encounter

If the vortex is entered at right angles to its axis, rapid vertical and pitch displacements with airspeed changes are likely. With an oblique entry, the most likely event will have symptoms of both. (See Figure 6.21).

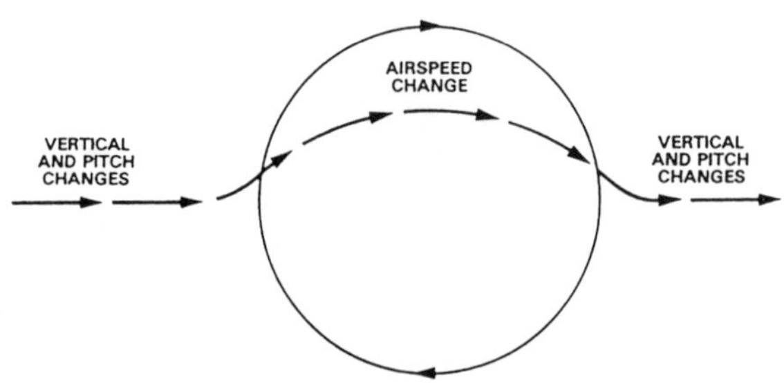

Figure 6.21 Right Angle Encounter

Vortex Ground Effect

Although a vortex encounter at altitude is very uncomfortable, not to mention alarming, the pilot can recover. If it happens closer to the ground there may not be sufficient height to recover.

A significant proportion of the incidents reported in the UK occur below 200 feet, generally just before landing, but some happen shortly after take-off, including one well documented fatal accident. This is when the affected aircraft is most likely to be directly behind a larger aircraft. I have personal experience of what can happen when you get into the vortex of a heavy jet – it is frightening. The incident happened as I was flying the approach to London Heathrow in a Citation 500 (MAUW 11,000 lbs). The weather was VFR and radar spacing seemed to have been reduced. My aircraft was behind a Boeing 747. It happened very suddenly. There was one tremendous jolt of turbulence and the Citation (which has light aileron response anyway) rolled to the right through about 110° before I could stop it. Then we were through and above the glideslope out of the way. We could easily have ended up completely inverted! What amazed me the most was that none of my passengers made any comment whatsoever.

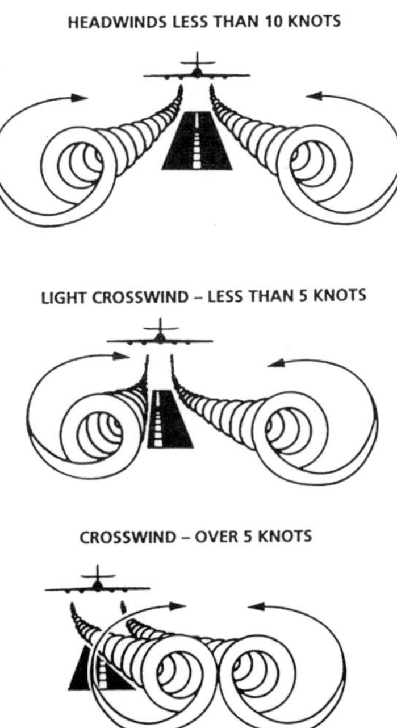

Figure 6.22 At very low altitude the area of hazard is not necessarily aligned with the flightpath of the aircraft ahead.

Vortices generally persist for about 80 seconds close to the ground where their effect is the most hazardous. They tend to move apart at about five knots in still air, so a crosswind component of five knots can keep the *upwind* vortex stationary on or near the runway. The *downwind* vortex will move away at about ten knots. In crosswinds of more than five knots, it is evident that the area of hazard is not necessarily aligned with the flight path of the aircraft ahead. (See Figure 6.22).

The Influence of Atmospheric Conditions

Vortices are especially persistent in calm conditions, temperature inversions and low windspeed conditions. Windy weather tends to shorten their life.

ATC and Vortex Separation

At most major airports, ATC will advise pilots of the necessary spacing interval; i.e. 'Skyways One Three Seven, you are number two to a Boeing 747, the recommended vortex wake spacing is six miles. Report final'. For VFR arrivals, vortex separation is a pilot responsibility, but the recommended spacing will be given by ATC (not AFISO/AIR GROUND RADIO). If in doubt always ask for a greater spacing.

Vortex Avoidance – Approach

Since the vortices are invisible (except on rare occasions when the cores become visible in very humid conditions) they are difficult to avoid. (Figure 6.19 is a prime example of heavy jet vortex wake).

There are two techniques which can be used:

- Distance can be judged visually by runway length. (Most major airports have runways between 6000 and 12000 feet long). So if the recommended spacing is six miles, then you need three to six runway lengths between your aircraft and the one ahead.
- If the aircraft on approach ahead of you is much heavier than your own type, try to keep it in sight. (This is obviously not possible in IFR conditions.)

In general, vortices drift downwards, so attempt to fly above and to the upwind side of the lead aircraft's flight path. Obviously as you get closer to the runway any lateral displacement has to be reduced, so land well up the runway – beyond the point where the heavier aircraft touched down (see figure 6.23).

Alternatively, if you are flying a STOL commuter aircraft, you might want to consider being high on the glideslope. You can always use full drag flap at the last minute and make a high angle short final approach. (This would not be feasible in heavy IFR if you were trying to get in with minimum weather conditions.)

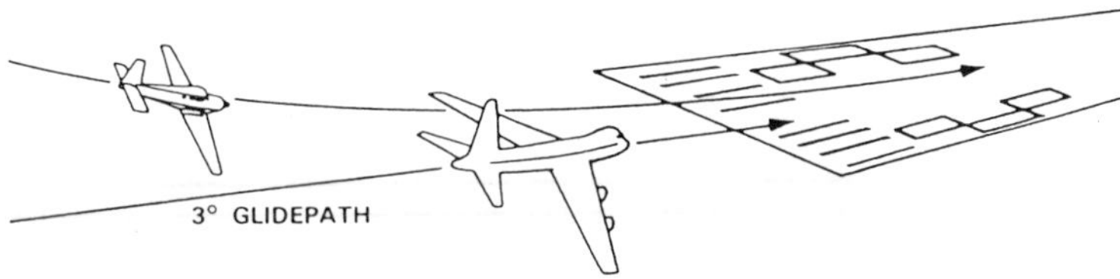

Figure 6.23 When landing behind a heavy aircraft, aim to touch down beyond the point where the heavy aeroplane landed.

The generation of vortices stops as the nosewheel contacts the runway (see Figure 6.24). The heavier the type ahead, the longer the landing roll is likely to be, so stopping a far lighter aircraft (especially one with STOL capabilities) should not present any difficulty. Heavy aircraft almost always approach on a 3° glideslope, so lighter aircraft can certainly accept steeper angles.

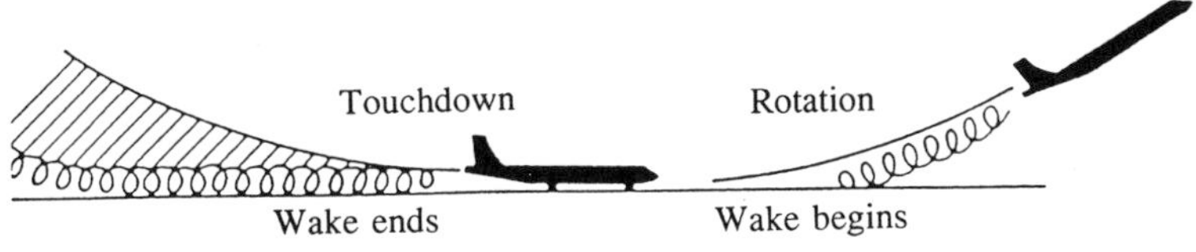

Figure 6.24 Vortex Generation on Landing and Take-Off.

Helicopters

It is considered that helicopters can generate more intense vortices than a fixed wing aircraft of the same weight. (Figure 6.25 is an excellent illustration of this phenomenon). When following helicopters, pilots of light aircraft should consider allowing a larger spacing than would normally be used behind a fixed wing aircraft of similar size.

Helicopters with rotors turning create a blast of air outwards in all directions, the strongest effect being downwind. This is not so significant when the helicopter is on the ground, with rotors turning. However, it is very severe during hovering and hover taxying, when the rotors are supporting the full weight of the helicopter, and this creates the greatest downwash. During your approach it may not be apparent which of the stages the helicopter is at. In these circumstances, pilots of light aircraft should aim to keep as far away as possible. In particular, if there is a helicopter on or near the runway, and if runway length permits, try to land further down to avoid being caught by rotorwash. If in doubt make an early decision to go-around.

Figure 6.25 Sikorsky S76. An excellent example of wake vortex. (Photo: FAA Technical Centre. By Mr J Sackett)

Wake Turbulence – ICAO Weight Parameters (Maximum Take-off Weight in Kg)

CATEGORY	ICAO AND FLIGHT PLAN
HEAVY (H)	136 000 OR GREATER
MEDIUM (M)	LESS THAN 136 000 AND MORE THAN 7000
SMALL (S) (UK ONLY)	–
LIGHT (L)	7000 OR LESS

Wake Turbulence Spacing Minima – Final Approach

Leading Aircraft	Following Aircraft	Separation Minima Distance and Time Equivalent			
		ICAO		UK	
		nm	min	nm	min
Heavy	Heavy	4	–	4	2
Heavy	Medium	5	2	5	3
Heavy	Small	NA		6	3
Heavy	Light	6	3	8	4
Medium	Heavy	3	–	*	*
Medium	Medium	3	–	3	2
Medium	Small	NA		4	2
Medium	Light	5	3	6	3
Small	Heavy	NA		*	*
Small	Medium	NA		3	2
Small	Small	NA		3	2
Small	Light	NA		4	2
Light	Heavy	3	–	*	*
Light	Medium	3	–	*	*
Light	Small	NA		*	*
Light	Light	3	–	*	*

These minima need to be applied when an aircraft is operating directly behind another aircraft and when crossing behind at the same altitude or less than 1000ft below.

*Separation for wake vortex reasons alone is not necessary

Wake Turbulence Spacing Minima – Departures

Leading Aircraft	Following Aircraft		Minimum Spacing at the Time Aircraft are Airborne
Heavy	Medium Small or Light	Departing from the same position	2 Minutes
Medium or Small	Light	"	2 Minutes

Leading Aircraft	Following Aircraft		Minimum Spacing at the Time Aircraft are Airborne
Heavy (Full length Take-off)	Medium Small or Light	Departing from an intermediate point on the same runway	3 Minutes
Medium or Small (Full length Take-off)	Light	"	3 Minutes

Faulty Approaches and Landings

Every pilot, at some time or another makes a faulty approach and/or a bad landing. Therefore we will now consider how to correct the various faults.

In addition to occasional errors in judgement during some part of the approach and landing, many variables, such as turbulence, shifting wind direction, gusts and other aircraft in the traffic (circuit) pattern create problems. These factors require the pilot to make corrections and adjustments to ensure an accurate approach profile at the right speed. Therefore the pilot must be aware of any changing situation and be able to deal with this immediately – not allowing any faults or potential faults to develop. *Anticipation* is the name of the game, because recovery from faulty or abnormal approach and landing situations, rates equally in importance with the skills exercised to accomplish a normal approach and landing.

In serious STOL flying, there is only a slim margin to correct any errors. Runways are short, approach angles are steeper, and flying skills and judgement have to be really sharp. So let's look at some common faults and how to correct them.

General Tips

Before making adjustments to any approach/landing problem – think basic. By that I mean understand which control has what effect, and the interrelationship of Power, Airspeed and rate of descent.

FIRSTLY, you must select a touchdown point or target area to aim for.

SECONDLY, there must be some form of visual gauge (a method) to assess your correct approach profile. An easy method is a visual, or 'mind's eye' mark one-third of the way up the windscreen. You can keep your touchdown point roughly aligned with this marker throughout the final approach.

THIRDLY, remember that:

- Power controls the rate of descent
- Speed is controlled by the elevators

(There is another method, but I don't want to confuse the issue here.)

Note: You do not want to be making radical speed or pitch angle changes (resulting in pronounced trim) during the approach. It makes control of the aircraft more difficult and is an unnecessary distraction. Also, I have noticed that many pilots (even quite experienced professionals) make large power changes during the approach, which often leads to the aircraft 'porpoising' above and below the correct glidepath. This is undesirable and can be eliminated if the basic approach guidelines are followed.

Rule of Thumb

- In an aircraft with a fixed pitch propeller, an adjustment of 100 RPM equals a change of 100 FPM to the rate of descent.
- In an aircraft with variable pitch/manifold pressure, an adjustment of 1 inch of manifold pressure equals a change of 100 FPM to the rate of descent.
- In a turbo-prop aircraft with variable pitch propeller, an adjustment of 1 inch (or 1 foot pound) of torque pressure equals a change of 100 FPM to the rate of descent.

By following this rule of thumb, then adjusting the speed with the elevators, an accurate approach will require only minor (control pressure/movement) changes.

These measures are rough guides, but the point I am making here is that by adjusting *any* approach profile faults, small (step by step) changes to the flight parameters makes for smoother, more proficient flying.

REMEMBER: *CHANGE – CHECK – HOLD* (LET AIRSPEED/ROD SETTLE) – *ADJUST* (FURTHER IF REQUIRED) – *TRIM* (WHEN SATISFIED).

A High, Fast Approach and 'Ground Shy' Landing

This is a common fault among relatively inexperienced pilots. It also happens sometimes in the initial stages of teaching the STOL approach and landing, resulting mainly from nervousness. In STOL, the problem lies in getting used to the high angle approach and much lower airspeed. But whatever the case, the answer once more lies in *basic procedures*. And this starts well before turning onto final approach.

- On the downwind leg slow the aircraft to maintain the correct circuit speed and height – 1000 feet AGL is normal.
- Choose your touchdown target area and turn onto base leg when the threshold is at an angle of 45°.
- Reduce power and set up a rate of descent not exceeding 400 FPM at the normal speed. Trim the aircraft. (Minor adjustments can be made as required and circumstances dictate.)
- Aim to turn finals at between 500–600 feet AGL.
- If your target threshold is moving down the windscreen in relation to the marker, you are overshooting. Therefore, reduce power by a small amount, sufficient to slow or stop the overshoot condition and so regain your correct approach profile. (The opposite will apply if you are undershooting.)

The Landing

Hold your approach profile down to the point of 'flareout'. This is reached at about 10–20 feet AGL. (Judged visually; see below.)

To ensure a smooth, accurate transition into the actual landing:

- Look about three-quarters of the way down the runway – not directly over the aircraft nose at the ground.
- Then when the ground (proximity) appears to visually and rapidly 'spread out' around the aircraft, the correct 'flareout' point has been reached.
- Check back on the yoke (elevators) sufficiently to place the aircraft in the level flight position, keep the wings level (ailerons), and complete the landing as normal, maintaining a positive back pressure on the yoke.

Low Final Approach

A low final approach usually starts with an excessively high rate of descent on the base-leg. Also not enough power, and/or probably too much flap.

If the altitude is excessively low, then considerable power must be applied to stop any further descent, and to reach a recovery point (intercepting the correct glidepath) from which a landing can then be made. *Do not* increase the aircraft pitch angle without applying power, because there will be a rapid decrease in airspeed. This can quickly reach the critical stalling angle of attack.

If there is even a small doubt about completing the approach and landing safely – take immediate go-around/missed approach action and start again.

Slow Final Approach

Slow final approach has been covered in depth during the explanation of STOL approaches. However, to summarise the main elements in general terms:

- At low airspeed we are flying close to the stalling angle of attack. Therefore close attention should be paid to the control of airspeed and rate of descent.
- The rate of descent must be controlled right down to the accurate judgement of the flareout, which will be minimal. Otherwise the aircraft may stall or sink rapidly, resulting in a hard impact with the ground.
- If a slow final approach is not the desired objective, then power should be applied to accelerate the aircraft and maintain the correct approach speed. If any doubts exist initiate a go-around.

Use of Power

Power can be used:

- To accelerate the aircraft to increase lift without increasing the angle of attack.
- To slow or stop excessive descent.
- In a slightly high flareout, the landing attitude can be maintained, and sufficient power used to ease the aircraft onto the ground.
- After touchdown the throttle(s) should be closed (if they are not already), so that no residual thrust or lift will remain during the after landing ground roll.

Flareout

In my experience, the *flareout* or *roundout* point presents many problems to pilots of all experience levels. Here are suggestions for eliminating faults.

Flaring Out Too High

Where to look and how to judge the 'flareout' point has already been covered. Now let us consider some specific points.

- During a high flareout the aircraft gives the impression it has stopped descending. In fact the flareout has been made too quickly, and the aircraft is in the level attitude at a greater height than it should be above the runway. (see Figure 6.26). If the flareout is continued in these circumstances, the airspeed would decrease rapidly, possibly resulting in the critical (stalling) angle of attack being exceeded.

- To avoid this happening, the pitch attitude should be kept constant. The aircraft will decelerate and start descending. The flareout can then be continued into the correct landing attitude. (This technique should be used only if there is sufficient airspeed; otherwise a small amount of power will be necessary to 'cushion' the loss of lift and check the rapid decrease in airspeed.)
- Maintain the aircraft attitude with back pressure on the yoke (elevator). Do not release the back pressure, otherwise lift will be lost and the nosewheel could contact the runway very hard, perhaps even collapse! If in any doubt during a high flareout, immediately apply full (take-off) power and go-around.

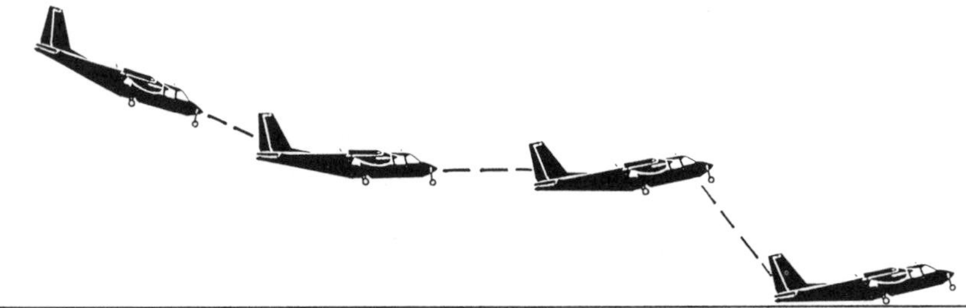

Figure 6.26 Flaring Out Too High

Low, or Too Rapid, Flareout

Flaring out too low or too quickly to prevent a hard (premature) touchdown, can lead to a very dangerous situation as sudden heavy G-load factor on the wings can cause an accelerated stall. The further effect of this would be an excessively hard landing, then a bounce back into the air. Due to the back pressure on the yoke (elevators), it is entirely possible the tail could hit the runway.

Recovery from this situation means an immediate application of a substantial burst of power to avoid a stall. If sufficient runway is available the situation can be recovered and a normal landing made.

Floating During Flareout

Floating is usually caused by excessive airspeed during the approach. The flareout will result in a long 'float', missing the selected touchdown point and shortening the available runway distance. (This is the worst scenario if attempting a STOL landing.)

Another way excessive 'float' can happen, is as a result of the pilot diving at his touchdown point (not following the normal procedure of a reduction in power to increase the rate of descent while keeping a stable airspeed). As a consequence the airspeed will increase rapidly. The pilot cannot then establish the correct touchdown attitude, because the flareout will increase the angle of attack and cause excessive lift. The aircraft will then float down the runway. (See figure 6.27).

Figure 6.27 Floating During Flareout

When floating, careful judgement is needed to control the aircraft (speed, height, rate of 'sink', keeping it straight with rudder). The pitch attitude must be smoothly and gently adjusted to ensure a normal touchdown. ANY ERROR IN JUDGEMENT AND TIMING WILL CAUSE EITHER BOUNCING OR 'BALLOONING'.

Recovery from floating will be affected by a variety of factors – crosswind component, length of the runway remaining (can the aircraft be stopped in the distance even if a landing is made) and, not least, the ability, skill and proficiency level of the pilot. Again, if you have any doubts (and especially on a short runway) – GO-AROUND.

Ballooning During Flareout

'Ballooning' is caused by the pilot misjudging the rate of 'sink' during a landing, i.e. thinking the aircraft is descending faster than it is, (probably by not looking in the right place down the runway to help with judgement of the flare). The sudden and rapid increase in pitch attitude, angle of attack and consequently lift, starts the aircraft climbing. This is 'ballooning'. (See figure 6.28). It can be dangerous if the gain in height is excessive, due to the above factors. However, if the ballooning is *slight*, the attitude should be held and the aircraft allowed to decelerate and settle onto the runway.

Figure 6.28 Ballooning During Flareout

Power can be used to cushion severe ballooning, but the throttle(s) (power levers) must be closed immediately after touchdown. However, it must be noted that torque will be produced when using power during ballooning, so rudder must be used to keep straight.

The sure, safe way to deal with *excessive* ballooning is to go-around. Attempting to salvage the landing could easily result in a stall.

With a crosswind, unless the pilot can accurately correct for drift, maintain directional control, and has the ability to carry out the correct technique – then the only thing to do is go-around.

Touchdown

Bouncing During Touchdown

The corrective action for a bounce is the same as for ballooning. However, when the aircraft makes a hard touchdown due to an excessive sink rate or an incorrect flareout attitude, the aircraft bounces back into the air. This is not a true bounce, as the undercarriage oleo units and tyres absorb some of the impact shock.

What actually happens is that the aircraft *rebounds* into the air, as the wing's angle of attack has suddenly increased, producing a much greater amount of lift. The instant change in angle of attack is the result of *inertia* forcing the aircraft tail downwards when the main wheels hit the ground. The harder the impact the higher the bounce, depending on airspeed and the amount of increase in the angle of attack. (See Figure 6.29).

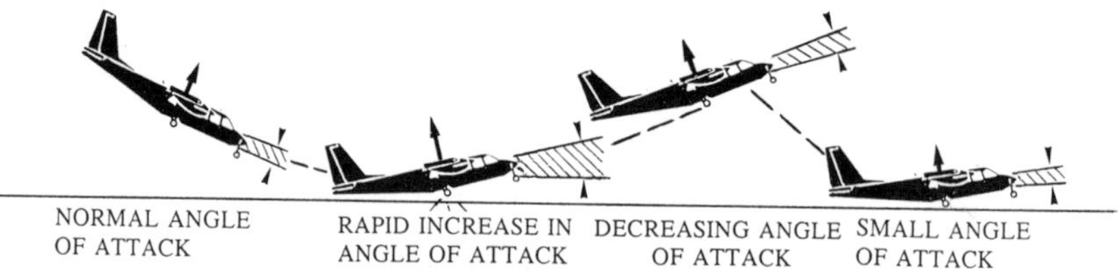

Figure 6.29 Bouncing on Touchdown

If the bounce is slight, all that is required to correct the situation is the application of sufficient power to cushion the subsequent touchdown, with a smooth adjustment to the pitch (landing) attitude.

In a crosswind, the crosswind correction must be maintained throughout the subsequent bounce until the next touchdown is made. But remember this will be at a lower airspeed (the upwind wing will therefore have to be lowered even further to compensate for drift). If no correction is held after the bounce, then the crosswind component will cause the aircraft to roll with the wind. This will expose more surface area and rapidly increase the drift.

For a severe bounce the safest action is to go-around immediately. Make no attempt to continue with the landing. However, even with full take-off power already applied, it is possible the aircraft may touchdown (bounce) again. So it is essential that directional control is maintained, with the pitch angle lowered to a safe climb attitude. *A stall must be avoided at all costs.*

Heavy (Hard) Landing

The purpose of oleo struts, shock absorbers, tyres and such, is to cushion the impact at touchdown and to increase the time in which the aircraft's vertical descent is stopped. When the aircraft contacts the runway surface, its *vertical speed* (ROD) becomes zero. If we didn't have 'shock absorbing' devices, the impact forces could be so great as to cause severe structural damage to the aircraft.

The shock absorbing devices do not provide all the cushioning effect. A considerable amount of help is provided by lift from the wings as the aircraft 'flares out'. But lift decreases rapidly as the aircraft forward speed decreases. At the point of touchdown the landing gear and other devices are compressed by the force of the touchdown (the aircraft inertia and weight). When the descent stops the lift will be almost zero, leaving the gear to carry the full burden of inertia and weight. Bear in mind that the instantaneous load experienced at touchdown can easily reach up to four times the weight of the aircraft, depending on the severity of the impact.

Touching Down with Drift (Crabbing)

It is a normal procedure for a pilot to correct for wind drift on final approach by 'crabbing' into the wind. If this attitude was held right through the flareout and touchdown – while the aircraft was still moving sideways – it would impose extreme side-loading (shearing effect) on the landing gear. In the worst case it can cause structural failure.

The best method of preventing drift is the 'wing down' (into wind) technique. This keeps the aircraft aligned with the runway and the direction the aircraft is moving during the approach, right through to touchdown. (Or a combination of crabbing and wing down as appropriate.) If there is insufficient corrective action to stop drift during a crosswind landing (wing down, crabbing – with any residual crabbing eliminated with the use of rudder prior to touchdown), *then gear side-loading will take place.*

The adhesion of the mainwheel tyres provides resistance to the aircraft's sideways motion causing abrupt deceleration. Inertia force takes over, and this produces a moment around the mainwheel on contact with the runway.

(see Figure 6.30). This will try to overturn or tip the aircraft. As the *windward* wing is raised by the moment, all the weight and impact of landing will be concentrated on one mainwheel. As stated, this can easily cause structural damage.

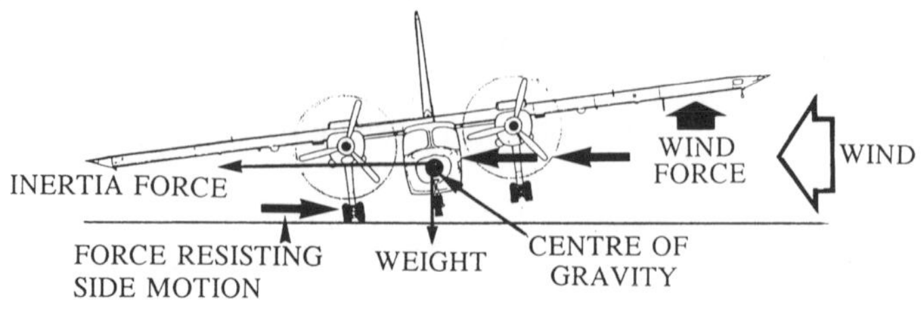

Figure 6.30 Drifting during Touchdown

The crosswind is also acting on the fuselage surface behind the main wheels. This tends to 'weathervane' (yaw) the aircraft into the wind. If it was allowed to continue it would result in a ground loop. However, nosewheel gear aircraft are less liable to ground loop, since the CG is located forward of the main landing gear. So any time a swerve does develop, centrifugal force acting on the CG will tend to slow or even stop the swerving action.
The corrective actions are as follows:

- Apply aileron towards the high wing.
- Stop the swerve with rudder.
- Brakes should only be used to correct for turns or swerves when the rudder control is inadequate.

Summary of Main Points

- Any time the landing attitude (as in the flareout) is excessively high, a high rate of sink or a stall situation must not be allowed to develop – use full power and go-around.
- Whether ballooning or bouncing if the aircraft is in danger of approaching a stalled condition; use full power, adjust the pitch attitude for the climb and GO-AROUND.
- Do not be hesitant about using full into-wind aileron when landing with even a light crosswind component.
- Revise and study this section on Faulty Approaches and Landings.

CHAPTER 7

MOUNTAIN FLYING – HOW TO LIVE AND FLY ANOTHER DAY

We never achieve mastery over the mountains, because the mountains are never conquered. They are permanent and implacable. Respect them at all times and know their dangers, and a remarkable sense of flying achievement will be yours.

Every STOL pilot at some time or another will be required to fly into short mountain airstrips. Some will be at the bottom of deep valleys, while others are perched precariously high up on the sides of steep slopes. Whatever the case, a great deal of caution is required.

Strong winds with mountain waves, up-draughts, down-draughts, turbulence, cloud covered ridges and a variety of other problems face the unwary or inexperienced pilot. So my intention here is to provide you with sufficient information to make your mountain flying safer.

In many mountain areas such as the Himalayas, only early morning (up to 1000 hours local) and late afternoon/evening flying operations (after 1600 hours local) are possible. This is due to heavy cloud formation, plus the very strong 'canyon' winds with associated turbulence which build up during the day.

The Importance of Maintaining Sufficient Ground Clearance

Close attention must be given to ALTITUDE when approaching mountains. Under average conditions a 2,000 feet ground clearance would be appropriate while building up experience. This will decrease as you develop a feel for the various types of conditions. With mountain waves, the ground clearance altitude will increase. This will be to avoid strong down-draughts (a considerable hazard for general aviation aircraft) but more importantly the *turbulence* which goes with it. If you do get caught in a down-draught, with adequate altitude there is manoeuvring space available towards lower ground. You can then climb in safety to get above it.

The initial approach to Jumla STOL airstrip is over a sharp 11,000 foot ridge. If there is a strong wind blowing then the approach is at a 45 degree angle WITH PLENTY OF CLEARANCE required because of turbulence and down-draughts. It was calm the day I crossed. Any cloud covering the ridge – and it's a 180° turn and return to base.

Figure 7.1

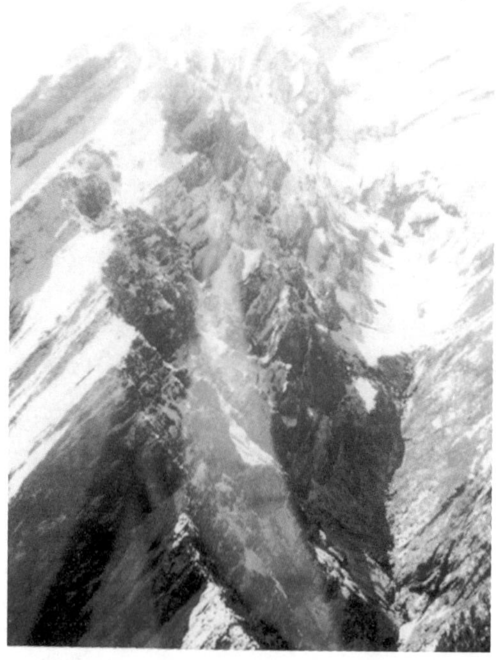

Figure 7.2

Crossing Ridges

If it is possible, always approach mountain ridges at a 45-degree angle in order to evaluate the actual air conditions (stability, turbulence). After safely negotiating the first ridge, you can evaluate the situation (weather ahead and escape routes to lower terrain).

If there is a wind blowing and there are strong down-draughts present, then you will have to alter heading accordingly to cross further ridges in your flight path at appropriate angles. BUT ALWAYS HAVE AN ESCAPE ROUTE IN THE EVENT OF AN EMERGENCY.

Even if you are confident when approaching a ridge with only a light wind, it can easily lull you into a false sense of security. A down-draught can suddenly affect the aircraft from as short a distance as 500 feet from the ridge, sometimes even less. Figures 7.1 and 7.2 show the initial approach to Jumla STOL airstrip which is over a sharp ridge.

What to Watch Out For

There is always the temptation to cross a ridge at low altitude. If you do this but notice that you appear to be climbing, or at least maintaining a height that enables you to see well ahead on the other side of the ridge – it is reasonably safe to continue. However, if your view of the other side is disappearing fast, turn away, climb and cross at a higher altitude.

Don't try to be a hero. The mountains are littered with crashed aircraft flown by so-called intrepid aviators who thought they could ignore the dangers of mountain flying. You can learn to live with them – but you can never beat them.

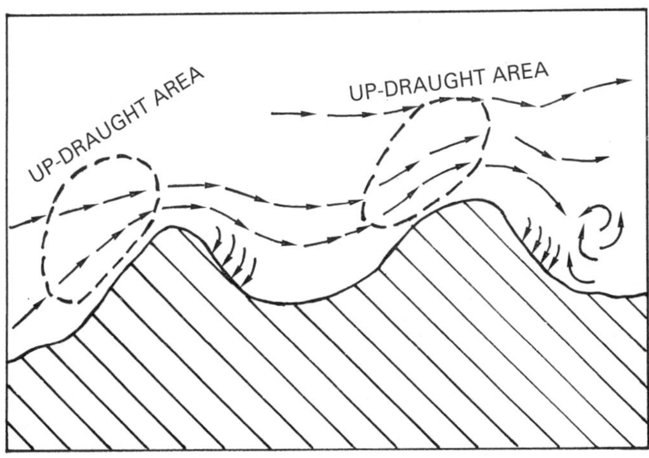

Figure 7.3 Strong Winds Blowing Perpendicular to the ridges

Now let's summarise other advice:

- Because of the cushion of air on the *windward* slopes, fly in the *downwind* direction, it will help to lift you over the ridge (See figure 7.3) (On the down-draught side you will be *flying away*).

Coping With Valleys

Whichever way you fly down a valley, use the up-draughts. The aircraft rate of climb will be better. By avoiding the lee side you will be out of the down-draughts and increased turbulence.

- Do not let your airspeed drop below V_Y (best rate of climb speed).
- If it is turbulent, make sure you have 20 knots above V_Y. This gives you a safety margin of error in case you have to turn back. You can trade the extra airspeed for altitude while turning.
  By flying the up-draught side of a valley you have:
  - More room to turn if necessary.
  - You can avoid possible wind shear in the centre.
- If you have to turn around for whatever reason (weather, technical), make it the shorter, upwind, climbing turn.
- If you are forced to turn quickly, make it a normal steep turn. No fancy aerobatic manoeuvres that could disorientate you in a critical (terrain) situation. You don't want to compound your problems with wing-overs or something more drastic. The presence of turbulence, up-draughts, down-draughts and the possibility of wind shear – not to mention the close proximity of cumulus granitus is a deadly combination.
- Be aware that wind direction can vary radically from one end of a long valley in a mountain range to the other; particularly as valleys rarely follow a straight line, so terrain features can quickly change from up-draught into down-draught areas.
- Avoid narrow valleys as you would the bubonic plague. A high percentage have 'dead-ends'. The definition of a narrow canyon is: 'If you have to turn around, the radius of turn is greater than 50% of the valley width'. If you are in a valley and it starts to narrow – *watch out!* Don't go beyond a point where you cannot turn around. A useful guide is; if you close the throttle on a piston engine – reduce the power levers to flight-idle on a jet-prop – there is still enough height to make a 180° turn.

One final word of advice. Never fly towards mountains head-on. Strong down-draughts and turbulence can easily force the aircraft down into a mountain slope. Use the 45° angle approach method – it could save your life!

Turbulence – How it is Produced

Turbulence is something a pilot has to cope with at all times to a greater or lesser extent. It can affect flight planning, principally the route and altitude chosen to the destination.

It can also vary in intensity from a few light bumps to severe turbulence, which can cause structural damage to the aircraft. Vertical gusts can change the angle of attack. This causes a variation in lift and in the flight load factor.

The first advice I can give you here is, when encountering moderate or severe turbulence, immediately slow the aircraft to the turbulence penetration speed given in the Flight Manual. If nothing is listed, then multiply the stall speed by 1.7 and use that.

Turbulence is associated with many varying weather patterns. A knowledge of how it is caused can help you avoid the worst areas. The main causes are:

- Wind shear (which we covered earlier in sufficient detail for a broad understanding).
- Wind blowing across mountains and along valleys.
- Air moving vertically in convective currents in warm to hot weather conditions.

A pilot can obtain information about turbulence from:

- His own experience of the weather conditions which produce it.
- Weather forecasts, met (synoptic) charts and pre-flight briefing from a qualified met forecaster.
- PIREPS (pilot reports).
- Radar, which also gives a good indication.

A pilot should never be afraid of turbulence. He should understand it and be able to deal with it from experience, avoiding the worst by pre-knowledge of the weather conditions which produce it.

The pilot of a light aircraft will be affected more by turbulence than a heavy jet in the same area. So his perception of the categories of severity will be different.

As far as the design of civilian aircraft is concerned, the design structural integrity of all types is very similar.

Classification of Intensity

Turbulence is divided into four degrees of intensity: Light, moderate, severe and extreme. As a yardstick to classify these degrees of intensity, a medium weight transport aircraft (F27) category was used.

- *Light*. Occupants of aircraft may be required to use seat belts at captain's discretion. However, objects such as passenger catering trays remain unaffected.

- *Moderate.* Occupants, including cabin crew, must use seat belts. Passengers are thrown against belts and unsecured objects in the cabin will move about.
- *Severe.* The aircraft can easily have brief periods where it is out of control. Passengers (and crew) are in for a rough time. They will be thrown continually against the back of their seats and onto their seat belts. Objects not secured in the cabin will be thrown about.
- *Extreme.* It isn't often any aircraft gets tangled up with this. The aircraft will be tossed about violently and will be virtually impossible to control. There is every possibility structural damage (or failure) could occur.

Different Types of Turbulence

Turbulence can be divided into four main types: convective, wind shear, clear air and mechanical. As we have covered the causes of *wind shear*, I'll deal only with the other three types here.

Convective Turbulence Also Called Thermal Turbulence

Experienced mostly by pilots of low flying aircraft on a hot day, convective turbulence is caused by localised air currents, both rising from and descending to ground level at the same time. Up-draughts and down-draughts develop in air whenever the lapse rate in temperature exceeds the dry adiabatic, and in saturated air when it exceeds the moist adiabatic lapse rates.

Cumulus clouds form in the hot air, and there are rising currents underneath and inside the clouds. In the clear air between them, there is a downward movement of air which is much slower and spreads over a larger area. (See Figure 7.4).

The force of convection currents is proportional to the difference in air density. Therefore the hotter the actual air temperature, the greater the proportional temperature difference between the rising and descending air. In very hot tropical climates, there will be a larger difference in temperature (and a greater speed of the currents) through a deeper vertical layer of air, compared to lower temperatures.

Rock and sandy surfaces heat faster than those covered with dense vegetation. Convective turbulence is most active in light winds. A strong wind will break up the air currents and the convective process will dissipate.

Clear Air Turbulence (CAT)

Clear air turbulence is not connected with any cloud formation. The exception to this is mechanical turbulence over mountains where no clouds are present.

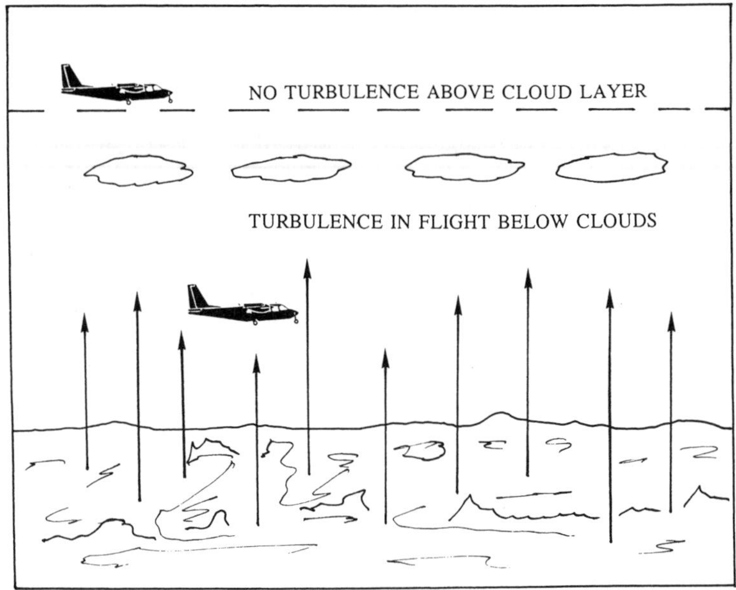

Figure 7.4 Convective Turbulence

If we take this one stage further, CAT is used to describe strong mountain wave turbulence which spreads a considerable distance away from mountains.

The true clear air turbulence is at high altitude, where wind shear turbulence occurs frequently in the area around a *jet stream*. This is a relatively narrow band of 'high-speed' air. The vertical and horizontal currents fall away rapidly at the edges and can generate some quite severe turbulence at times. The height of CAT varies from winter to summer from approximately 30,000 to 34,000 feet.

Outside of jet streams CAT is difficult for the met forecaster to predict, being scattered and patchy in nature. Upper air charts give little or no clues to the position of CAT.

Mechanical Turbulence

Mechanical turbulence is caused by obstruction to the wind flow. When wind hits an object it is forced to change direction and go over the top and around. After passing behind, it returns to its original course and turbulent eddies of air are formed in the *lee* of the object. These eddies are called mechanical turbulence.

Where there are numerous objects of all shapes and sizes, such as buildings, areas of trees and undulating rough ground, the smooth uninterrupted flow translates into a maelstrom of wind eddies. This will produce mechanical turbulence which will be felt for several hundred feet above the ground.

If we move this one stage further, to a strong wind blowing over large mountains, we can see a dramatic increase in the overall effect. Figure 7.5 shows what happens. The wind blowing up the windward slope is stable and reasonably smooth. When it spills over the top and down the *leeward* side it develops strong down-draughts and turbulence. These down-draughts are dangerous, and can pull an aircraft into the side of a mountain without the pilot being able to do anything about it!

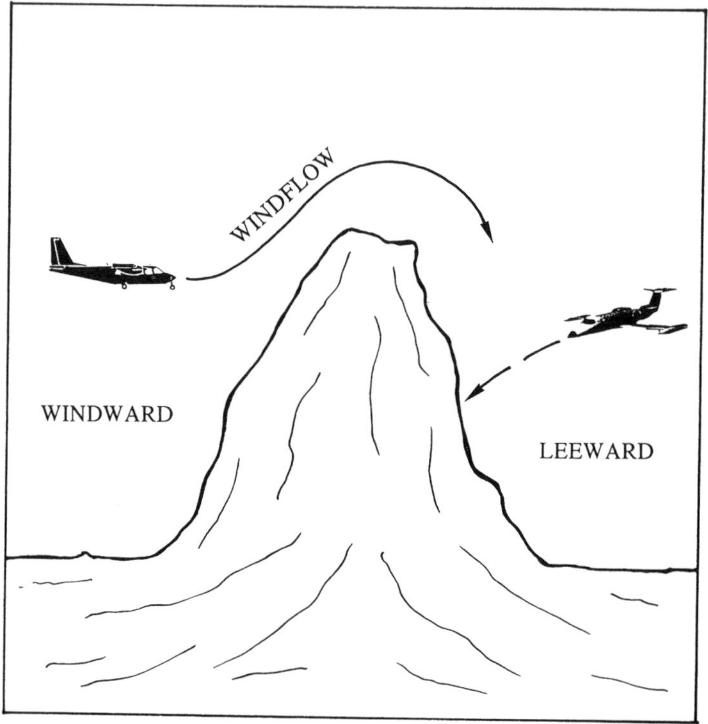

Figure 7.5 Mechanical Turbulence Caused by Mountains

As I stated earlier, pilots should allow *a minimum safety altitude of at least 2000 feet above the highest ground.* If the wind is really strong – above 30 knots – then a much higher safety altitude is recommended. Climb to this altitude *well before* reaching a point where you are faced with climbing in a down-draught, because you might have to abandon the climb and turn away. Do this before the situation becomes critical.

Be aware that if the winds are blowing directly towards a mountain range and are reaching speeds of 50 knots or more, then severe turbulence can be expected. You might consider turning back and taking the advice as per the title of this section on mountain flying.

The effects of *mountain waves*, or *standing waves* generated by major mountain ranges, can extend as far as 300 miles downwind. Expect anything up to *severe turbulence*.

When there is sufficient moisture in the air, stationary lens-shaped lenticular clouds form. If there is enough moisture 'rotor' clouds will appear near the surface. These contain wind shear and violent air currents. Sometimes there is not enough moisture to form these clouds, so no 'rotor' action will be visible. The most violent areas are close to the steepest leeward slopes, which often drop almost vertically into deep valleys. They also precede line squalls.

Near the surface, the action of the rotor can pick up loose debris which then whirls around making it visible. Pilots who have experienced its effects have compared it to a horizontal tornado!

Chapter 8

Operation at Minimum Level

In STOL operations as well as normal flying, there are often circumstances that require the planning of a low level flight. Not enough (instructional) attention is paid to this, which means that even some experienced pilots can be caught out when faced with this situation.

Here are the basic guidelines for consideration and review.

The Need for Special Training

Operational flying at minimum level is very different from early concepts of an exercise known as *Low Flying*, which accomplished nothing beyond experiencing and learning the technique of handling the aircraft very close to the ground. The exercise was carried out in a variety of weather conditions within preselected training areas.

Low level operations require a higher standard of flying ability, self-discipline and decision-making qualities, all of which will be essential during flights which are more difficult than when flying at higher, safer altitudes.

Hand flying a STOL, or any other aircraft at around 500 feet for any period of time, is mentally and physically exacting on even experienced pilots. It poses additional problems of judgement, and often involves variations in aircraft handling techniques that can only be acquired by suitable training.

Attempting this type of flying in poor weather conditions (low cloud, restricted visibility and perhaps strong winds) without proper training is a dangerous undertaking. Certainly low level *navigation* must be avoided until the pilot is thoroughly proficient in all normal visual dead reckoning (DR) navigation and map reading at normal cruising altitudes. (We will be looking at this in some detail later on in this section.)

Self-Discipline

A low level flight should only be considered, or flown, when there is no other alternative. It requires a high standard of flying ability, self-discipline and confidence (not over-confidence).

I have never indulged in low flying just for the thrill, and have encouraged any pilots I have trained to follow the same rule. Low flying is a serious operation, to be carried out only as the need arises, for example on some occasions during a medical emergency evacuation flight. However, never attempt to continue such a flight *regardless of deteriorating weather conditions*. Always make an early decision to return to base, or divert if this can be done safely.

Low-Level Operations

In civil flying there are several instances when deliberate operation at minimum level will be necessary:

- The planned entry into the VFR Entry/Exit lanes associated with certain Controlled and Special Rules Airspace; usually to provide separation from IFR traffic.
- An unplanned operation at low altitude due to deteriorating weather during a navigation exercise, or in the local flying training area, and for practice in bad weather circuits.
- A complete flight in actual bad weather for training.
- An operational low level flight caused by high average terrain heights, which can then involve flying below low cloud bases due to the lack of instrument let-down aids at remote destination areas in the wilderness. (This happened to the author regularly in countries such as Ethiopia, Iran and South America, on international aid relief flights and *medevac* emergencies.)

Low-Level Familiarisation

During any operation at minimum level, the pilot will need to understand the change in several factors from flying at a higher level. For instance, the requirement to map read, interpret ground features and *accurately* keep track of and identify the aircraft's position at all times, which becomes more difficult at low level. Weather conditions, including low cloud, bad visibility, turbulence, wind shear and strong winds all add to the overall problems that can be experienced.

The development of an awareness of all these problems will be essential to the safe conduct of any low-level flight. Methodical cockpit procedures and close attention to fuel management and aircraft systems become even more important:

- FUEL: in a piston engine aircraft, mixture to *rich*. Fuel contents noted and monitored closely. When fitted with electric fuel pump(s), this should be 'ON'. In both piston and turbo-prop aircraft any noticeable fuel imbalance should be rectified without delay.

- SYSTEMS: Ammeter(s) and Suction Gauges must be checked to ensure serviceability.

  Compass systems – DGI, Magnetic Compass (slaved or 'whisky' standby compass) serviceable and no unacceptable errors. The DGI in particular, if it is not 'slaved', then precession must be within an acceptable range. (Accurately synchronising the DGI with a compass in low level turbulence is difficult.)
- ALTIMETER: check accuracy and set to regional QNH datum. On a relatively long flight from base, note the average barometric pressures for the route from the preflight met forecast, then note any radical variations.
- ENGINE(S): carefully check temperatures and pressures. If the aircraft is piston engined with carburettor heat, then it is essential this is functioning properly. Remember that carb icing can occur from -5°C to +25°C in suitable conditions.
- RADIOS: UHF will have a limited range at low level. If HF (or VHF) is used for longer range, check those.

Aircraft Configuration and Airspeed

A normal cruising speed will usually provide an adequate safety margin to initiate avoiding action for obstructions and high ground.

If the flight is taking place in poor visibility it might be more appropriate to use a low safe cruising speed – no problem for a STOL aircraft. If this is the case, the use of around 10° flap will allow flight at the same airspeed, but a lower nose position (increased forward visibility).

Range and endurance can be significantly affected at very low levels, so this should be worked out and carefully considered before any flight.

A check of fuel remaining and fuel needed to return to base (if this is the best option), must be calculated at regular intervals. The actual fuel state versus fuel burn, will have increasing importance if 'dog-leg' diversions are forced on the pilot by bad weather or terrain.

Height Keeping at Low Altitude

Once the aircraft is in level flight at the (low level) cruising altitude 500–600 feet, the changed perspective of ground features from that at a higher altitude can be clearly seen, as can the difficulties experienced in maintaining height by ground reference. Frequent scanning of the instruments is essential, particularly the altimeter. It is important to note that *the lower the aircraft is flown, the more oblique the view of the ground features will be.* Map reading will therefore become more difficult.

Practise along easier low level routes gives the trainee pilot the opportunity to study and mentally assimilate this changed perspective and will develop the ability to more easily interpret the ground features shown on the map. I have flown a great many hours on low level operations, and after a while you break through an initial period of trying to keep up with the faster speed with which the ground features appear. It's simply a question of getting used to landmarks viewed from an oblique angle. You feel that your map reading will never catch up – but it does. At that point you are really beginning to get into the swing of the exercise.

It is important to bear in mind that marked obstructions less than 300 feet AGL, as well as unmarked obstructions of all kinds, could be present up to a height of 299 feet AGL.

If you are in a region where snow has fallen, the snow will mask certain ground features, blending them with one another. This will make it more difficult to keep track of the aircraft position.

An optimum low level cruising height of 500–600 feet is suggested to avoid the unmarked obstructions. However, there is a real possibility you might have to fly lower in areas where the ground has pronounced vertical ridges and in restricted visibility. (Be aware of the minimum 500ft AGL rule.)

The Effects of Speed and Inertia on Turns

Due to its inertia an aircraft does not begin to turn immediately bank is applied. The higher the speed the greater this effect will be. It also follows that the higher the speed the greater will be the radius of turn for any given angle of bank.

While the effects are less important at normal cruising levels, they must be considered at low level. Turns must be anticipated and commenced in good time to be completed within the available air space.

The Effects of Wind

We are aware that movement due to the speed of the aircraft is more noticeable at low level. So are the effects of wind upon that movement. This is most apparent when flying into wind and downwind. In both these cases there is a very noticeable difference in ground speed, giving the appearance of a change in airspeed.

When flying downwind this gives a totally misleading visual impression. There is a strong temptation for an unaware pilot to alter the power setting without even looking at the airspeed indicator. (The other impression is that

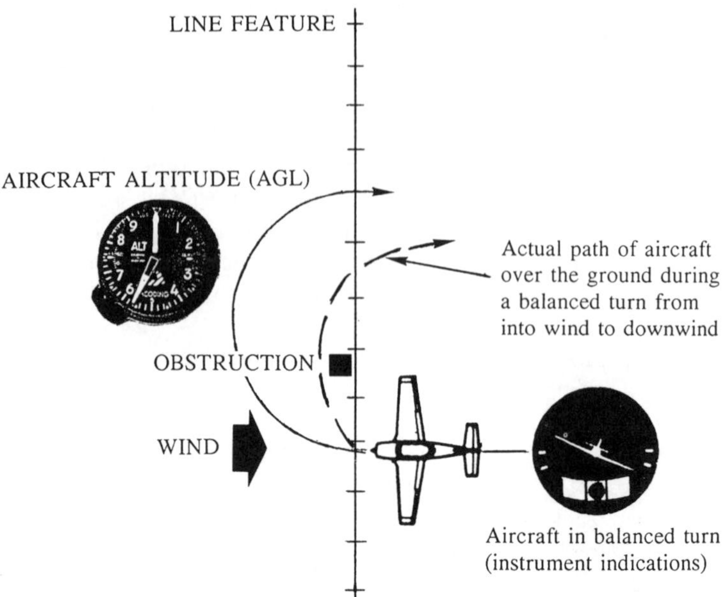

Figure 8.1 Into Wind to Downwind

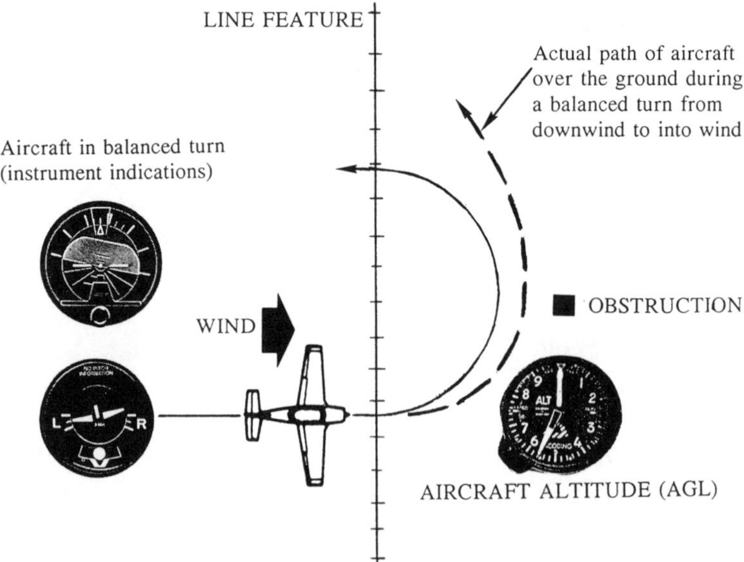

Figure 8.2 Downwind to into Wind

the aircraft *appears* to be 'slipping in' during the turn.) This is a potentially dangerous situation, as a reduction of power when flying downwind – thinking the airspeed has increased, could easily result in an inadvertent stall.

When turning into wind the opposite will happen, and the pilot will think the aircraft is in unbalanced flight and skidding towards the outside of the turn. (See Figure 8.2). This is the time to rely on the BALANCE INDICATOR to help in maintaining a balanced flight condition, ignoring the incorrect illusion.

Drift becomes more apparent at very low altitude when flying *crosswind*, specifically when turning. It gives a false visual impression of unbalanced flight, even when the aircraft is perfectly balanced. This is an optical illusion and rudder must not be used unless the balance indicator requires it.

However, the drift itself is very real, and its effect upon the radius of turn must be allowed for when it becomes necessary to alter heading and avoid obstacles (Figures 8.1 and 8.2 illustrate the potential danger). When flying downwind, it is necessary to commence both turns and climbs earlier to avoid obstructions or high ground.

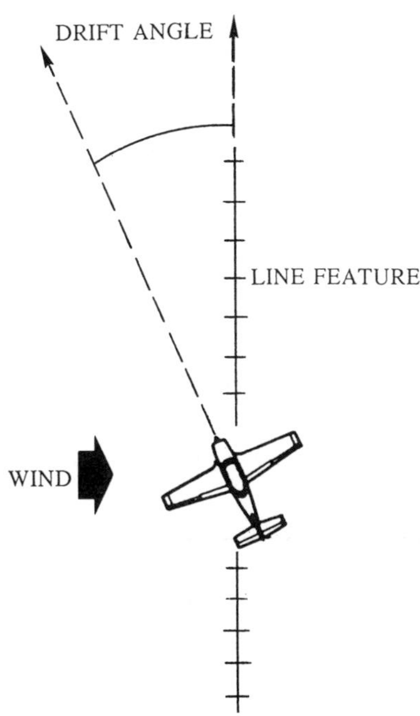

Figure 8.3 Drift Angle Along a Line Feature

The Effects of Turbulence

Severe turbulence can be encountered at low level. There are a variety of reasons for this, although strong winds are the primary cause. Ground which is undulating or hilly is one, and turbulence will always exist to some extent downwind of wooded areas, especially forests. This type of turbulence can become a real hazard as it can happen very suddenly and without any warning. So the use of power to avoid sudden height loss must be anticipated over this type of terrain.

Even over rough ground which is relatively flat, mechanical turbulence and wind shear effects are particularly marked in moderate to strong winds.

Low down, *vertical wind shear* effects assume greater significance. The effect of vertical gusts on the aircraft is the important factor in relation to aircraft structural considerations. Vertical gusts will increase the angle of attack, causing an increase in the lift generated at that particular airspeed – and therefore an increased load factor. If the angle of attack exceeds the critical angle, the wing will stall. (See Figure 8.4). This can occur at a speed well above the published 1g stalling speed. The top of the GREEN BAND on the ASI (Vno) relates to load factors as a result of gusts during turbulent conditions.

Load Factor, which we know as *G-force*, is a measure of the stress on the aircraft. Each category of aircraft is built to withstand certain G-forces which are laid down in the Flight Manual. It is important these G-forces are not exceeded.

Therefore we must fly the aircraft at the best turbulence penetration speed (which is usually slower, by around 10–20%, than the normal cruise speed), but nowhere near the aircraft stalling speed. We must remember that the stalling speed in turbulence is higher than published in the Flight Manual.

Horizontal shear will cause sudden changes in the wind component and its effects on the aircraft flight path. This will cause sharp variations in airspeed. The consequence of this will be a sudden loss of lift and height. Therefore the pilot must be ready to counteract this.

Turbulence makes control of the aircraft more difficult, which affects accuracy. On a long, low level flight fatigue can occur very quickly.

High Ground, Obstructions and Contours

Hilly country with many undulations presents special problems for low level operation. You cannot make an unwavering rule to fly only at 500–600 feet AGL. It will depend on the weather (wind strength, cloud base). Therefore choose a height that will give adequate clearance over the highest points – then maintain it.

There is always a great temptation to ‘ride the contours’, but this is a very

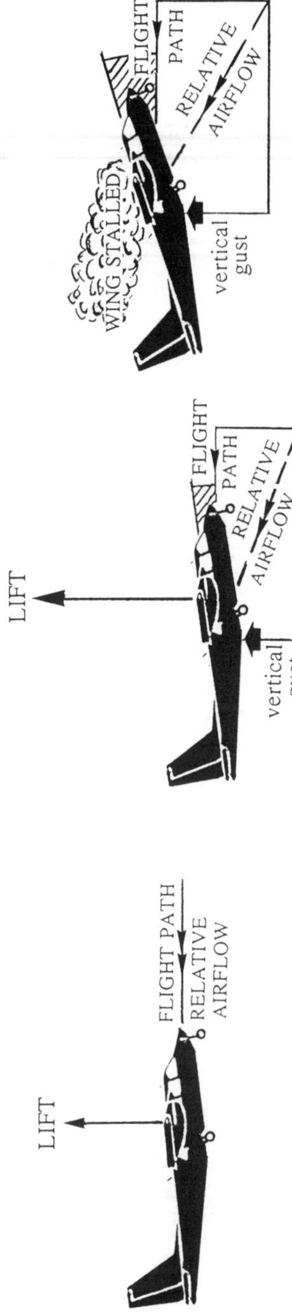

Figure 8.4 Vertical gusts increase the angle of attack, which increases the load factor and can stall the wing.

dangerous practice. You can easily meet an uphill gradient that is steeper than the aircraft's angle of climb. Only jet fighters with enormous amounts of thrust can cope with this sort of situation.

Flying along valleys in mountainous country requires special care – and a great deal of experience in mountain flying. A wrong turning into a 'blind' valley can lead to disaster. Climbing into cloud with the hills obscured would be folly.

Unless the weather is reasonable to good, any low level flight should either be postponed or, if possible, rerouted in to an area where conditions are acceptable.

The Effects of Precipitation

Before any flight, windscreen demisters and/or rain repellent systems should be checked and serviceable.

Light rain does not normally result in a visibility problem. But heavy rain, sleet or snow can seriously reduce forward visibility, often to almost zero, the same condition as being in cloud. This must be avoided at all costs in low level operations. Dog-legs around thunderstorm areas or rerouting should be undertaken as required.

Whenever rain in the form of large drops is present, great care should be taken. Raindrops on the windscreen cause distortion to forward visibility. This is due to refraction and diffusion of light waves and the danger of this effect can mislead pilots into believing the aircraft is higher than it really is. Figure 8.5 shows the effect en-route and during an approach to land.

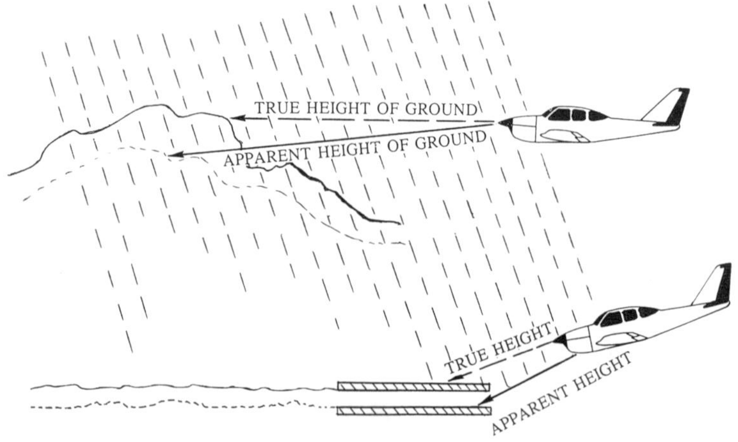

Figure 8.5 Apparent and true height is distorted by the effects of precipitation both en route and during an approach to land

Whenever precipitation is seen on the windscreen the demister should be selected on. I normally leave it on 'low' all the time.

If there is a serious loss of forward vision through the windscreen in heavy rain, it may be improved by reducing the aircraft's speed.

If you are flying a piston engine aircraft, always be alert to the possibility of carburettor icing. This can get worse in conditions of high humidity combined with low cloud and rain.

Make sure the pitot heater is on (and checked serviceable on pre-flight inspection). Guarding against the possibility of problems with the ASI is of vital importance at minimum level, as this can become a real problem in an already high pilot workload situation.

Flying Over Water, Snow or Featureless Ground

When flying over a calm sea, especially if the conditions are hazy, visual judgement of height is very difficult. Certainly there may be little difference in the appearance between 100 feet or 1,000 feet.

Real problems can occur when the horizon merges with the surface of the water. If the haze is very thick with no visual horizon, the aircraft will have to be controlled by reference to instruments. Such conditions can rapidly lead to a sensation that the aircraft is not level – even though the instruments show it is. A great deal of discipline has to be exerted to continue believing the instruments. The feeling can become particularly strong when the sun can just be seen through the haze. This seems to add to the difficulties instead of helping the situation. Flight in these circumstances is probably the most difficult and hazardous of all. It should not be attempted by inexperienced pilots or those not competent in instrument flying.

Flying over snow can produce a similar effect. The problems relate to the positive identification of landmarks which may become obscured, or so changed in appearance that they become difficult to recognise. In both cases, the navigational problems are increased by the fact that *drift* is very hard to see and calculate.

Remember that weather conditions in which you operate under normal circumstances, can easily become dangerous at low level over the types of surface described here.

Flying and Navigating in Reduced Visibility

As already mentioned above, flying in reduced visibility is one of the most difficult aspects of low level operations.

The visibility limits imposed on any low level operation, without dramatically increasing the danger level, depend very much on the flying ability and experience of the pilot. An additional factor concerns knowledge of the route.

In conditions of thick haze with no visual horizon (especially flying into sun) controlling the aircraft on instruments, plus visual navigation by ground features, becomes very difficult. It can easily lead to the wrong impression of the aircraft's attitude.

If you are committed to continue a flight in these conditions, the following tips will be helpful:

- Within the height parameters you have set for the operation, fly at the height which gives the maximum horizontal visibility and view of the ground as long as this is not below the minimum for obstacle clearance.
- If changes of height do not make any apparent difference, fly as high as possible within your set limits, while still maintaining a reasonable view of the ground (to navigate).
- Consider the possibility of reducing speed to help map reading and the avoidance of unexpected obstacles. Note. It may not be necessary to reduce speed to the extent that some flap has to be used. This will depend upon the type and speed of the aircraft, and whether flap can be used in the slow cruise configuration.
- Use whatever additional navigation aids you have available. If you have GPS, cross-check the accuracy of the navigation data being displayed.
- Choose landmarks such as line features running across the track which will not be missed if a track error develops. By keeping a careful time check, anticipate the time such features will be seen.
- Landmarks on the down-sun side of the track are easier to see, so use these as much as possible.

- If checkpoints (landmarks) are missed:
  a) Maintain an accurate course (heading).
  b) Check the time flown since the last known checkpoint, and work out your probable position.
  c) When this is done, decide on another prominent landmark which you estimate is still ahead of your position. Then work out an ETA.
- If you are following a line feature, river, railway line or road, keep it on the left and always reconfirm its identity by comparing the aircraft magnetic heading with that of the line feature. Prominent landmarks can also be related to it.

Revision and Summary of Navigation at Minimum Level

Because normal cockpit tasks happen so much faster during low level operations, the pilot is more likely to feel increased anxiety/stress because it is easier to get lost.

At minimum altitude, the necessity to fly accurately will be greatly increased. This is mainly due to the difficulty in map reading at low levels, and the dependence on the technique of DR navigation.

Trying to map read and *continuously* identify ground features is most unlikely to be successful. It is more appropriate to concentrate on easily identifiable and prominent ground features, rather than a mass of confusing detail.

The main problem with navigating at low level is to avoid concentrating exclusively on the ground immediately in front of the aircraft. This is not only a bad habit, but can lead to a lack of awareness of upcoming obstructions, high ground or deteriorating weather (lowering cloud, heavy rain, etc) ahead of the aircraft. I am not saying you should avoid looking immediately in front of the aircraft, just be conscious of the problems.

The lower the altitude you are flying the more difficult and exacting it will be to make flight log entries. If the overall navigation task-loading starts to overwhelm you, make sure that above all else you enter *accurate times* over *known checkpoints* – the high level of cockpit distractions can easily lead to you missing a checkpoint. (If you do miss one (on DR estimation) don't despair, assume you have already overflown it and look ahead for the next checkpoint.)

Use of Major Line Features

It is often the case that even in remote wilderness areas you can clearly identify a line feature, such as a major river, coastline, even a railway line or road. (Be careful of roads, they can be misleading.) If the feature ends or is close to your destination, I have found it to be a wise policy to follow it. Even if it means a few more minutes added to the flight time, it's worth it – for peace of mind! I once overflew a desert airstrip in Saudi Arabia by fifteen minutes, because I took (what I thought was) a short cut by not continuing to follow a prominent line feature.

> N.B. Don't forget, when following any line feature, to keep it on the left side of the aircraft.

Uncertainty of Position

Any visual and DR navigation in association with map reading, needs the pilot to maintain accurate headings and identification of ground features. There will be times, however, when a pilot will be unable to fix the position of the aircraft by a positive identification of a ground feature using a map. It can happen to anyone and is not a situation for panic (which is almost certain to result in a radical degradation of situational awareness and flying ability).

The main causes of becoming lost can be narrowed down to:

- An incorrectly synchronised or faulty (excessively precessing) DGI.
- A sudden and marked change in wind velocity.
- Mistakes in the (elapsed) time calculations in the flight log.
- Incorrect identification of a previous checkpoint. (Often difficult to determine after the event.)
- Reduced visibility due to weather deterioration, increased cockpit workload and distractions.
- Unscheduled diversions from the original track.

Initially in this situation, it is best to assume that you have overflown the checkpoint, and therefore continue to maintain the heading until the next designated checkpoint, usually never more than about ten minutes away. If for some reason this checkpoint does not appear at the estimated ETA, you can then think about using a 'Lost Procedure'.

The following list of actions provides a guide:

- Make sure the DGI is synchronised with the compass.
- Check the correct (compass) heading is being flown when compared to the flight (navigation) log.
- Quickly re-assess the ETA for the checkpoint which has been missed.
- Estimate the present DR position and mark a circle of uncertainty on the map. (This is a 10% radius of the distance flown since the last KNOWN checkpoint.)
- Try to identify a feature within the circle of uncertainty, not forgetting to read from the ground to the map.

Analysing the Weather Forecast

Like a doctor diagnosing the symptoms of a patient, so does a weather forecaster 'diagnose' all the ingredients that make up the weather – temperature, dewpoint, barometric pressure, windspeed and direction – then makes the necessary 'predictions'. Each are professionals, the doctor and the met forecaster, and would like us to believe they are dealing in an exact science. But in medical problems and weather forecasting there are always unpredictable factors.

When considering the weather, the cautious, and therefore the safe pilot, regards aviation forecasts merely as a guideline to what is going to happen. Because weather is constantly changing, the longer the forecast has been out, the greater the probability some part of it will be inaccurate.

Research into aviation forecasts indicates:

- If bad weather is forecast to occur within *three to four hours*, the chances of the forecaster being right exceeds 80%.

- A good weather forecast for up to twelve hours ahead with VMC conditions, has a greater probability of being accurate than if the forecast was below VMC.
- When there is a marked weather system such as frontal, trough, area of general rain, the first few hours of the forecast which predicts poor flying conditions, or worse, are more reliable.
- However, the weather associated with traditionally fast-moving cold fronts and squall lines, are the most difficult to predict accurately because of the unpredictability of the rapidly changing elements within them. (Forecasters can only supplement their scientific knowledge by using 'pattern recognition' based on their local regional knowledge and experience.)
- Visibility on the surface is more difficult to forecast than cloud ceilings. (While I was flying as pilot to a North Pole expedition, a senior forecaster with many years experience told me that predicting visibility in snow conditions is the most difficult and inexact of all.)
- The fallibility of weather forecasting is highlighted when trying to predict when bad weather will occur at a specific forecast time.

If we take note of the points made here, our flying will be safer, our (aviation) decision making ability will improve, which will in turn lessen the cockpit stress factors.

Effects of Low-Level Flight on Range and Endurance

Briefly, a low level flight would be ideal for maximum endurance flying, but range is normally reduced at lower levels. If the aircraft is then flown at speeds below the figure recommended for range, it is again reduced.

If partial flap is used for minimum (cruise) speed in poor visibility, the result would be a considerable reduction in range. (Refer to the performance graphs in the Flight Manual for accurate information.)

If range is a critical consideration for any flight, a regular running check of fuel against distance flown will give early warning if consumption becomes excessive.

Summary and Consolidation of the Main Factors in Operations at Minimum Level

In planning, or having to cope with a low level flight, each pilot must pay particular attention to *airmanship*.

We must look closely at:

- Our sense of weather awareness.

- Accurate knowledge of the aircraft position.
- The wind direction and strength.
- The height of terrain and any individual obstructions (in relation to the proposed track).
- The need for a good look out.
- Self-discipline (to maintain an even more heightened situational awareness).
- The hard decision-making capability to make firm 'go–no go' decisions. An indecisive or press on regardless attitude could prove fatal! (In essence, this means recognising and then deciding on the safest course of action through previous training and overall aviation experience.)

If you are intending to undertake a complete low level flight from the outset, then plan systematically, taking into account the following points:

- Objective(s) of the flight. (Other than for training, is it really operationally necessary?)
- Consideration of all the flight planning ingredients – (availability of navigation aids, fuel required, ATC rules as applicable, aircraft equipment, selection of suitable alternate (diversion) airfields, controlled airspace entry-exit lane procedures if applicable. Pilot qualifications and experience level (you might be qualified – but do you have the right experience?))
- Familiarity (proficiency) with low level operation (including height keeping and visual impressions at low altitude, effect of speed and inertia during turns) effects of wind and turbulence.
- Be aware that the most common errors in handling the aircraft and making decisions, will arise from a *lack of anticipation and awareness*.
- Our planning should also take into account the weather considerations, specifically as they relate to low level operations:
  - Low cloud and good visibility.
  - Low cloud and poor visibility.
  - Effects of precipitation (avoidance of moderate to heavy rain showers).
  - Approaching destination and joining the circuit (positioning and speed according to visibility).
  - Bad weather circuit procedure, final approach and landing.
  - Action in the event of a 'go-around'.

Note of Caution. Simulating and practising bad weather circuit joining, including approaches and landings, in good weather is no substitute for practise in actual bad weather conditions. Therefore it is essential for flight safety reasons to practise one or two flights in varying degrees of bad weather with a fully qualified and experienced instructor. This applies from PPL level through to experienced commercial pilots.

When considering diversion due to weather the following points must be considered.

When diverting back to departure point:

- The likely cloudbase across the route to be flown. Consideration of obstructions.
- The possibility of further weather deterioration.
- Variation in expected visibilities for flight below cloud, including areas of precipitation.
- Difficulties that could be encountered in map reading and maintaining an accurate track for the existing weather conditions.

When diverting to an alternative airfield:

- The expected weather conditions along the diversion route.
- The type of terrain that will be encountered.
- The *fuel state* and *daylight remaining* versus the *distance* to the alternate airfield.

In conjunction with all the points made here, *maintain good overall airmanship practices at all times*. Also, a regular flight review of the exercises outlined in the section on SLOW FLIGHT will provide proficiency practice and valuable psychological confidence-boosting for actual low level operations in bad weather.

Chapter 9

How to Survive an Emergency (Including a Crash Landing)

A very good pilot-examiner friend of mine (now in his late eighties and actively examining until he was eighty-one), said that during his early flying career every time he flew a state of emergency existed. This was due to the unreliability of engines, which had a nasty habit of failing without any warning. It was not an altogether unusual occurrence for bits of the airframe to drop off as well!

With the development of the jet and turbo-prop engine and their high standard of reliability, malfunctions and shut-downs are rare. As a result, the *actual* engine-out performance of many modern light twins is not fully understood by the average general aviation pilot. I don't care what the manufacturers say, an engine failure at or near maximum gross weight is a drift down situation. The 'live' engine is only giving you time to choose where the aircraft will force (crash) land. In reality, having one engine shut down means you have lost *more* than 50% of your aircraft performance.

However, it can also be said that any aircraft, piston or jet, is only safe until the pilot boards. After that a whole variety of things can go wrong. Just one example: statistics show that around 20% of the total aircraft accidents happen because of engine failure brought about by the pilot mismanaging one of the associated engine systems. The one cause that stood out among all others concerned the fuel supply.

If we are honest with ourselves, each one of us, at some time or another has been uncertain exactly which fuel tank switch position feeds which engine during a crossfeed in a multi-engine aircraft. I bet that you simply left it alone and hoped you wouldn't be forced into using it. The answer of course, is to read the section on fuel management in the Flight Manual, then run the engines on the ground and try it all out. That is the time to sort out the mistakes. Not only that, proving the fuel crossfeed system is an essential pilot check (naturally we will already have checked the crossfeed fuel drain for water!) Remember, if an engine inadvertently stops in the air through your mismanagement you may not be able to get it started again.

A small confession. I was undergoing my biannual multi-engine instructor renewal on a Partenavia P68. The examiner was a very experienced RAF Central Flying School check pilot. I had flown the Partenavia, but not for some years, and my examiner had hardly flown it at all. To cut an embarrassing story short, we ran through the checklist together and the examiner started the engines (from the left-hand seat). We were about to commence the 'after start' checks when both engines suddenly stopped within seconds of each other. The examiner had misread the 'fuel on' positions and actually switched them to 'off'. Not only that, *I* had missed the mistake as well (unfamiliarity with the aircraft type). So if two experienced pilots with over 20,000 flying hours between them can make such a potentially serious error, what could happen to rookie pilots? I was glad we were on the ramp and not airborne!

The correct use of checklists is covered in part III of chapter 1. Checklists should be followed and a sense of awareness developed about how systems can be mismanaged, as these factors are just as important as understanding the correct profile and technique for take-offs and landings, or stall recovery. In many instances a properly trained and aware pilot can think, act and often avoid a potential emergency before it happens.

Having said all that, this chapter is aimed at coping with an emergency if it happens for real, then what to do to survive the sequence of events that follows.

What many pilots do not realise is that almost any type of terrain, even mountainous, can be used for a *survivable* emergency (crash) landing. However, the pilot must know how to use the aircraft structure to protect both himself and the passengers in order to minimise any injuries.

Obviously, there is no *practical* training that can be given. We could not just crash-land an aircraft on any old rough ground just for practice! Nevertheless we can prepare ourselves for an emergency landing by studying the techniques outlined in this chapter. I have personally experienced several actual emergency landings in different parts of the world, and survived by applying the advice given here.

As a flight instructor, I have tried to instil the need for recurrent practice in all emergency procedures. From the single-engine 'let's try and get into that field down there', type of exercise, to the more advanced, multi-engine and emergency crash-land advice given on the following pages I have added the results of my own practical reservoir of knowledge.

My maxim is – *You can survive an emergency crash-landing with the right knowledge, mental attitude and training.*

As previously mentioned, modern aero-engines, particularly jet and turboprop, are very reliable and fortunately there are few in-flight shutdowns. It is true to say, though, that it is the pilot-induced factors that contribute most to emergency crash landings. By this I mean inadequate flight planning, fuel management and getting lost in marginal weather conditions. Another contributor is the failure to use carburettor heat in piston engine aircraft, or not knowing how to use it properly.

Classification of Emergency Landings

Emergency landings can be broken down into three different types:

Forced Landings

Forced landings are mainly associated with single-engine aircraft following an engine failure, therefore requiring an immediate landing. This can be immediately after take-off (EFOTO), or at any point during a flight (ENROUTE), the pilot having no option but to carry out an emergency landing procedure.

Precautionary Landing

A precautionary landing can be associated with both single and multi-engine aircraft. It is a planned 'diversionary' landing, on or off an airport/airstrip, when continuing a flight is considered hazardous or operationally inadvisable by the pilot. For example: an engine or a systems problem that could get worse and develop into a full emergency, making an early landing the safest option. This could also cover events such as deteriorating weather, shortage of fuel, being lost, or approaching darkness in difficult (mountainous) terrain without any instrument (landing) aids at the destination airfield.

Ditching

A ditching is a forced, or precautionary landing on water. Either one is a full emergency.

General Aspects of Crash Safety

Let us consider the most important points for a pilot faced with an emergency landing in difficult terrain where major damage to the aircraft is inevitable.

Minimising/avoiding major crash injuries means preserving the complete flight deck and cabin area structure more or less intact. This can be accomplished by using other (non-occupied) parts of the aircraft to absorb the violent 'impact-force' of the uncontrolled stopping process before occupants suffer injury. The wings will provide the main cushion, together with the landing gear and underside of the fuselage. This has to be effective *before* the severe stopping process injures the occupants.

On a retractable gear aircraft it might sometimes be better to make a 'gear up' emergency landing, depending on the roughness of the ground. What must be avoided at all costs, are the wheels hitting rocky outcrops or holes in the ground. This can easily cause the aircraft to 'cartwheel', or dig in and flip over onto its back. If this happens there is a good chance of the aircraft catching fire.

I've pulled off two successful and deliberate wheels-up emergency landings. One was a Cessna 310 on an undulating, sandy surface covered with pockets of soft sand. The second in a DC-3, which I put down in a rice-paddy on one engine. This was after extensive damage during a military operation. The wheels-up landing was the best option in both cases.

With the Cessna, the long nose leg of the undercarriage stood a high chance of collapsing, with the narrow main-wheels easily sinking into the soft sand. The DC-3, being a large tail dragger, would almost certainly have flipped over onto its back in the shallow, muddy water of the rice-paddy. The alternative was thick jungle and tall trees. In both these instances, I firmly believe that with gear down the results would have been catastrophic. As it turned out there were only very minor injuries on both landings.

As with all flying, you have to think fast and make the best decisions according to your experience and training. But only knowledge and training will give you the edge (see chapter 1, PRACTICAL COCKPIT MANAGEMENT).

The pilot of this twin made a forced landing with the undercarriage down. As we can see it absorbed the crash 'impact' even though it collapsed, making it a survivable emergency landing. Notice the pilot even managed to feather both propellers before the initial impact point.

Figure 9.1

Airframe Versus Impact Absorption

The results of many accidents have shown that the crushable integrity of the aircraft has a direct relationship to the extent of damage in a crash landing. The first point of impact is usually the worst. So it is the resistance of the structure to the initial and most severe crash forces that dictate the 'survivability' of the occupants. Investigations have shown that it is best to collide with an object directly ahead, rather than crash into it sideways.

The aircraft structure is not the only consideration when planning a crash landing. Outside objects such as trees, dense vegetation, even cultivated crops, make excellent energy absorbing medium. They help to bring the aircraft to a progressive stop, like an arrester wire on an aircraft carrier. Vegetation and crops have the best cushioning/braking effect without causing extensive damage to the aircraft.

General avaition aircraft of the type mentioned in this book are designed to provide impact protection up to 9 Gs.

Speed Versus Stopping Distance

How fast and severe the actual stopping process is during a *controlled* crash landing, depends on the aircraft speed over the ground (groundspeed). *The faster the speed, the greater the destructive energy.*

Therefore the initial impact (touchdown) speed is critical. For instance, doubling the groundspeed means the total destructive energy is *four times* as great. So you can see it is far safer to impact at 70 knots than 100 knots plus. Not only that, but at 100 knots the stopping distance is almost *four times as long* as 70 knots. Therefore you should be aiming to reach your minimum approach speed immediately before the flare out.

I have instructed many military pilots in low level reconnaissance techniques, mostly in STOL aircraft like the Britten Norman Defender and the Short's Skyvan, ideal for LAPES extractions. On many occasions it meant flying at treetop height over tall, tropical forest trees in low visibility monsoon conditions. Therefore I repeatedly stressed the importance of flying at an airspeed that would give them adequate time for obstacle clearance. (It is easy to fly and control both these aircraft at a low safe cruise of 75 knots with flap extended.) You certainly stand more chance of getting away with inadvertently touching the top of a tree at low speed as well. To my embarrassment I actually knocked the flag pole off the top of a building in a BN Defender on one sortie. Luckily I was only flying at 65 knots, but it still destroyed the fairing surrounding one of the fixed undercarriage legs. I hate to think what would have happened at 130 knots.

When pilots are asked what they consider is the best place for an emergency landing, most will say the largest available field, or open area that is flat. However, very little stopping distance is required if the aircraft deceleration speed can be spread evenly over the selected emergency distance.

By understanding the requirement for a steady slowing process in rough terrain, the pilot has the knowledge to choose *where* the best touchdown can be made. This will make the best use of the crash-absorbing aircraft structure over a short landing distance, and noticeably reduce the peak deceleration of the flight deck/cabin area after the initial impact.

Because the aircraft's vertical component of velocity will become zero with ground impact, the rate of descent should be kept completely under control. Accurately judging the flare is essential. Ground contact that is too flat at a high ROD on any surface can cause physical injury (especially spinal) without destroying the airframe. This is particularly so with low wing aircraft due to the rigid bottom structure of the airframe.

On soft terrain (mud, snow, sand) an excessive sink rate could easily cause the nose to dig in. At the very least there will be a severe deceleration, or more probably the aircraft could flip over onto its back.

Most STOL aircraft I know are high wing, with a strong undercarriage that can be fitted with high flotation gear in the form of wide, low pressure tyres. These are more resistant to high impact stresses, and are more likely to cope with a variety of soft surfaces. Nevertheless, physical injuries can still be caused by high ROD impacts.

Training and Cockpit Perspective

Although I said there was no *practical* training that could be given in crash landing techniques, there is one exercise that is very useful to practise. This entails flying out over a remote country area (no towns, villages, etc) and simulating "crash-land" approaches right down to minimum level.

To save on training costs, the exercise can be undertaken, where appropriate, during empty legs with no passengers on board (or all-cargo flights, which has the advantage of aircraft handling at a realistic in-service weight). However, I recommend that the initial training session be set up without the pressure of any other flying duties. The preflight briefing would include an explanation of the psychological points made in this chapter of the book. Such practice will allow a pilot to gain the low-level cockpit *perspective* and build up confidence to be able to cope with the real thing.

The best way to train is a combination of normal two-engine, plus simulated asymmetric approaches. This develops accuracy, judgement and the planning technique for the various types of terrain you might encounter for an emergency landing and, above all, *confidence* in your ability to accomplish it. Like any other flying exercise though, it is essential to have regular training sessions so that you always have an acceptable proficiency level if the worst happens.

Some pilots I have instructed had initial problems controlling the aircraft

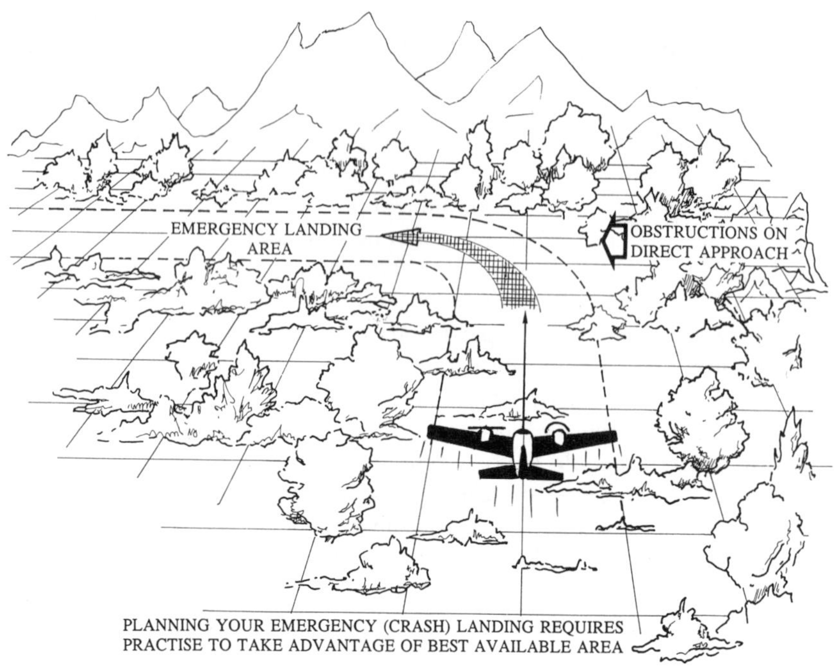

Figure 9.2

rate of descent in the final stages of the approach. When this happens the airspeed and altitude start to fluctuate, which causes excessive use of the elevator trimmer, plus a loss of concentration and perspective of the selected landing area at the most critical time.

The problems stemmed from:

- *Lack of experience* in off-airport operations. The runway, or airstrip always provides some form of perspective to judge a circuit and landing profile.
- *Nervousness/Fear*. The natural reluctance of the pilot to believe he could be faced with a real emergency crash landing (it will only happen to some else syndrome). This probably combines with a mental aversion to the prospect of destroying the aircraft. I had one very experienced pilot (ex-Navy) who absolutely refused to even participate in such an exercise. He said that as the aircraft (it was a Twin Otter) did not have an ejector seat, any emergency that would lead to a crash landing could be faced *if* it happened – the whole matter was out of his hands. I certainly hoped I would never fly as passenger on board his aircraft!

- *Indecision.* Not being able to select a precise 'impact point' for the landing. The pilot changes his mind at least twice which leads to an aborted (practice) approach. I continually point out you cannot do this in a real emergency so don't get into the habit of doing it in practice! This is partly due to a combination of the previous two points.

Body Restraints – Seat Belts

Of course it is not just the aircraft structure that helps us to survive a crash landing. Seat belts (and shoulder harness for the crew) provide firm bodily restraint to help prevent violent impact with the interior of the aircraft, where incapacitating injuries would occur. Restraints are provided so that the human body can decelerate at the same rate as the surrounding structure. If these were not fitted, the sudden stop that results (known as the second collision), would cause extensive injury and possibly death to passengers being thrown forward. This would cancel out any advantage of the crash-absorbing structure.

I do not know of any civil aircraft that has a shoulder harness fitted to the passenger seats, not even a single cross-over strap. (I'm discounting some light, single-engine aircraft where the rear seat does have them.) Shoulder harnesses would certainly provide much better protection. In view of their absence, the pilot should try to avoid a direct, head-on collision against solid objects such as large trees, resulting in the most violent, sudden stop.

Conclusions

We can see that there are many factors which interfere with a pilot's ability to act promptly when faced with an emergency. And this covers the whole spectrum of flying experience.

- A *psychological reluctance to accept the possibility of an emergency crash landing*. Which leads to a lowering of flying skills (control of altitude, airspeed and vital decision-making).
- *A pilot mentally expects to be able to reach a safe landing area* (airport, airstrip, emergency landing field), particularly if the aircraft is still able to fly and maintain altitude on one engine.
- *The desire to save the aircraft.* In the back of the pilot's mind is the opinion that an undamaged aircraft means there will be no injuries. Certainly in a real emergency the pilot should not be concerned about destroying the aircraft. He should be thinking about how he and his passengers can walk away from it!
- *The fear of serious injury or death.* We know that fear is the most important mental mechanism that triggers the human process of self-preservation. In flying, fear has to be controlled by the continual

process of training and experience. Flying is not natural for humans. We have all heard the well-known saying used by people who are afraid to even get into an aircraft, let alone fly one: 'If God had wanted me to fly, He would have given me wings'. Some fear/apprehension in a pilot is healthy, but if it is allowed to develop into panic the worst scenario can quickly follow. Pilots who maintain their cool and use the emergency training they have been given over the years, are the ones who live to write the survival reports.

Facing an emergency landing head-on, because there is no other way to do it, involves continual psychological preparation just as much as it does honing physical flying skills. Remember that the insurance company will always buy a new aircraft – but it cannot buy you or your passengers new lives.

Emergency Field Length

The main consideration when selecting an emergency area to land in, is having sufficient *width* to allow for correction of approach errors. The overall length is not quite so vital as we discussed earlier in this chapter (initial impact, rapid dissipation of crash energy on rough ground help deceleration). It is better to hit an obstruction at the *end* of the landing run, than put a wing into a tree at flying speed on the final part of an approach.

Landing into a strong wind will also cut down the distance required, as will an upslope. Try to avoid a downwind landing unless there is an overwhelming reason for doing so (landing up a very steep slope or to avoid bad obstructions); even a better area with a strong cross-wind might be preferable.

Once you have selected your emergency area – stick to it. Changing your mind at the last moment could be disastrous.

Estimating Wind Direction

There are several ways of estimating wind direction:

- Drifting smoke: if it is slow rising and drifting almost intact, the wind-speed is very low. Rising smoke which suddenly parallels the ground in a ragged line, indicates a strong surface wind with the possibility of turbulence and perhaps wind shear over rough ground.
- Long grass and cultivated grain fields sway and bend in the direction of the wind with a sort of rippling effect. So do lakes and other areas of open water.
- In desert areas, blowing sand and established lines of sand dunes also provide excellent wind direction indicators.

- In cattle country such as Australia and some parts of North and South America, cattle face downwind while eating if the wind is any stronger than a light breeze.
- If none of the above applies and all else fails, use the same wind as your departure airfield.

Advice About Confined Areas

Out in a remote, wilderness area, a river or creek bed might seem to be a suitable place for an emergency landing, particularly if the surrounding terrain is exceptionally rugged. But you have to assess if there is sufficient width to reach it without hitting an obstruction with a wing tip.

This also applies to landing on roads and highways. I have landed on many road-strips, specifically designed for aircraft operations, but they are generally clear of obstructions. Remember, man-made structures such as power lines are often difficult to see, and frequently follow the line of a road as well as bisecting it. So beware!

Avoid restricted open areas surrounded by tall trees or other high obstacles. In theory they may well be long enough. However, in practice you will almost certainly never reach a practical touchdown (impact) point, because you have to maintain excessive height to clear obstructions on the final approach. This considerably cuts down the available landing distance.

If you do approach a confined area, and then find the distance is too short to avoid heavy contact with obstructions at the far end – force the aircraft onto the ground. Any aircraft will decelerate faster after the first impact.

You might consider ground-looping a fixed-gear aircraft, or retracting it on other types. If collision with substantial tree trunks is inevitable, aim the aircraft between two suitably spaced trunks. The simultaneous impact of both wings will greatly reduce the forward speed and bring the remainder of the airframe to a stop. What you have to avoid at all costs is a head-on collision with a hard obstruction.

Landing on Forest Trees

I've flown over many forests around the world and certainly would not relish the prospect of an emergency landing in trees. Nevertheless, here are a few pointers to assist in making such an experience survivable:

- Approach into wind as for a normal landing, with gear down and full flaps. You want the lowest possible groundspeed.
- Do not stall into the tops of the trees; make the initial contact at

minimum airspeed. This will help to avoid 'hanging' the aircraft in a nose-high landing attitude in the branches.

- Land with wings level to ensure the maximum simultaneous cushioning effect from the entire underside of the aircraft. This will help to maintain the attitude and prevent a wing breaking off, which could hasten a descent to the ground. (A fuselage hung up at a high angle is difficult to get out of with any safety.) A level attitude helps avoid penetration of the cockpit windshield – where you are sitting!

  (I went to the crash site of a DC-3 in the tall rain forests of the New Guinea highlands some years ago. The pilot had unfortunately 'nosed in' with gear retracted, instead of using the full cushioning effect of the airframe. I consider the DC-3 one of the most 'survivable' aircraft in a crash landing from my own personal experience).
- Avoid direct contact with more widely spaced, heavy tree trunks.
- The dense overhead canopy of a tropical rain forest is a good bet, not tall trees with thin tops and trunks clearly visible. Closely packed, small forest trees with dense top foliage are also acceptable. Remember that if the aircraft weight has little resistance, then it will crash freely down to ground level resulting in a severe impact.
- If there are areas of young, slender trees (as in reforested areas) plan to land in those. Individual trees are widely spaced to allow room for growth, and trunks will break off easily resulting in a good deceleration effect.

Landing in Mountainous Terrain

The very thought of an emergency landing in mountainous terrain would make most pilots shudder. However, STOL aircraft are sometimes the only aircraft that can use some of the high airstrips in such an area.

I flew extensively in the Himalayas using a Twin Otter and I consciously avoided situations which would lead me into an emergency. Bad weather conditions along valleys with peaks rising to well over 20,000 feet are to be avoided like the plague. So is unnecessarily low and/or slow flying over ridges and mountain peaks with the danger of standing waves and turbulence.

Every time I fly into or over a mountainous region, I am always on the look out for at least an emergency route out at a lower altitude (maybe along a valley at or below the single-engine service ceiling). This increases the *effective* altitude and the choice of emergency landing areas.

Forget about looking for any emergency landing area on high slopes. Even if you did put the aircraft down safely, altitude, low temperatures, difficulty of rescue and the time it would take, are all factors against survival.

Concentrate on the valleys where there are at least small villages, roads or tracks and running water. Even a rocky ravine with a river is preferable.

Refer also to the advice given about landing in CONFINED AREAS earlier in this chapter.

Emergency Ditching on Water

A well performed ditching on water has been researched as involving less violent *deceleration* than landing on rough terrain or onto a tall canopy of rain forest trees. However, 'Putting down in water', has traditionally met with a great deal of reluctance from the majority of pilots I have questioned on the subject. One reason is the certainty of losing the aircraft, but the overriding fear is that of getting trapped, then death by drowning as the aircraft sinks.

As a matter of record, a fixed wing aircraft ditched at minimum approach speed in the normal landing configuration will not sink immediately. The large wing area will provide considerable flotation. Near empty fuel tanks considerably assists this process. Ditched aircraft have been known to float from a few minutes up to several hours in calm water, even if the flight deck and cabin is below the water line as in a high-wing aircraft.

Ditching on a wide expanse of smooth water, especially in bright sunlight with considerable sun reflection, can cause a serious loss of depth perception. This leads to two problems. The first is flaring out *too high* and stalling-in from an excessive height. The second *not flaring out at all* and flying straight into the water. To avoid either of these eventualities, a long, shallow approach with a low rate of descent will solve the problem.

On low-wing aircraft no more than half flap is recommended with gear retracted, because with full flaps the force of water resistance could easily result in one flap breaking. This asymmetrical situation can cause one wing to dig in with obvious results.

All occupants must be cautioned to keep their seat belts fastened and their body and head forward in the crash position, certainly until the aircraft has completely stopped in the water. This is a necessary safety measure to prevent passenger disorientation/injury. It minimises the likelihood of injuring themselves, or injuring/delaying any of the other passengers at a critical time. All occupants are then in an ideal position to disembark into the water, or life rafts.

There are a few important factors to consider when looking at the possibility of ditching:

- How close you are to land.
- The availability of life vests, dinghies or rafts.
- The time of year. Winter and a very cold water temperature can mean

only a short survival time. For example, with water only a degree or two above freezing, the average person would be lucky to last an hour.
- If you have elderly, sick or injured on board, their prospects of surviving would be very low unless rescue is almost immediate.
- The number of passengers and the position of emergency exits.

How to Land on Snow

There is very little difference between the techniques required for landing on snow and ditching on water. The aircraft configuration is exactly the same. In fact, the loss of depth perception in white-out conditions is worse (uniform whiteness between sky and snow in bad visibility on a large, open expanse of snow). Even a relatively light wind can whip up light, powdery surface snow, creating an opaque layer several feet deep.

As I found in the Arctic, a deep, even snow layer often covers sharp, rocky ground that otherwise would not be suitable for landing. The danger lies in the 'humps' hiding larger obstructions. These cannot easily be seen during an approach in the conditions described above.

If the aircraft is fitted with skis, or wheel-skis, the prospects of surviving an emergency (ditching) landing are considerably enhanced.

During the North Pole expedition when I flew a Twin Otter on wheel skis, I considered every landing on the pack-ice as an 'emergency landing'.

A Few General Tips

- We know that flaps improve manoeuvrability at low speed, as well as lowering the stalling speed. But remember, only use full flap when you are *assured* of landing within your selected *emergency area*. The premature use of full flap and the large increase in *drag* can easily spoil a good approach.
- Switching off the aircraft *electrical master switch* before touchdown reduces the possibility of a post-crash fire. However, it should not be switched off until there is no longer a need for electrical power to operate any vital aircraft system (e.g. some aircraft have electrically operated flaps).
- Your primary consideration above all else during the final part of the approach, is to *maintain positive control of the aircraft*. This takes precedence over aircraft configuration and cockpit checks.
  GOOD LUCK.

Suggested List of Items to Carry in Your Aircraft Survival Kit

Planning and creating a first aid and survival kit is a serious business because you may have to use it.

The medical items should be compiled with expert medical advice. This can be supplemented as required according to the number of passengers carried on the aircraft and the area of operations. Alternatively, there is a selection of good aviation first aid kits available from professional aviation suppliers.

The list given here as a guide would be suitable for a light, twin-engine aircraft operating over difficult (SAR) terrain. Therefore you can supplement the quantities as necessary for the type of 8–30 passenger STOL aircraft mentioned in this book.

A BN Islander flying over the Papua New Guinea highlands. It has taken off from the difficult bush airstrip at the bottom of the deep valley behind. Each of these STOL aircraft carries a suitable survival kit as part of the essential aircraft equipment.

Many aircraft have totally disappeared after crashing in the rain forest, where trees are up to 200 feet high. Search and rescue is all but impossible in the mountainous, dense tropical rain forest. It has swallowed many aircraft without trace.

Figure 9.3

Aircraft First Aid Kit

QTY	ITEM	USE
•32	Adhesive bandages	
•3	Spools of adhesive tape	
•3	Stretch bandages	
•10	Steri-pad gauze flats 4in x 4in	Cover large abrasions.
•2	Roll of roller gauze	Holding gauze flats in place.
•10	Butterfly bandages	
•3	Triangular bandages	For supporting arm and protecting dressing from any contamination.
•20	Thick dressing pads	Cover large cuts/wounds.
•12	Butterfly Bandaids – various sizes	For closing lacerations.
•3	Large compress bandages	For large, bleeding wounds. (It is absolutely essential that clean, absorbent dressings be applied completely over the wound and sufficient pressure applied to stop bleeding.)
•2	2in rolls non-waterproof tape	For sprains and securing dressings in place.
•Box	Assorted Bandaids	For minor cuts (it is important to keep these clean as they can rapidly become infected).
•1oz bottle	Tincture of Benzoin	To hold tape in place and protect the skin.
•1 pkt	Molefoam	For padding/protecting blisters.
•1 pkt	Assorted needles	For puncturing blisters and removing splinters which can become easily infected.
•1 roll	Strong thread	Repairing torn garments to prevent them becoming unwearable.
•1 doz	Safety pins	
•1 bottle	Salt tablets	To prevent exhaustion and cramps due to heavy perspiring.
•1 bottle	Friars' Balsam	For repair of foot blisters

QTY	ITEM	USE
		once punctured. It hurts initially but toughens underlying skin enough for you to walk on.
•Small pack	Micro touch latex medical gloves	To keep blood off person administering first aid and help prevent cross-infection.
•12	Iodine wipes	
•1 bottle	Eyewash, Optrex or similar	Helps sore eyes and mild infections.
•3	Eye pads	Keep dust/insects from infected eye.
•1 bottle	Antiseptic eyewash	Prevents minor infection spreading – clears up existing ones.
•1 bottle	Antihistamine tablets	One tablet every four hours for insect bites, cold or hives.
•2 boxes	Imodium capsules (take as directed by brand manufacturer)	Relief of diarrhoea. (As we all know, diarrhoea can be very debilitating and lower resistance, thus the ability to function properly in a survival situation.)
•1 box	Aspirin/Paracetamol or similar	1 to 2 every four hours to relieve pain.
•1 box	Antacid	For indigestion and heartburn.
•1 pair	Tweezers	Removal of deep splinters.
•4	Ammonia inhalants	
•12	Burn treatments	All burns should be treated promptly to prevent infection.
•1 can	Insect repellent	Brand which can be used on exposed skin (arms, face).
•1	Mosquito net	For use of immobilised, injured person.
•3	Wire or similar splints	For immobilising broken limbs.
•1	Forceps	
•1	Bandage scissors	

QTY	ITEM	USE
•3	Rescue blankets	Size 56in x 84in. For use by injured or elderly.
•A/R	Emergency aluminium 'space blankets'	Sufficient number for one to each person.
•1	Thermometer (oral and rectal combination)	To obtain temperature of injured person, or water if treating frostbite.
•1	Bottle sun block lotion	Good quality brand name.
•1	Bar anti-bacterial soap	Mild antiseptic for cuts and abrasions.
•fi	Bottle brandy	'Morale booster' (for un-injured).
•1	Utila fold-up stretcher	This is the more compact, lighter version of the Furley stretcher and is standard first aid equipment. (See also improvised stretcher).
•1	First aid instruction book and copy of international ground signals for communicating with SAR aircraft	First aid instructions ensure treatment is complete and correct. Take particular note of the way to splint suspected forearm, wrist or ankle fractures. (International ground signals are covered later in this section.)

[This does not cover survival at sea after ditching. Aircraft will be suitably equipped with life-vests/life-rafts containing survival package. Of course, life-vests can be salvaged from a crash aircraft and worn by survivors if a river has to be crossed on land.]

QTY	ITEM	USE OR INFORMATION
•Assorted pack	Dehydrated food sufficient for seven days	This can be obtained through camping supply outlets.
•1 box	Bottled water	
•1 pkt	Water purification tablets.	
•1	100-foot length of thin climbing rope.	Multiple: including securing locally made survival shelter, roping people together whilst climbing/crossing rivers.

QTY	ITEM	USE OR INFORMATION
•1	'Bowie' knife or one of similar strength and size.	
•1	Whistle.	
•1	Fishing line – packet of hooks.	
•1	Small mirror or Mylar reflective sheets.	For signalling/attracting attention
•1	2in wide roll parcel tape	Good for binding anything together, repairing damaged shoes, spectacles. (Waterproof).
•1	Fold-up military style trenching tool.	Digging holes, etc for shelter.
•1 roll	Large, thick plastic dustbin (trash) bags.	Shelter or ground. They are very effective as an emergency sleeping bag to keep warm and dry.
•1	Hunting rifle and ammunition – bolt action gun with folding stock. Calibre sufficient to stop animal size of polar bear/mountain lion.	For use as defence/hunting in real wilderness/jungle/ mountains/arctic.
•6	Smoke flares.	For use only when sound of aircraft heard in order to attract attention.
•2	Boxes matches in waterproof box/packet.	
•1	Pocket field compass.	
•	Spare flashlight/battery.	
•1	Tron 1E Mk 2 emergency beacon.	*To supplement aircraft ELT.* Jotron transmits on the aircraft and regional mode SARSAT/COSPAS freq. 121.5 mHz. Can be bulkhead mounted. N.B. Lithium battery has up to 10 year storage life. (Recommend change after five years). Weighs only 260 grams.
•1	Hardback notebook for keeping daily journal/accurate	Encourage survivors to contribute. Brings sense of

QTY	ITEM	USE OR INFORMATION
	record of events, treatment of injuries, etc.	order – organisation – positive thinking of group. Important to have team-work. Even injured can participate.

Survival Food

Nutritionists tell us that the average person, with a normal lifestyle needs approximately 2,500 calories per day. Persons involved in hard physical labour, or living and working in an extremely cold climate will need more, but it is the military who has the greatest need for 'survival' food that will sustain personnel in combat conditions, often in a harsh environment.

During and since WWII, 'compo' rations have changed from bulk (and heavy) canned rations, to lightweight, dehydrated and rehydrated foods. Now *rehydrated* survival meals are favoured because they need only a small amount of water to heat them in sealed, self-contained pouches. However, as they are already pre-cooked, they can be eaten cold if required.

There is a good variety of menu combinations which does help to cater for a wide cross-section of taste.

Given here is a sample of rehydrated food combinations as used by Western Coalition Forces in the Gulf War. These are standard issue to British Army combat troops. This type of food is ideal for stocking *aircraft survival kits.* I used them during a North Pole expedition, and have recommended them since.

The amount you would carry depends on the number of passengers, but provision for *seven days'* ration would seem a reasonable amount.

In the United Kingdom they can be purchased *retail* at selected sports/camping outlets for the equivalent of $US4.60 (£3.00) per meal.

Rehydrated Meal Information

(Source: Manufacturer)

Nutritional Information (ave. per 100g)		**Energy kj/kcal**	**Protein**	**Carbohydrate**	**Fat**
Main Meals	Beans & Bacon in Tomato Sauce	451kJ/106kcal	9.4g	14.3g	1.4g
	Beans & Sausages in Tomato Sauce	672kJ/160kcal	5.3g	19.7g	6.7g
	Sausage Casserole	422kJ/101kcal	5.4g	9.0g	4.8g

Nutritional Information (ave. per 100g)		**Energy Kj/kcal**	**Protein**	**Carbohydrate**	**Fat**
	Chicken Casserole	633kJ/152kcal	9.3g	8.2g	9.1g
	Chilli Con Carne	582kJ/138kcal	10.1g	13.5g	4.9g
	Beef Stew & Dumplings	456kJ/109kcal	5.9g	12.3g	3.9g
	Lancashire Hot Pot	372kJ/75kcal	7.7g	6.0g	2.3g
	Spicy Vegetable Chili	301kJ/71kcal	4.0g	13.2g	0.3g
	Golden Vegetables & Dumplings	421kJ/100kcal	3.9g	12.2g	3.9g
Sweet Meals	Fruit Dumplings with Butterscotch sauce	1009kJ/241kcal	1.9g	31.3g	12.0g
	Chocolate Pudding with Chocolate sauce	936kJ/233kcal	32.g	30.0g	9.8g

Packaging: Main Meals 12 x 300g per case
Sweet Meals 12 x 200g per case

Shelf Life: 3 Years from date of manufacture

Storage: Store unopened pouch in cool, dry conditions

Heating: Place the pouch in boiling water for 7–8 minutes (all products are pre-cooked, therefore, can be eaten cold if required)

Meals can be supplemented with special chocolate and similar energy producing products, which collectively will maintain 'survivors' in a reasonable physical condition until rescue arrives.

Stay cool, think clearly and positively and you have every chance of surviving if the worst happens.

The following items are highly recommended to every pilot as part of a personal survival kit.

QTY	ITEM	USE OR INFORMATION
•1	PLE-7 personal locator beacon	Lightweight, compact, can be worn around the neck. Has built-in antenna. Transmits on 121.5 mHz.

QTY	ITEM	USE OR INFORMATION
		Fireproof and waterproof. Battery powered, measures only 73 x 70 x 29mm. N.B. Typical homing range to SAR aircraft at 2000ft AGL is 10 miles.
•1	Jotron AQ-4 high intensity strobe light	Small enough for the jacket pocket but provides up to 10km range. Will penetrate fog/rain. Emits dazzling white flash 50 times per minute. Weighs 190 grams and 15cm long by 4.5cms diameter. US Coast Guard approved.
•1	VHF transceiver. Hand-held, two-way communications	Direct ground-to-air link with SAR or other aircraft
•1	Hand-held GPS (GARMIN GPS 90 or similar).	
•1	Leatherman 12-in-1 survival tool or Swiss army knife	Multiple uses and almost indispensable in a survival situation.
•1	Small pair binoculars	
•1	Goretex bivvy bag.	As used by special forces. Compact, lightweight sleeping bag. Easily carried in belt pouch. Keeps body dry and warm in survival situation.
•1	Army-type water bottle	One that will clip onto a belt.

Chapter 10
Lift and High-Lift Devices

'Anyway, what is lift?'

Lift

What every STOL aircraft manufacturer strives for is more lift. That is to say, to improve the wing's actual performance. And in turn the experienced STOL pilot tries to use every last bit of this lift to the best (aerodynamic) operational advantage.

Lift is derived from the forward motion of an aircraft wing through the air. In turn, the shape of the wing determines how much lift can be obtained. The design construction of the wing – in other words the *wing shape*, has been developed over the years to take advantage of the air's response to certain physical laws. (A typical aerofoil section is shown at Figure 10.1).

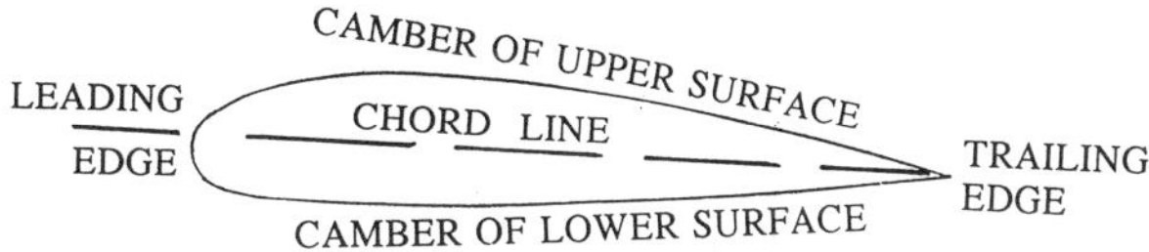

Figure 10.1 Typical Aerofoil Section

Two actions result from the air mass below the wing, and a negative-pressure lifting action from lowered pressure above the wing. As the airstream strikes the flat lower surface of the wing at a small angle of attack to its forward direction, the air is forced to rebound downwards. This causes an upward reaction in positive lift. At the same time, the airstream striking the upper curved section of the leading edge of the wing is deflected upwards.

Therefore, a wing shaped in such a way as to cause an action on the air – forcing it downwards, will provide an equal reaction from the air, forcing the wing upwards. (See Figure 10.2).

The aerodynamic fact is that a wing is designed in a shape to ensure a greater lift force than the total weight of the aircraft so that it will fly. The upward component of this force is called LIFT.

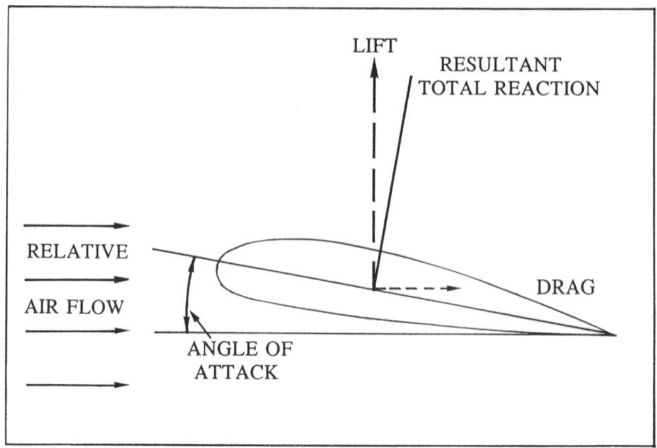

Figure 10.2 Aerofoil v Lift

Under some conditions, disturbed airflow around the trailing edge of the wing could be so excessive that it will cause the aircraft to lose both speed and lift.

The remainder of the lift needed by the aircraft is derived from the airflow above the wing. This is the key to flight. Most of the lift is the result of the airflow downwash from above the wing. To know what lift is and how it works this must be properly understood.

We could get the impression that the lift and drag forces are more or less equal. This is not so. An aerofoil produces lift way in excess of its drag value.

Bernoulli's theorem, specifically his Principle of Pressure, explains how the pressure of a moving fluid (whether this be liquid or gas) varies with its speed of motion. He stated that an increase in the speed of movement, or flow, would cause a decrease in the fluid's pressure. This is precisely what happens to air passing over the curved upper surface of an aircraft wing. The most practical example of Bernoulli's theorem is the VENTURI TUBE, also known as a STREAM TUBE. This has an air inlet which narrows to a throat, being the most constricted point; then an outlet section whose diameter at the outlet is the same as the inlet. (See Figure 10.3).

- At the throat the airflow *speeds up* and the *pressure decreases.*
- At the outlet the airflow *slows down* and *pressure increases.*

The reduction in pressure over the upper surface of the wing caused by the faster airflow, provides approximately two-thirds of the lift made by the wing. Figure 10.4 illustrates the general pressure distribution over the surfaces of a wing at a small angle of attack.

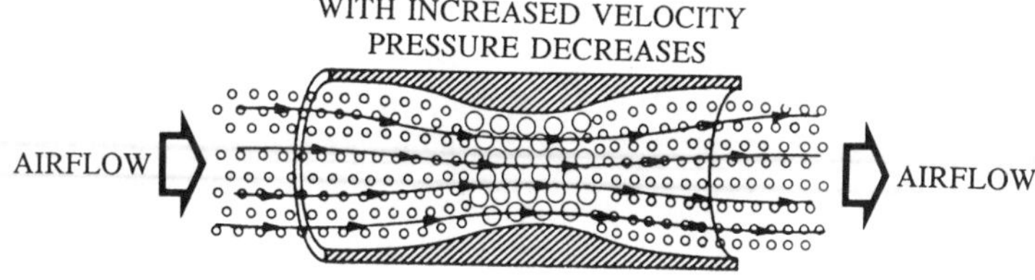

Figure 10.3 Air Pressure Decreases in a Venturi

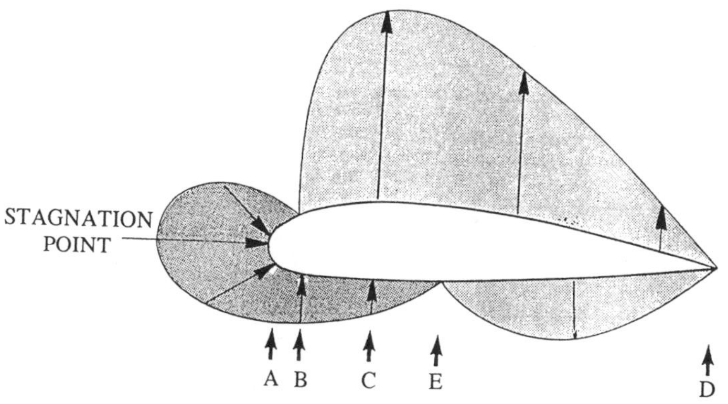

Figure 10.4 Air pressure around a wing at a small angle of attack

As we can see, the upper surface of the wing produces a considerable reduction in pressure, but the lower surface gives a mixture of increase and decrease in pressure as well.

Examining the diagram in detail shows that:

- At the leading edge of the wing, point A, the *full pressure* is felt. This is the stagnation point.
- As the airflow moves over the upper surface of the wing towards point B, it is reaching an area of *lower pressure*. At point B, it is just *atmospheric*, or *static pressure*.
- The air pressure steadily reduces until it reaches its minimum value at point C, as indicated by the longest arrow.
- Towards the trailing edge of the wing, moving over the top of the wing from C towards D, the airflow is encountering an adverse pressure

gradient. (This is an important factor when we consider stalling.)

- On the under-surface of the wing at point A the pressure is above static. In fact, the full *dynamic pressure* is felt there, and to some extent an increase in pressure is felt on the under-surface of the wing up to about point E. After that, the wing under-surface produces a small venturi of its own. This gives a reduction in pressure, so in order to limit this reduction, the curvature of the wing is considerably less on the under-surface than the top.

The pressure distribution shown in Figure 10.4 was for a relatively small angle of attack, about four degrees. Changes in the angle of attack of the wing produce very considerable changes in the pressure distribution. Figure 10.5 shows what happens at a high angle of attack – around 12 degrees.

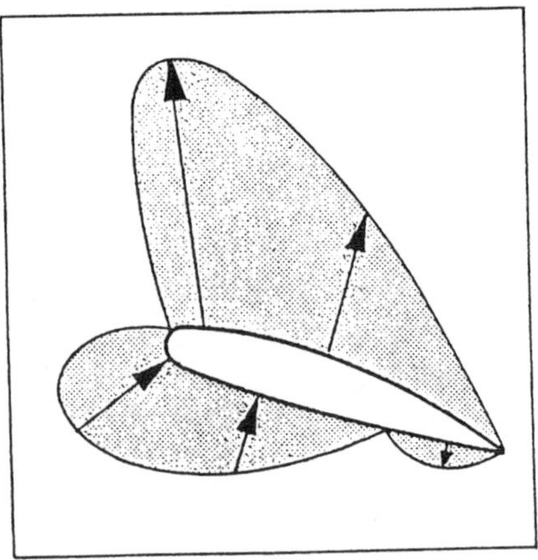

Figure 10.5 Air pressure distribution around a wing at about 12° Angle of Attack

The most obvious difference between Figures 10.4 and 10.5, is the change of shape of the below static pressure on top of the wing. The main feature is that the *point of minimum pressure* is much closer to the leading edge than it was before.

This means the airflow from C to the trailing edge has to deal with a considerably longer and much larger adverse pressure gradient. The only way the air can travel against this adverse pressure gradient is by its own kinetic energy – its energy of motion. If that adverse pressure gradient proves to be too great for the air's kinetic energy, it will break away from the wing. This is called a stall.

On the under-surface of the wing the effect of the increase in pressure is enhanced. This provides more lift, and the small amount of negative pressure towards the trailing edge has been reduced.

The overall effect of the increased angle of attack is to increase lift, but this can only go so far then the wing stalls.

Angle of attack versus lift is illustrated by Figure 10.6. There is a steady increase in lift as the angle of attack increases. At the stalling angle (about 15°) there is a sudden decrease.

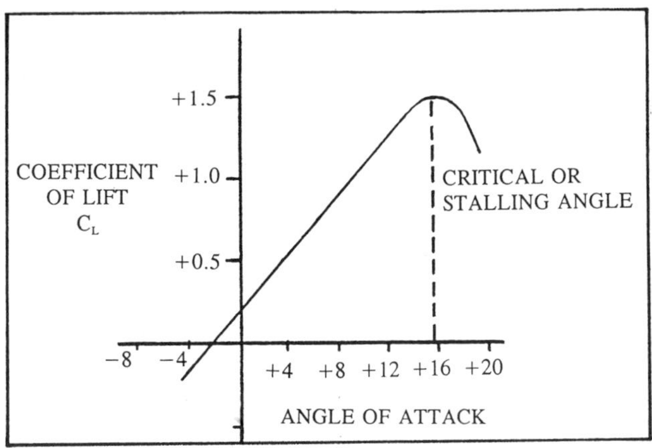

Figure 10.6 Relationship between angle of attack and lift

Having said all this, it should be noted that the percentage of lift generated by the upper part of the wing, compared to the under surface, will vary. This is mainly because they are not constant values. The variations not only change with flight conditions, but with different wing designs. Naturally this is something we will look at with our STOL aircraft wing.

Aircraft are designed for different purposes, and this dictates the shape of the aerofoil. The most efficient aerofoil for producing the greatest lift was discovered many years ago. It had a concave, or scooped out lower surface. The disadvantage of this type was it sacrificed too much speed while producing lift, so it was unsuitable for high speed flight. But the evolution of aerofoil design has turned full circle with modern engineering progress. High speed jets are now taking advantage of the concave high lift characteristics.

When leading edge *Kreuger* flaps and trailing edge *Fowler* flaps are fitted to the basic wing structure, they literally change the wing shape into the original concave form. This generates far greater lift during slow flight, as in take-off and landing.

Therefore the shape of the wing influences the amount of lift that can be generated. This produces a factor (dependent upon the cross-sectional area of the wing) called the coefficient of lift (C_L). This C_L is in fact a compound of the *wing shape* and its *angle of attack*.

For the technically minded readers, here is the *LIFT EQUATION*.

The basic factor controlling the *value of lift* is dynamic pressure, so it can be said that:

$$\text{LIFT} = \tfrac{1}{2}\rho V^2$$

The size of the wing will obviously affect the amount of lift, therefore this must be added to the equation:

$$\text{LIFT} = \tfrac{1}{2}\rho V^2 S \text{ (where S is the wing's } \textit{area}\text{)}$$

If we look at the C_L together with the angle of attack, we can see that it will have a direct influence on the amount of lift generated.

The full lift equation is completed thus:

$$\text{LIFT} = \tfrac{1}{2}\rho V^2 S C_L$$

The shape of the lift curve for any wing will be more or less the same, but it should be noted that the higher the camber of a wing the greater the lift it will develop. Figure 10.7 shows the max C_L comparison between that of a cambered and non-cambered symmetrical wing and angle of attack. As a matter of interest the cambered section still generates lift at a zero angle of attack, while the symmetrical one does not. So it is the highly cambered wing that manufacturers use for STOL aircraft together with other high lift devices (as in flaps, slots, slats, etc.), which we will cover later in this section.

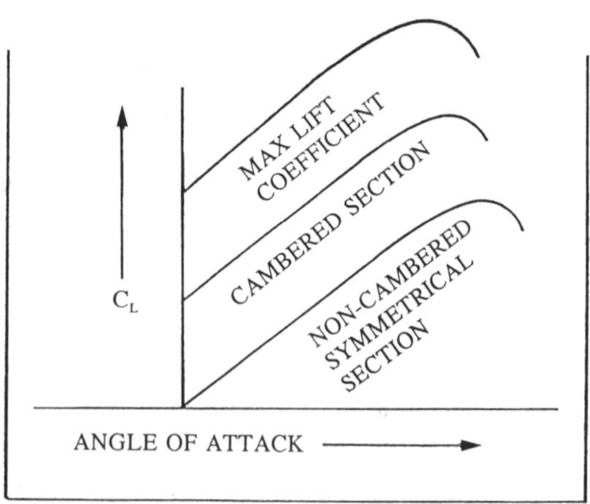

Figure 10.7 The Relationship between C_L, Camber and Angle of Attack

The other important fact is, any *increase* in camber *decreases the stalling angle of attack*. Another plus factor as far as our flying is concerned. (Remember, flaps increase camber, therefore lift.)

At the opposite end of the scale, an aerofoil that is perfectly streamlined and offers little wind resistance, can reach the point where it does not have enough lift to get the aircraft off the ground. So the fact is, modern aircraft have to compromise between extremes in design versus the operational needs the aircraft is required for. This has led to aviation engineering companies specialising in modifications to existing aircraft types, so that they can perform specific roles.

In the STOL field, the Robertson STOL conversion for certain general aviation aircraft types is a typical example. It has a dramatic effect on the short-field performance, allowing operators to get into airstrips they would normally have ruled out.

Lift and Centre of Pressure

The angle of attack is generally defined as *the angle between the chord line of the wing and the relative airflow*. See Figure 10.8. It is often referred to as the *aerodynamic angle of incidence*.

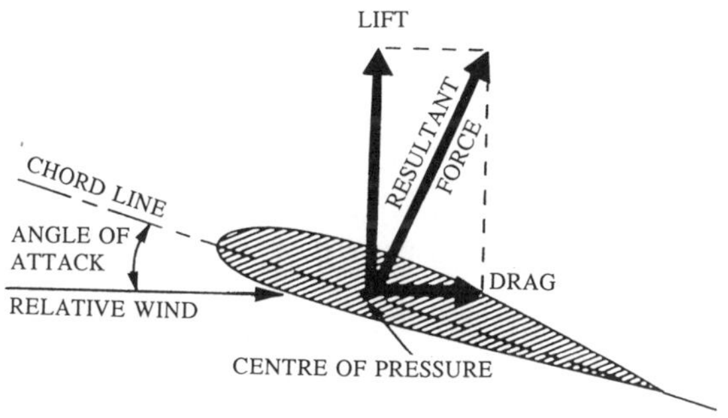

Figure 10.8 Force Vectors on an Aerofoil

It is, however, sufficient to say that the angle of attack is simply the angular difference between where the wing is heading and where it is actually going. Figure 10.9 shows that this angle may be precisely the same for climbs, descents and level flight. Or it can be quite different, even when maintaining level flight.

What complicates matters is that, with certain exceptions, we have no way of actually seeing the angle that the wing meets the airflow. (Only jet aircraft are fitted with angle of attack indicators.)

When we come down to it, angle of attack is the basic ingredient of what

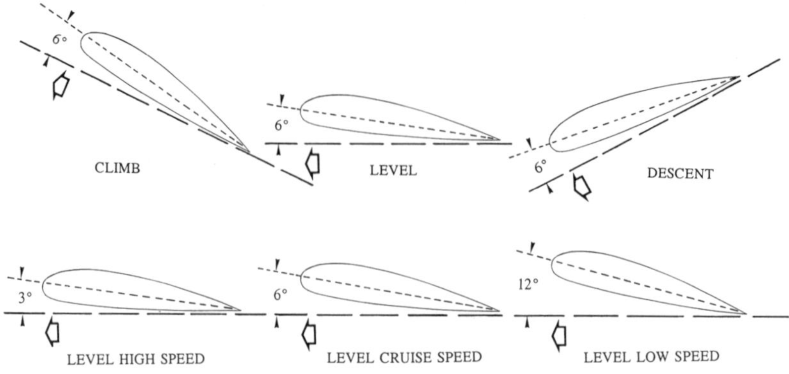

Figure 10.9 Angle of Attack Versus Altitude and Speed

'flying' is all about. The pilot can control lift, airspeed and drag by changing the angle of attack. As we saw in chapter 3, even the total aircraft weight, which is supported by the wings, may be varied with different angles of attack. When this also involves power changes and the use of other devices such as flaps, slots and slats, we are talking about the heart of the aircraft control.

As the angle of attack changes, so does the pressure distribution around the wing. In turn, this has a direct relationship to the movement of the centre of pressure (CP). The centre of pressure is defined as the point on the chord line through which the lift can be considered to act (see Figure 10.8). The lift vector always acts at 90° to the relative airflow. Throughout the aircraft's normal range of flight attitudes, if the angle of attack is increased, the CP moves forward and if it is decreased the CP moves rearward – see Figure 10.10. (The total range of movement of the centre of pressure is about 12 degrees of the chord line, i.e. 12°–32° back from the leading edge.)

Since the CG is fixed at one point (apart from in-flight variations within the CG forward and aft limits), it is clear that as the angle of attack increases, the CP moves ahead of the CG. This creates a force which raises the nose of the aircraft, with still more increase in the angle of attack. If the angle of attack is decreased, the CP moves aft and lessens the angle.

Up to now in this chapter we have discussed the wing in isolation to any other 'lifting' surfaces. However, by itself, the wing is unstable because it must have a longitudinal balancing force. This is provided by the horizontal and vertical tail plane with elevator and rudder attachments. The aerofoils of these devices have the same aerodynamic characteristics as the main wings.

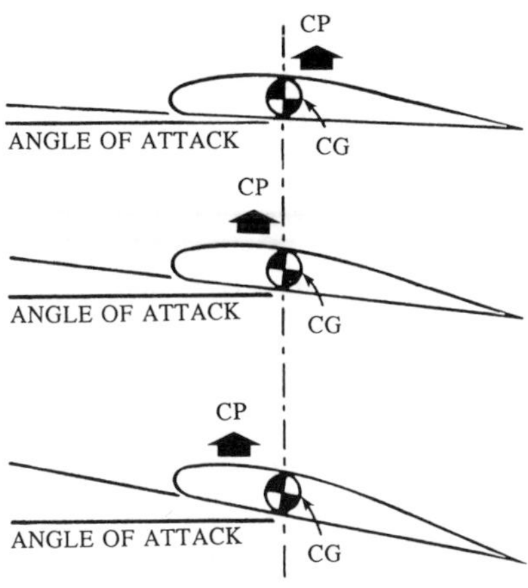

Figure 10.10 Centre of Pressure Movement with Angle of Attack

Spanwise Distribution of Pressure

The amount of lift produced by the upper surface of the wing will gradually decrease from root to tip. This means that although the pressure on top of the wing is all below static pressure, it is much lower near the root than it is near the tip.

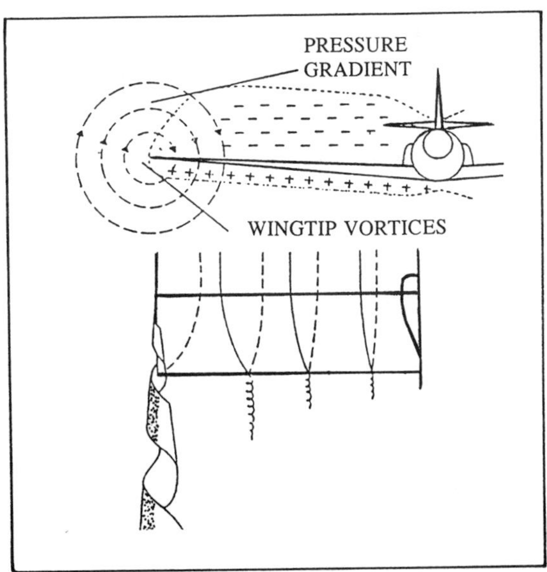

Figure 10.11 Spanwise Distribution of Pressure

On the underside of the wing the same applies in reverse, and the pressure near the root is much higher than it is near the tip. This will cause the air flowing over the *upper surface* of the wing to be *deflected inwards*, and the air flowing over the *under side* of the wing to be *deflected outwards* (see Figure 10.11).

When the two airflows meet at the trailing edge of the wing they are moving in different directions, and the result is to form a sheet of vortices. If we were able to stand behind the trailing edge of the wing and see the air, the vortices on the right-hand wing would be rotating anti-clockwise, and clockwise on the left-hand wing.

The result of these vortices is to impart a downward velocity to the airflow. This downward movement of the air as it passes over the trailing edge of the wing is called DOWNWASH. (See section on WAKE TURBULENCE in chapter 6).

Lift/Drag Ratio

The total resultant force from a wing can be resolved into two parts, LIFT and DRAG. The whole object of the exercise is to produce lift, and in an ideal situation this could be produced without any drag. Unfortunately, in the real world of flying this is never possible. But it is of great importance to know the ratio between lift and drag, so that the aircraft can be flown in such a way that we can get the maximum amount of lift for the minimum amount of drag.

We know that lift and drag vary with the angle of attack and the variations of these are shown in Figures 10.12 and 10.13.

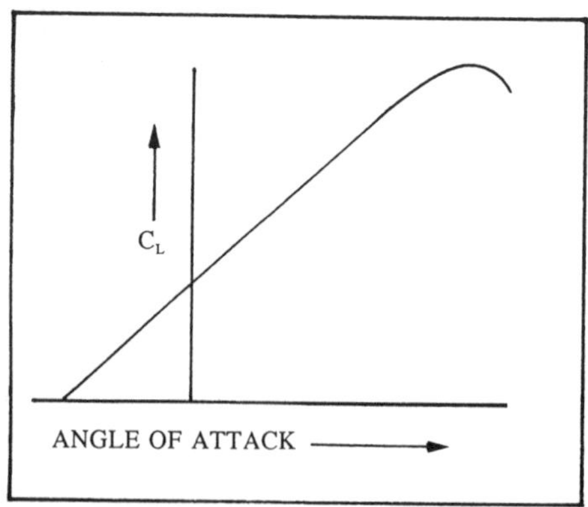

Figure 10.12 C_L Versus Angle of Attack

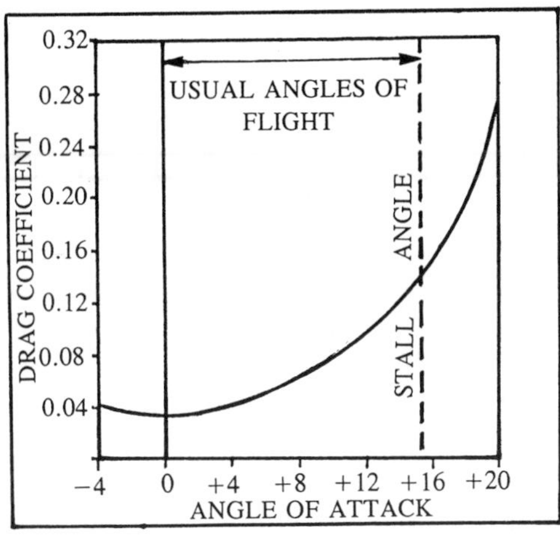

Figure 10.13 Drag Coefficient v Angle of Attack

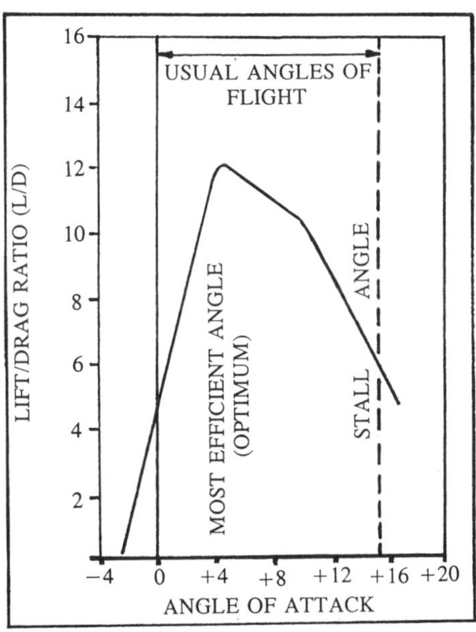

Figure 10.14 Mathematical Combination to Show Increase in Lift/Drag Ratio, which is Desirable up to 4° Angle of Attack

You might be interested to know that the lift/drag ratio for the average aircraft in level flight is between 18:1 to 20:1, which equates to a 4° angle of attack. While a glider has a ratio of 55:1, a considerable difference. So we can extend the lift equation thus:

$$W(\text{LEVEL FLIGHT})=L=C_L\tfrac{1}{2}\rho V^2S$$

High-Lift Devices

In STOL flying we are interested in any device that will improve the lift of our aircraft. High-lift devices are attached to aircraft wings to reduce the distance required for both take-off and landing.

Having made that simple statement, we all know there is more to it than that:

- The distance the aircraft uses during take-off and landing depends on the speed involved.
- This in turn is directly related to the stalling speed of the aircraft.
- The higher the stalling speed, the longer the distance required to complete the landing run. An aircraft cannot make an approach to land below its stalling speed, that is obvious.
- The same applies for take-off. The aircraft will not be able to leave the ground until it has reached flying speed (above the stall). The lower the stalling speed – the less the distance required.

All high-lift devices have the same effect – they increase the coefficient of lift (C_L) of the wing. The methods used are:

- Flaps
- Slots
- Boundary layer control

Flaps

A flap is a hinged aerofoil section which can be mechanically lowered, either from the trailing or leading edge of the wing.

The effect of lowering flap is to increase the overall camber of the wing, thus increasing the C_L. In addition, some types of flap increase the wing area, so augmenting the additional camber and producing even more lift.

There are many different types of flap in general use, some of the more usual ones are given here.

Plain Flap

The plain flap is illustrated in Figure 10.15 and, as can be seen, it is an aerofoil section that hinges down from the trailing edge of the wing.

Figure 10.15 Plain or Simple Flap

Split Flap

The split flap hinges down from the under surface of the trailing edge (see Figure 10.16). This has the advantage that the camber of the upper surface of the wing is not disturbed, but it will produce a considerable amount of drag.

Figure 10.16 Split Flap

Slotted Flap

One of the problems with flaps is that at large flap angles, the air tends to separate away from the flat upper surface reducing its effectiveness.

This can be minimised by putting a small slot between the *trailing edge* of the wing and the *leading edge* of the flap, as in Figure 10.17.

The slot produces a venturi effect which increases the speed of the airflow giving it more kinetic energy. It enables the airflow to follow the contour of the flap further back before it breaks away.

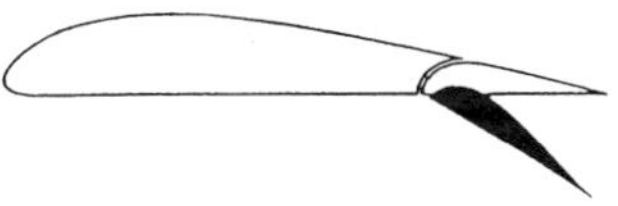

Figure 10.17 Slotted Flap

Fowler Flap

In addition to moving downwards, the Fowler flap also moves rearwards in sections when lowered. In addition to increasing the camber of the wing it also increases the wing area. This will result in a very large increase in the coefficient of lift. It is also quite usual for Fowler flaps to have slats, and this type of flap is illustrated in Figure 10.18.

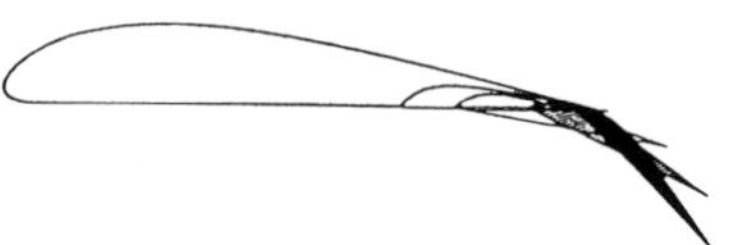

Figure 10.18 Fowler Flap

Kreuger Flap

The Kreuger flap is a leading edge flap which increases the leading edge camber, as shown in Figure 10.19.

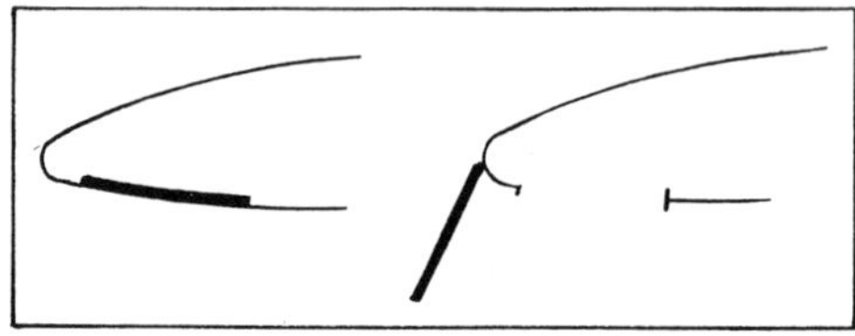

Figure 10.19 Kreuger Flap

Leading Edge Droop

In the leading edge droop system the entire leading edge of the wing is mechanically lowered. This has the effect of increasing the leading edge camber (see Figure 10.20). As can be deduced, the mechanism for lowering the leading edge must be complicated, and as a result this type of high-lift device, although effective, has not found general favour with aircraft operators.

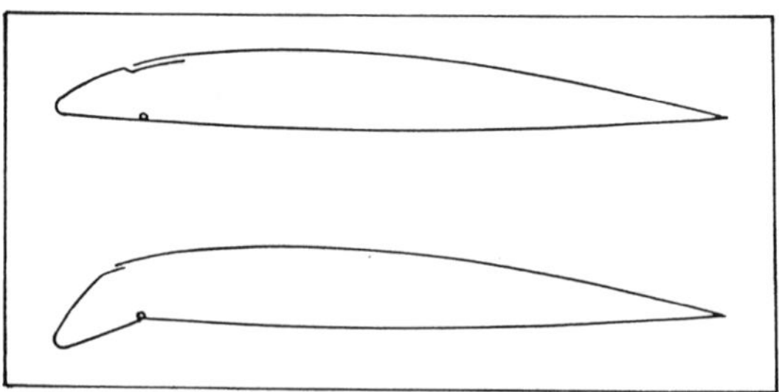

Figure 10.20 Leading Edge Droop

The Effect of Lowering Flaps

The increase in camber caused by the lowering of flaps produces more lift from a given wing section. If we consider straight and level flight, when we lower flaps, the greater lift will enable the angle of attack or the speed to be reduced. Generally speaking though, a compromise is reached between these two factors, and the speed is considerably reduced with a small reduction in the angle of attack.

The effect of lowering flaps is not constant from zero angle to full deployment. When selecting 30° of flap it will give a very large increase in lift for a relatively small penalty in drag. (The Short's SKYVAN uses 30° of flap for a short-field STOL take-off – see the performance charts given in chapter 5 THE WHY AND HOW OF STOL). When the flap angle is increased to around 60° flap it will produce very little further lift – but a considerable increase in drag.

In considering the required take-off distance, the first thought might be that the lowest speed for take-off would give the shortest distance, this whole effect being achieved by a large flap angle. Unfortunately, this is not the case. We know that a large flap angle gives us a very high drag penalty, which reduces the acceleration of the aircraft. You would certainly end up with a considerable take-off run before reaching unstick speed. A lower flap angle gives a higher unstick speed, but better acceleration with less drag. In practice, a compromise is reached between these two limits, and the flap setting for take-off is something in the order of 10°–12°.

The distance required to land depends on the touchdown speed. The lowest speed will be achieved with full flap – this giving the lowest stalling speed. The selection of full flap will produce a very considerable amount of drag which will assist in the deceleration of the aircraft on landing.

Slats

A slat is a lift augmentation device which resembles a small auxiliary aerofoil. It is highly cambered, adjustable and situated next to the leading edge of a wing (forming a SLOT), usually along the complete span (see Figure 10.21). Control is either automatic, or manual by the pilot.

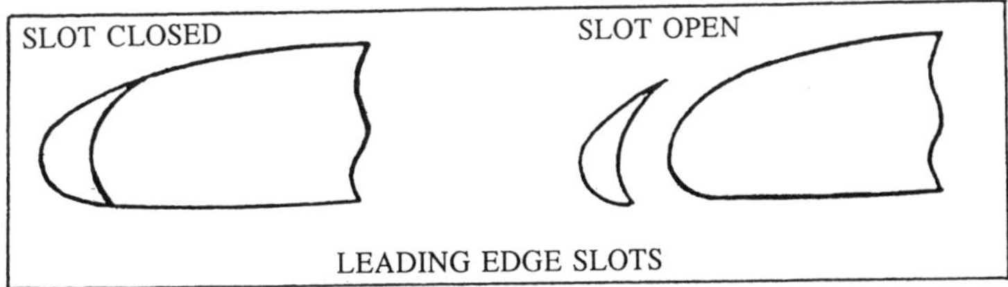

Figure 10.21

When the leading edge slot is open, it prevents the airflow from breaking away at the normal stalling angle. This allows the wing to be used at higher angles of attack, giving higher C_L and so lower speeds.

The effect on the C_L and angle of stall/attack is seen in Figure 10.22. The C_L is increased by approximately 70% and the stalling angle around 10%.

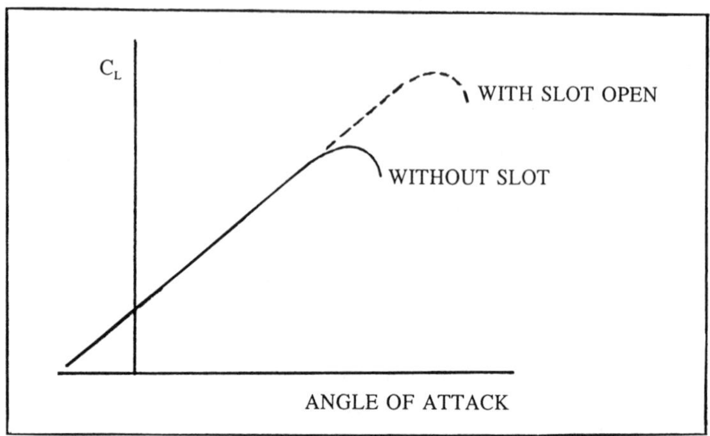

Figure 10.22 Effect of Leading Edge Slots on C_L

The effect of the slat is to prolong the lift curve by delaying the stall until a higher angle of attack.

When operating at high angles of attack, the slat is generating a high-lift coefficient because of its marked camber. Aerodynamically, the resultant action is to flatten the marked peak of the low pressure envelope, changing it to one with a more gradual gradient, Figure 10.23. This flattening means that the boundary layer does not undergo the sudden thickening due to negotiating the sudden pressure gradient which existed behind the former peak, so retaining its energy. This enables it to penetrate almost the full chord before separating.

Figure 10.24 also shows that the pressure distribution is flatter, and the area of the low pressure region is unchanged or even increased.

The passage of the boundary layer over the wing is assisted by the air flowing through the slot – between SLAT and leading edge (LE) – being accelerated by the venturi effect. This adds to the kinetic energy, helping it to penetrate against the pressure gradient.

Summary of the Effects of Slats

Slats have the effect of delaying separation until a 25°–28° angle of attack is reached. During this time the C_L has increased by approximately 70%. It

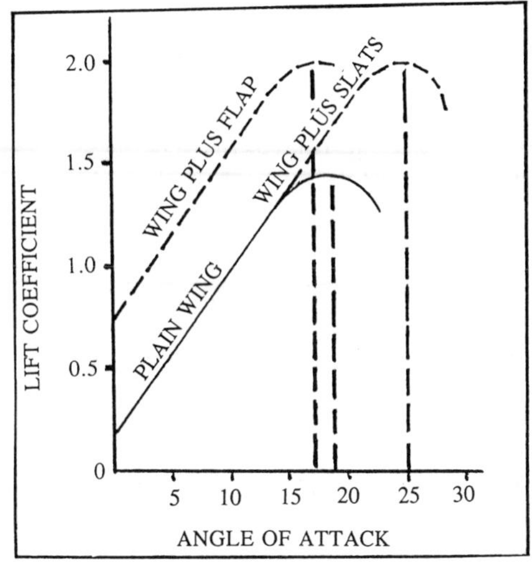

Figure 10.23 Comparison of Flaps and Slats

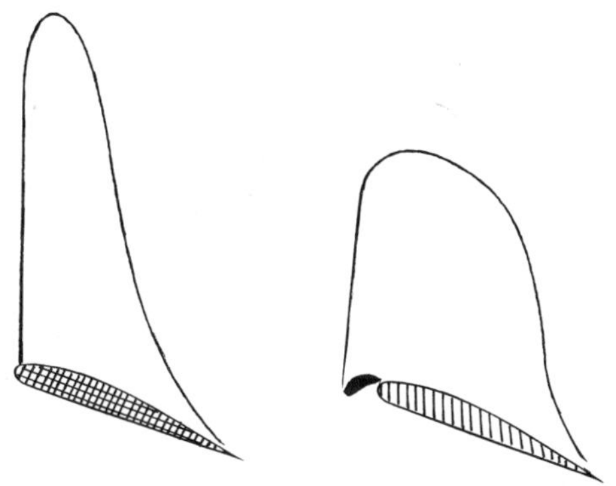

Figure 10.24 Effect of Slats on Pressure Distribution

should be evident that the stalling speed of a slatted wing is significantly reduced, e.g. if an *unslatted* wing stalls at 100 knots, a *slatted* wing would stall at about 80 knots. The exact amount of reduction depends on the length of LE covered by the slat, and the chord of the slat.

Slat Control

Since slats are only useful at high angles of attack, some method must be used to fair the slats with the LE, thus eliminating increased drag at the normal flight configuration. If the slats are small and the drag is negligible, they may be fixed, i.e. non-automatic. Large slats are normally automatic types. They have a mechanical control with hydraulic actuators – selection being mechanically 'gauged' to flap selection. The linkage is such that slats are extended *before flap*, and prior to the normal approach speed.

The opposite occurs on take-off, when slats are fully in only *after* flap retraction at the correct airspeed.

In the event of a flap or slat malfunction, it is usual to be able to 'split' the linkage between the two, isolating the inoperative system. It allows the serviceable unit to function normally.

On some aircraft the stall sensing unit may be used to extend flaps if the sensor is activated by approaching the stall angle.

Summary of High-Lift Devices and Flaps

High-lift Devices	Increase of maximum lift	Angle of basic aerofoil at max. lift	Remarks
Basic aerofoil	–	15°	Effects of all high-lift devices depend on shape of basic aerofoil.
Plain or camber flap	50%	12°	Increase camber. Much drag when fully lowered. Nose-down pitching moment.
Split flap	60%	14°	Increase camber. Even more drag than plain flap. Nose-down pitching moment.
Zap flap	90%	13°	Increase camber and wing area. Much drag. Nose-down pitching moment.
Slotted flap	65%	16°	Control of boundary layer. Increase camber. Stalling delayed. Not so much drag.

High-lift Devices	Increase of maximum lift	Angle of basic aerofoil at max. lift	Remarks
Double-slotted flap	70%	18°	Same as single-slotted flap only more so. Treble slots sometimes used.
Fowler flap	90%	15°	Increase camber and wing area. Best flaps for lift. Complicated mechanism. Nose-down pitching moment.
Double-slotted Fowler flap	100%	20°	Same as Fowler flap only more so. Treble slots sometimes used.
Kreuger flap	50%	25°	Nose-flap hinging about leading edge. Reduces lift at small deflections. Nose-up pitching moment.
Slotted wing	40%	20°	Controls boundary layer. Slight extra drag at high speeds.
Fixed slat	50%	20°	Controls boundary layer. Extra drag at high speeds. Nose-up pitching moment.
Movable slat	60%	22°	Controls boundary layer. Increases camber and area. Greater angles of attack. Nose-up pitching moment.
Slat and slotted flap	75%	25°	More control of boundary layer. Increased camber and area. Pitching moment can be neutralised.

High-lift Devices	Increase of maximum lift	Angle of basic aerofoil at max. lift	Remarks
Slat and double-slotted Fowler flap	120%	28°	Complicated mechanisms. The best combination for lift; treble slots may be used. Pitching moment can be neutralised.
Blown flap	80%	16°	Effect depends very much on details of arrangement.

The Boundary Layer

The boundary layer is best described as the layer of air extending from the wing surface to the point where no drag effect is measurable. Or, that region of airflow in which the speed is less than 99% of the free stream flow, which exists in two forms – laminar and turbulent. Figure 10.25 shows the boundary layer.

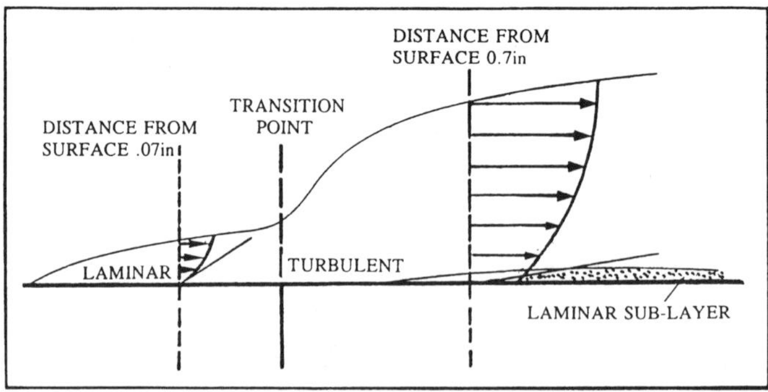

Figure 10.25 Boundary Layer

In general, the flow at the front of a body is laminar and becomes turbulent at a point some distance along the surface. This is known as the TRANSITION POINT. By reference to Figure 10.25, it may be seen that the rate of change of velocity is greater at the surface in the turbulent flow, than in the laminar. This higher rate of change of velocity results in greater surface friction drag.

The nature of this boundary layer is a controlling factor in the amount of surface friction drag which develops. But even more important, the nature of the boundary layer determines the aircraft's maximum C_L, the stalling and high speed characteristics of the wing and the value of form drag.

The boundary layer cannot be entirely eliminated. Although some measure of control may be helped by wing devices (one already dealt with being LE Slots, Figure 10.21). These have the effect of re-energising the boundary layer. Others are:

- *Boundary layer fences* which restrict the boundary layer outflow. They also check the growth of the separation 'bubble' along the leading edges.
- *Boundary layer suction.* Suitably placed suction points draw off the weakened layer. A new high energy layer is then drawn to take its place.
- *Boundary layer blowing.* High velocity air is injected into the boundary layer to increase its energy.
- *Vortex generators.* These re-energise the boundary layer and are usually positioned ahead of control surfaces.
- *LE extension.* Also known as 'saw-tooth' LE. It restricts the outflow of the boundary layer.
- *LE notch.* This has the same effect as LE extension.

Stalling

In a considerable amount of our STOL flying we are frequently operating close to the stall. So it's a good idea to review our knowledge of the subject and see exactly what happens. I call this part of our STOL work – 'flying the edge', because we are very close to the bottom end of our aircraft's flight envelope.

Previously it was shown that lift produced by a wing steadily increased as the angle of attack increased. But this was only up to a certain point. Past this angle of attack the lift decreased rapidly. This critical angle (of attack) is known as the *stalling angle*.

A stall is produced when the air flow has broken away from most of the upper surface of the wing. The only factor affecting this is the angle of attack. (The wing always stalls at a fixed angle, usually in the region of 15°). The cause of a stall is the inability of the air to travel over the surface of the wing against the pressure gradient, which is behind the point of minimum pressure. Figure 10.26 shows the pressure distribution at a normal in-flight angle of attack of about 4°.

The minimum pressure point is at B, and the air travels from A to B without difficulty as it is moving from high to low pressure. However, from B to C it is being forced to travel from low to high pressure – against an adverse

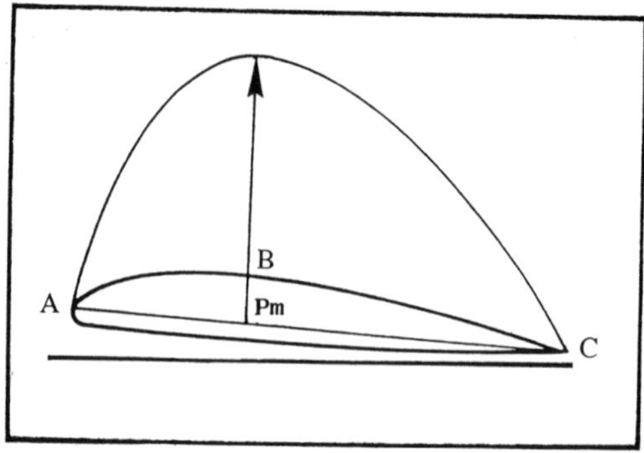

Figure 10.26 Air Pressure Around a Wing at a Small Angle of Attack

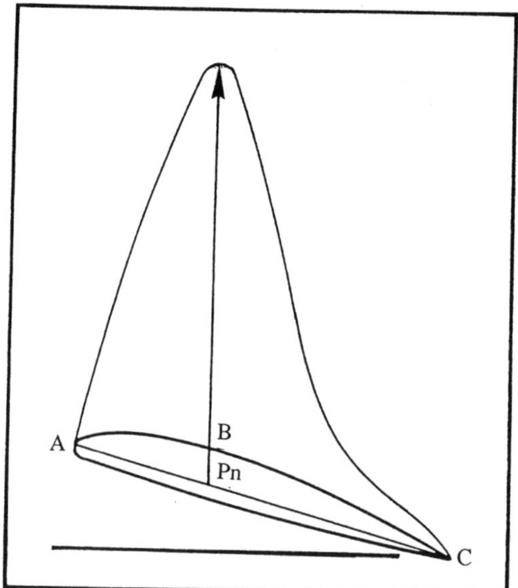

Figure 10.27 Air Pressure Distribution Around a Wing at about 12° Angle of Attack

pressure gradient. This poses no problems at low angles of attack, as the kinetic energy of the air is adequate to take it to the trailing edge.

As the angle of attack is increased the minimum pressure point moves forward, and the distance B to C increases. When it reaches the stalling angle it covers most of the wing. Figure 10.27 refers.

When the angle of attack reaches a certain value, the air runs out of kinetic energy and breaks away from the surface of the wing in a random manner. Lift decreases sharply and drag increases considerably.

In straight and level flight at the stall, the cross-section, weight and lift is a fixed value for a given wing area. This is fortunate when we consider the lift equation:

$$\text{LIFT} = \tfrac{1}{2}\rho V^2 SC_1 + \text{ANGLE OF ATTACK}$$

At the stall, lift, angle of attack, wing area and C_L are also constant. In view of this, the total value of $\frac{1}{2}\rho V^2$ is also unchanging. ($\frac{1}{2}\rho V^2$ is dynamic pressure shown on the airspeed indicator). This is the reason that, for a given weight, the aircraft will always stall at the same indicated airspeed regardless of height.

Any change in weight will require a different value of lift for straight and level flight. So an increase in weight requires an increase in lift.

If we consider level flight at the stalling angle, we can see that the higher the weight the greater the lift required, and logically – the higher the stalling speed. To find out how much the stalling speed has increased due to additional weight, we can use a rule of thumb to guide us:

The percentage increase in stalling speed due to an increase in weight, is half the percentage increase in weight.

For example:

- Weight 2000 lbs, normal stalling speed 100kts.
- Weight 2200 lbs, percentage increase 10%, stalling speed increases 5%, i.e. to 105kts.

The same effect happens during manoeuvres such as turning, which produce a G-loading. During a turn the lift not only has to balance the weight, but the centrifugal force of the aircraft in a curved path. The result of this lift has to be greater than in level flight. So provided the speed is kept constant, the only way to obtain extra lift is to increase the angle of attack. But the problem with this is that it puts the aircraft wing closer to the stalling angle. Therefore the net result of producing more lift is that the aircraft weight appears to have increased – hence the expression G-LOADING.

The increase in stalling speed is calculated by taking the level flight stalling speed for the aircraft's weight, then multiplying it by the square root of the G-loading.

For example:

- Normal stalling speed 100kts,
- stalling speed in a 2-G turn = 100 x square root 2
  = 100 x 1.4
  = 140kts

The one thing we must always be aware of is that a wing does not normally stall over its entire length at the same moment – it starts from one part of the wing.

Wherever this happens to be – either the root or tip – it then spreads over the rest of the surface. The factor controlling where the stall starts is the shape of the wing.

What we want to avoid is the stall starting at the wing-tip because of difficulties for the pilot controlling a wing drop. If it isn't handled promptly and correctly it may well lead to a spin. The correct technique for stopping a wing drop is to use OPPOSITE RUDDER to the dropping wing. Remember the further effect of YAW is ROLL. So if you use a large amount of aileron on the same side as the dropping wing, you can easily induce a more pronounced stall – then spin.

A further advantage of having a wing root stall – instead of the tip – is that aileron control can be maintained up to the point of full stall. The separated airflow from the wing root will cause buffet over the tail which acts as a stall warning.

Various design features can be incorporated in the wing which will help to ensure the wing root stalls before the wing tip. These are:

- The wing may be twisted so that the tip is at a smaller angle of incidence than the root. This will make sure that the root stalls before the tip.
- The cross-section of the outer wing may be given a higher camber than the root, which will increase the C_L.
- A stall-inducer can be fitted to the wing root. The effect of these strips (as in Figure 10.28) is to reduce the camber of the root. In turn this reduces C_L and will cause it to stall before the tip.

The Effect of Engine Power

With propeller-driven aircraft, there will be a marked difference between the power-off stalling speed and one with power. Power reduces the stalling speed. It is also helped by:

- The vertical component of thrust – at a high angle of attack the thrust line is inclined upwards. This vertical component of lift boosts the wing's C_L, which gives additional support for the aircraft weight and delays the stall.
- The propeller slipstream over the wings – this speeds up the air over the wing which delays the stall.

Caution should always be exercised in power-on stalls, as their effect may result in a tip stall from a wing that normally stalls from the root. The results can be dramatic, rapid and alarming. Without full and precise corrective action the aircraft can easily end up in a spin – sometimes inverted.

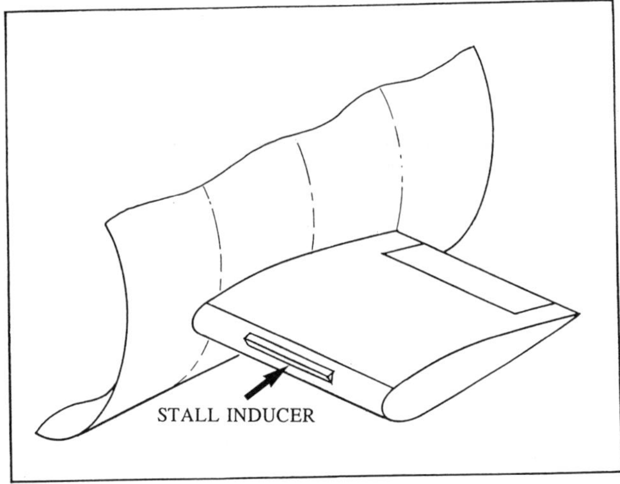

Figure 10.28

The Position of the Centre of Gravity

We have covered this in the Weight and Balance section, so only a brief recap is necessary here.

The stalling speed will be affected by the centre of gravity (CG). If the CG is forward of the centre of pressure (CP), a down-load is required from the horizontal stabiliser. Now the lift is not only supporting the weight through the CG, but also the down-load on the tail. Therefore the lift will have to be increased which will mean a higher stalling speed. The closer the CG gets to the CP, the less will be the down-load with a consequent reduction in the stalling speed.

Icing

Ice formation on a wing distorts the camber and reduces the C_L. This can occur with thin layers of ice, even hoar frost. So the utmost care must be taken to de-ice wings immediately prior to take-off. (Remember, de-icing lasts for a very limited period only – and never more than 30 minutes – otherwise the de-icing procedure must be repeated.)

The effect of ice drastically reduces the C_L, which decreases the stalling angle of attack. (See Figure 10.29).

Stall Warning Devices

STOL aircraft are not fitted with angle of attack indicators, these are more likely to be found in high-speed jets and large jet transport aircraft. We are more likely to have some other form of stall warning. This could be operated

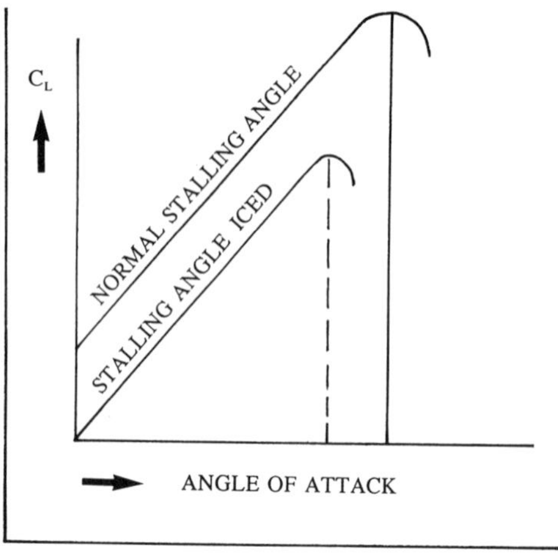

Figure 10.29 Effect of Ice on C_L

from a sensitive stall warning vane fitted to the leading edge of the wing and de-iced. The warning in the cockpit can take the following forms:

- A flashing light prominently displayed on the instrument panel.
- An audible warning such as a horn, perhaps a stick knocker.

For medium/heavy aircraft:

- A stick shaker
- A stick pusher, or both.

A stick pusher is operated by an angle of attack sensor on the fuselage (which is de-iced); this senses when the angle of attack is approaching the stall. Signals are then sent to an electro-hydraulic system, thus preventing the aircraft from stalling. It is fitted to heavy transport aircraft which must be prevented from entering an unrecoverable deep stall.

Summary of Factors Which Affect the Changes in the Basic Stalling Speed (V_S)

- A change in the aircraft weight.
- Manoeuvring – load (G) factor.
- Aircraft configuration (flaps, slats, slots)
- Power – slipstream.

Note: There is a quiz on Lift and High-Lift Devices at the rear of the book for revision purposes.

Chapter 11

Understanding Performance

Know your aircraft and how it performs

The word PERFORMANCE in the aviation context can cover a very wide technical area. But ask the average pilot what it means, and the answer will invariably refer to take-off and landing data on performance charts. When I have asked them to be more specific, such as calculating a take-off performance problem, in some cases there is hesitation, although an answer is usually forthcoming. More blank looks occur when you talk about, 'a reduced take-off distance because of a temporary obstacle so many metres from the threshold of a particular runway'. And I give it a bearing of so many degrees, just within the limits of the take-off flight path. Then more variables such as surface conditions, wind, a low barometric pressure (a pressure altitude calculation) and ask what is 'factoring', and immediately there is a real depth of understanding problem. I'm talking about professional pilots here.

If there is a lack of understanding in such performance basics, then a deeper operational knowledge has to be sketchy at best. And as we know 'working the charts' is just one part of a much broader performance picture.

Therefore PERFORMANCE in the wider sense, could certainly be used to describe the ability of an aircraft to perform certain specific flight operations for a particular purpose. For example, a Boeing 747 is used for long-haul, multiple hundreds of passengers and cargo carrying between major world centres, while a Twin Otter can be used for remote area STOL and commuter flying from restricted minor airports.

Two of the most important elements when we consider performance, are the take-off distance (TOD) and landing distance (LD). When we combine this with rate of climb, service ceiling, range, speed, payload, manoeuvrability, fuel burn and overall stability, we are beginning to coordinate other important ingredients.

Although this book relates predominantly to STOL flying, most aspects of performance are also common to our studies.

The Importance of Performance Data

The performance, or operational information section of the aircraft Flight Manual/Owner's Handbook, contains the relevant data to enable the pilot to calculate performance for take-off, climb, range, endurance, descent and landing. This information provides the backbone in flying operations, and is mandatory to ensure safe and efficient flying.

The study of, and familiarity with, this material, will give you a better working knowledge of the aircraft. In conjunction with all the other information contained in the Flight Manual, it will provide complete technical reference material on the aircraft.

It should be pointed out that the data given by different aircraft manufacturers has not always been standardised, and still isn't. Some technical support departments present information on the basis of ISA conditions, using pressure or density altitude. So the performance information in aircraft handbooks has little practical value unless the users (pilots, other air crew, flight dispatchers, operations department personnel) recognise the differences and variation of presentation. Only then will there be a complete understanding.

Having said all this about actual aircraft performance, we cannot study the subject by looking at the aspects I have mentioned in total isolation. We need to know something of what happens in the atmosphere around us – the air we fly in– and how our engines perform.

Properties of the Atmosphere

The Atmosphere

The gaseous envelope surrounding the Earth is called the atmosphere. There is no defined upper limit to the atmosphere, but much of this study is limited to the first 60,000 feet where most aviation activity is conducted.

Gas Composition

Gases are found in the atmosphere in the following proportions by volume:

- Nitrogen 78%.
- Oxygen 21%.
- Other gases 1% (eg. argon, carbon dioxide, water vapour).

Oxygen is essential for the sustenance of life and the combustion of materials. In the context of aviation, oxygen is required for the combustion of fuel, a deficiency of this gas resulting in incomplete burning and reduced engine efficiency.

Water vapour is present in the atmosphere in varying proportions, and is responsible for the weather around the earth, which in turn affects aircraft operations and performance. Additionally the presence of water vapour may cause icing of the airframe or engine, which can impair an aircraft's performance.

Regions of Atmosphere

The atmosphere is divided into a number of layers (see Figure 11.1):

- The Troposphere – where temperature decreases with increase of height. In this region nearly all significant weather occurs.
- The Tropopause – the upper limit of the troposphere where temperature stops decreasing with an increase of height. The tropopause is therefore the upper limit of significant weather, the first point of lowest temperature, and additionally it is the region for maximum wind strengths. The height of the tropopause varies with latitude, season of the year and prevailing weather conditions, such that it is usually higher in low latitudes in summer and in fine weather. Typical heights for the tropopause are:

Latitude	Tropopause Height	
Equator	53,000 – 57,000 feet	(16-17km)
45N/S	33,000 – 39,000 feet	(10-12km)
Poles	25,000 – 29,000 feet	(7½-9km)

- The Stratosphere – extends from the tropopause to approximately 50km amsl, and is characterised by the temperature being steady or increasing with height.
- The Mesosphere – extends from 50km to 80km; the temperature generally decreases with height.
- The Thermosphere or Ionosphere – where temperature increases with height.

Temperature

The temperature scales most commonly used are Celsius (or Centigrade), Fahrenheit and Kelvin (or Absolute). The first two scales are based on the melting point of ice being 0°C and 32°F respectively, and the boiling point of water being 100°C or 212°F.

Being a form of energy, heat is related to the random movement of molecules in a substance. If heat is reduced, the molecules become more orderly. The minimum temperature to which a substance can be reduced is approximately –273°C, and this is known as absolute zero, or 0°K. Correspondingly, the melting point of ice is equivalent to 273°K and the boiling point of water 373°K.

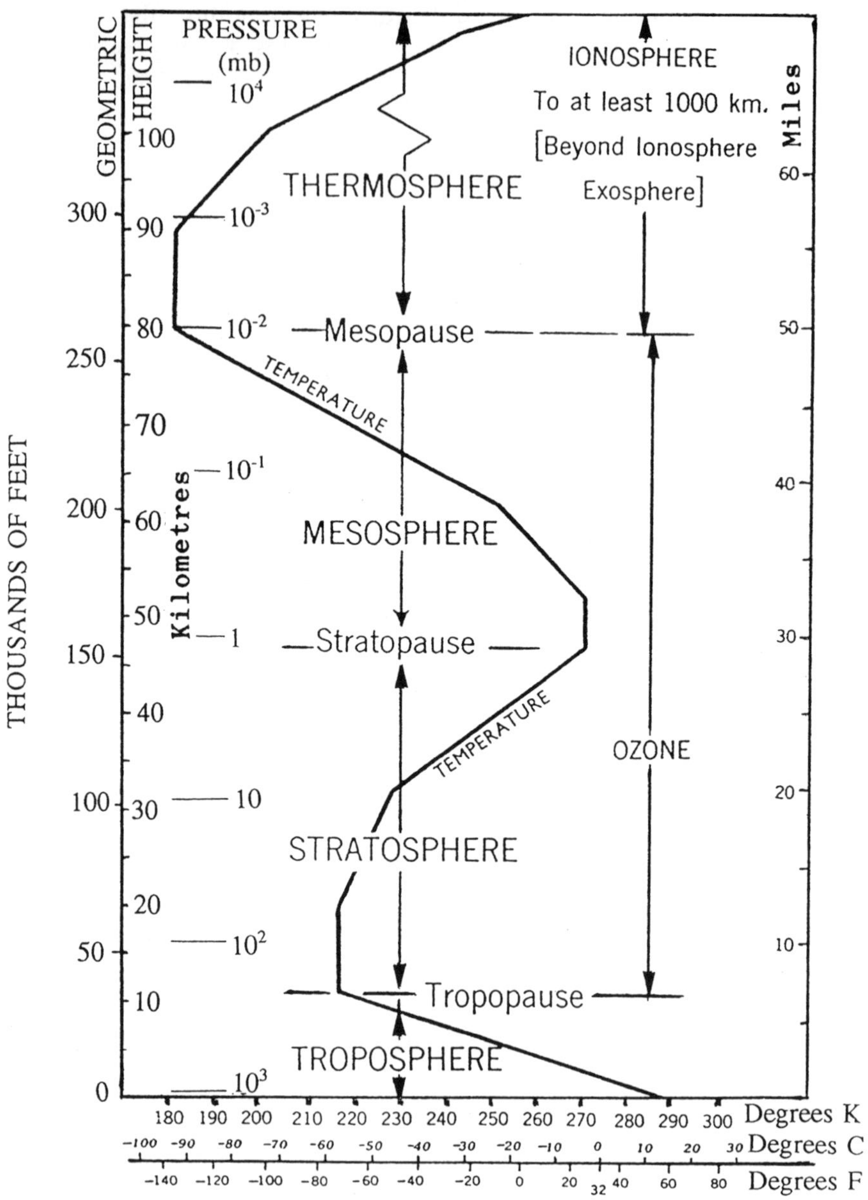
GEOMETRIC HEIGHT
PRESSURE (mb)
IONOSPHERE
To at least 1000 km.
[Beyond Ionosphere Exosphere]
Miles
THERMOSPHERE
Mesopause
TEMPERATURE
THOUSANDS OF FEET
Kilometres
MESOSPHERE
Stratopause
TEMPERATURE
OZONE
STRATOSPHERE
Tropopause
TROPOSPHERE
Degrees K
Degrees C
Degrees F

Figure 11.1

To convert from one temperature scale to another, the following formulae may be used:

$F = \frac{9C}{5} + 32$ [Example: $20° \times \frac{9}{5} = 36 + (32) = 68°F$]

$C = \frac{5}{9}(F-32)$ [Example: $68°F\ (-32) = 36 \times \frac{5}{9} = 20°C$]

K = C+273 [Centigrade + 273 = Answer]

TEMPERATURE VARIATION IN THE TROPOSPHERE

At ground level, in general, the temperature increases with decrease of latitude. With increasing altitude, the conductive and convective effects from the earth are reduced so that temperature will usually decrease with height up to the tropopause.

Typical values of temperature found at the tropopause are:

Latitude	Temperature
Equator	–80°C
45N/S	–56°C
Poles	–45°C

There is, therefore, a reversal of temperatures with latitude in comparison to those found at ground level. This is partly explained by the fact that the tropopause is higher at the Equator and the temperature decrease is effective over a greater height. (See Figure 11.2).

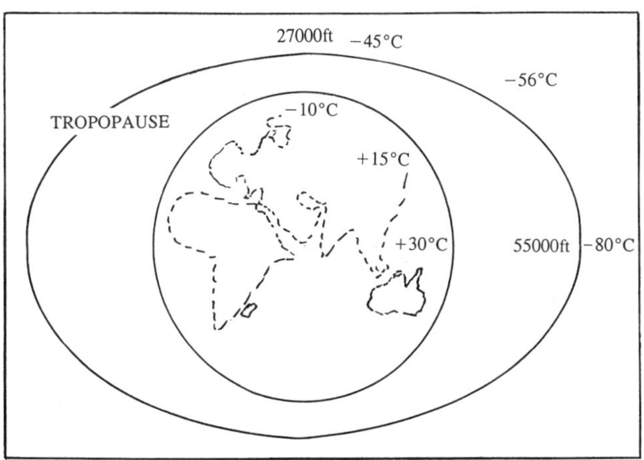

Figure 11.2 The Tropopause

Lapse Rates

The temperature decrease with increase of height is referred to as the lapse rate.

A representative value of 2°C/1000ft is a typical value for the troposphere and this figure is used as the reference for the Jet Standard Atmosphere (JSA).

The International Standard Atmosphere (ISA) uses the comparable value of 1.98°C/1000 feet.

For meteorological purposes, differentiation between dry (that is, not saturated) and saturated adiabatic lapse rates is made, and the values of 3°C/1000ft and 1.5°C/1000ft respectively are used. The difference of lapse rate for saturated air is caused by the release of latent heat during condensation, thus reducing the temperature change.

Temperature and Aircraft Performance

At a given pressure, an increase of temperature results in a reduction of density.

Firstly, considering airframe performance, a reduction of density (ρ) reduces lift (L). This may be counteracted by increasing the true airspeed (v) to achieve the required amount of lift (L).

$$L = C_L \tfrac{1}{2} \rho V^2 S$$

where: C_L = coefficient of lift
and S = surface area

The dynamic pressure is gained at the expense of an increased take-off run, cruising TAS or landing run according to the stage of flight.

On the credit side, drag (D) reduces with increase of temperature.

$$D = C_D \tfrac{1}{2} \rho V^2 S$$

A piston engine's performance is related to the temperature of the air being drawn into the cylinder head. The higher the temperature, the lower the density and weight of fuel/air mixture that can be burnt in the combustion chamber. The power output of the engine therefore falls with increase of temperature.

For a propulsion system, piston or jet:

Thrust = mass of air x acceleration to which air is subjected.

Thus an increase of temperature will reduce the mass flow, and therefore the thrust.

Pressure

Definition

Pressure is the force exerted on a unit area, that is:

$$\text{Pressure} = \frac{\text{Force}}{\text{Area}} = \frac{\text{Mass x acceleration}}{\text{Area}}$$

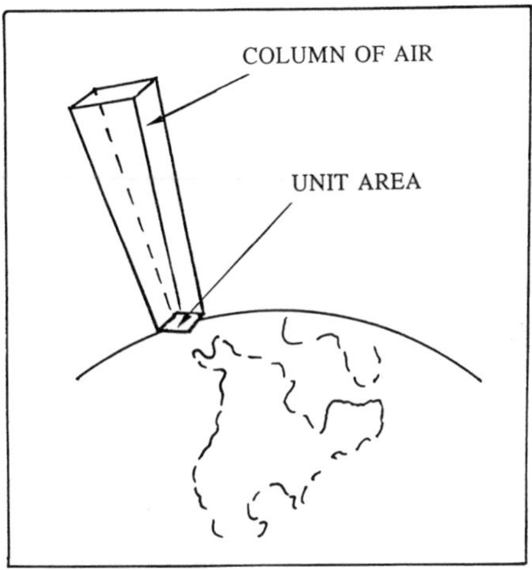

Figure 11.3 Definition of Pressure

In the atmosphere, pressure is caused by the mass of the gaseous molecules acting under the force of gravity on a given area. As all molecules act under gravity then the pressure can also be considered to be the weight of a column of air on a unit area. (See Figure 11.3)

Units

The metric units of pressure are dynes per square centimetre, where the dyne is the force required to accelerate 1 gram by 1 centimetre per second.

The International units of pressure are Newtons per square metre, where the Newton is the force required to accelerate 1 kilogram by 1 metre per second. The Newton is equal to 10^5 dynes.

Although largely obsolete, the Imperial system of units is still widely used, and pressure is expressed in pounds per square inch.

In meteorology the unit of pressure is the millibar (mb), which is equivalent to 1000 dynes per square centimetre.

Before the introduction of the millibar, meteorological pressure was measured in terms of the length of a column of mercury in a barometer that the weight of the atmosphere could support (see Figure 11.4).

Variation of Pressure in the Atmosphere

At sea level, pressure generally varies between 950 and 1050 mb. However, in tropical revolving storms and tornadoes, pressures may fall much lower.

With increasing altitude the mass of overlying air decreases and so the

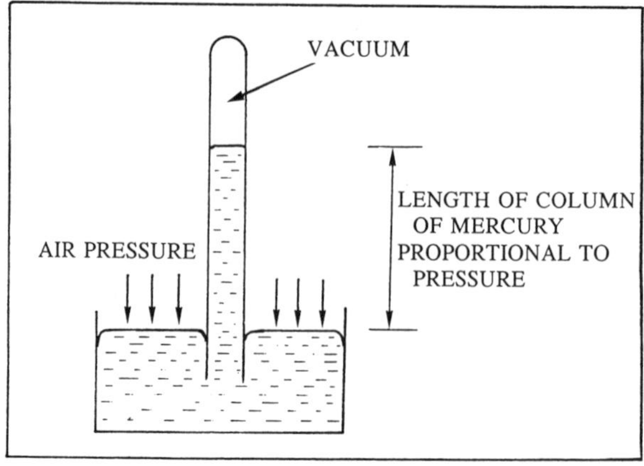

Figure 11.4 Column of Mercury Measures Pressure

pressure falls. Pressure values of the International Standard Atmosphere are recorded below:

Altitude	Pressure	Pressure	Pressure	Pressure
(ft)	(mb)	(psi)	(in HG)	(mm)
40 000	187.6	2.72		
30 000	300.9	4.36		
20 000	465.6	6.75		
10 000	696.8	10.11		
0	1013.25	14.7	29.92"	760mm

From the table it should be noted that at about 18 000ft, the pressure is half the sea level value.

Also, it should now be apparent that the rate of pressure decrease with height is not constant. In the first 10 000ft, the pressure falls at a rate of approximately 1mb per 30ft (see Figure 11.5), but between 30 000ft and 40 000ft the pressure decrease is closer to 1 mb per 88ft.

Density

Definition

Density is the mass per unit volume of a substance at a specified temperature and pressure.

$$\text{Density} = \frac{\text{Mass}}{\text{Volume}}$$

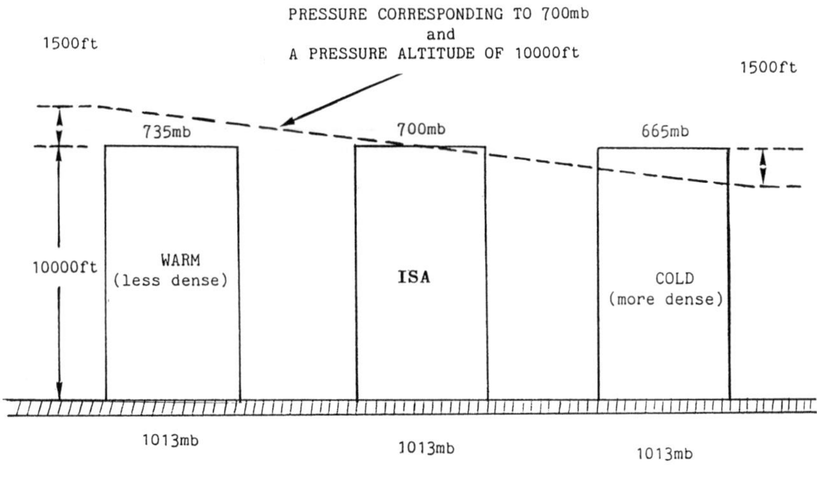

Figure 11.5 Field Elevation Versus Pressure Altitude

Units

Density is expressed in grams, or kilograms per cubic metre for metric or S.I. units, respectively. The Imperial units are pounds per cubic feet.

The factors affecting density when considering a gas are:

$$\text{Density} = \frac{\text{pressure}}{\text{gas constant} \times \text{Absolute temperature}}$$

For a given temperature, therefore, an increase of pressure increases density, or, at a given pressure a decrease in temperature increases density.

Variation of Density in the Atmosphere

At sea level, densities vary between 1.200 and 1.550 per cu. m, the higher values are usually associated with the colder temperatures of higher latitudes, and the lower values typical of equatorial latitudes.

Air at lower levels in the atmosphere is compressed by the mass of the overlying air. With increasing altitude, the overlying mass reduces and air can now expand, resulting in further reduction of pressure.

With increasing altitude the temperature also decreases, but at a rate lower than the pressure. Density, therefore, decreases with height.

Density values of the International Standard Atmosphere are shown below:

Altitude (ft)	Density (kg/cu.m)
40 000	.302
30 000	.458
20 000	.653
10 000	.905
0	1.225

At about 22 000ft, the density is half the sea level value.

We have already seen that density at sea level tends to be higher at the Poles than at the equator. However, at 26 000ft, the density value is similar at all latitudes.

Variation of Density with Humidity

The total pressure of the atmosphere is equal to the sum of the individual pressures of the gases. The pressure of moist air is less than that for dry air, and so humidity decreases the total pressure. From the gas equation, it can be seen that the reduction in pressure results in a lower density. The greater the humidity, the lower the density falls.

Density Altitudes

Density Altitude is defined as the altitude in the International Standard Atmosphere at which a given density is found.

Note: Hot, humid air is less dense. Water vapour is lighter than air.

Aircraft performance is largely dependent on density altitude as opposed to true or pressure altitude.

Density and Performance

The effects of density on lift, drag, power and thrust have been considered in the section concerning temperature. There are however, additional effects of density performance.

Above about 300 kts TAS, air becomes significantly compressed and locally increases the density. At much higher speeds this may give a marked increase in drag and, when increasing altitude, this can offset the otherwise reducing drag value.

A similar compressibility effect increases drag on a propeller blade, reducing its efficiency, particularly at higher altitudes. A jet engine's performance though, is enhanced by this compressibility effect as mass flow is improved.

Air Density and the Human Body

The reduced density of air with increasing altitude means that, in a given volume of air breathed in, the oxygen content has decreased. Above 10 000ft this reduction leads to hypoxia, its effects ranging from lack of judgement to sleepiness or collapse, according to the pressure height of the aircraft cabin. At night, the reduced intake of oxygen impairs night vision at altitudes of 4000ft and above.

To counter these problems, aircraft operating above 10 000ft must have an enriched oxygen supply, either in conjunction with a pressurised cabin, or through face masks. At night, oxygen should be available from ground level upwards.

Performance Ceilings

Service Ceiling

The service ceiling is defined as the altitude at which the rate of climb of an aircraft falls to a specified figure, usually 100fpm for piston-engined aircraft, and 300fpm for jets.

Absolute Ceiling

The absolute ceiling is the altitude at which the rate of climb of an aircraft falls to zero.

Piston-Engined Aircraft

For piston-engined aircraft operating under 26 000ft the improved atmospheric density found in winter in high latitudes will give the highest ceiling.

Jet-Engined Aircraft

As most jet engined aircraft operate above 26,000ft the best performance ceiling will be found at the highest tropopause where the temperature is lowest – that is in summer and at low latitudes.

The Gas Laws

Whilst air is not an ideal gas, it does conform within close limits to the results of Boyle's and Charles' laws.

Boyle's Law

The volume (V) of a given mass of gas at constant temperature is inversely proportional to pressure (P).

- If you double the pressure you halve the volume.

- By halving the pressure you double the volume.

$$V + \frac{1}{P} \text{ OR } PV = \text{CONSTANT}$$

This can be expressed in the form:

$$P_1 V_1 = P_2 V_2$$

Charles' Law

The volume of a given mass of gas at constant pressure, increases by 1/273 of its volume at 0°C for every 1°C rise in temperature.

$$V \times K \text{ or } \frac{V}{K} = \text{Constant (Volume x Temperature = Constant)}$$

The alternative expression below is also useful.

$$\frac{V_1}{K_1} = \frac{V_2}{K_2}$$

Combined Boyle's and Charles' Law Equation

The results of both laws may be combined in one equation, expressing the behaviour of a gas under varying conditions of pressure, volume and temperature.

$$\frac{P_1 V_1}{K_1} = \frac{P_2 V_2}{K_2}$$

$$\frac{\text{Pressure Volume}}{\text{Temperature}} = K \text{ (Constant) } \frac{P_1 V_1}{K_1} = K$$

The International Standard Atmosphere

In order to provide a common datum for aircraft performance calibration, an assumed set of conditions has been determined. This is known as *The International Standard Atmosphere* (ISA). Although representative, these conditions do not necessarily reflect actual conditions in the atmosphere. The values used are listed below:

- Temperature of 15°C (59°F) at MSL.
- Decreasing at 1.98°C (3.5°F) per 1000ft up to 36,090ft (11km) where the temperature remains constant at –56.5°C until 65,617ft (20km).
- Barometric pressure of 1013.25mb (29.92in) at MSL.
- Air Density 1.225kg/cu.m at MSL.

Pressure Altitude

Pressure altitude is the altitude in ISA corresponding to a particular pressure level.

The pressure altitude can be determined by either of two methods:

- By setting the barometric scale of the altimeter to 1013.3mb (29.92in), and reading the indicated altitude.
- By applying a correction factor to the elevation according to the reported 'altimeter setting' (see Figure 11.6).

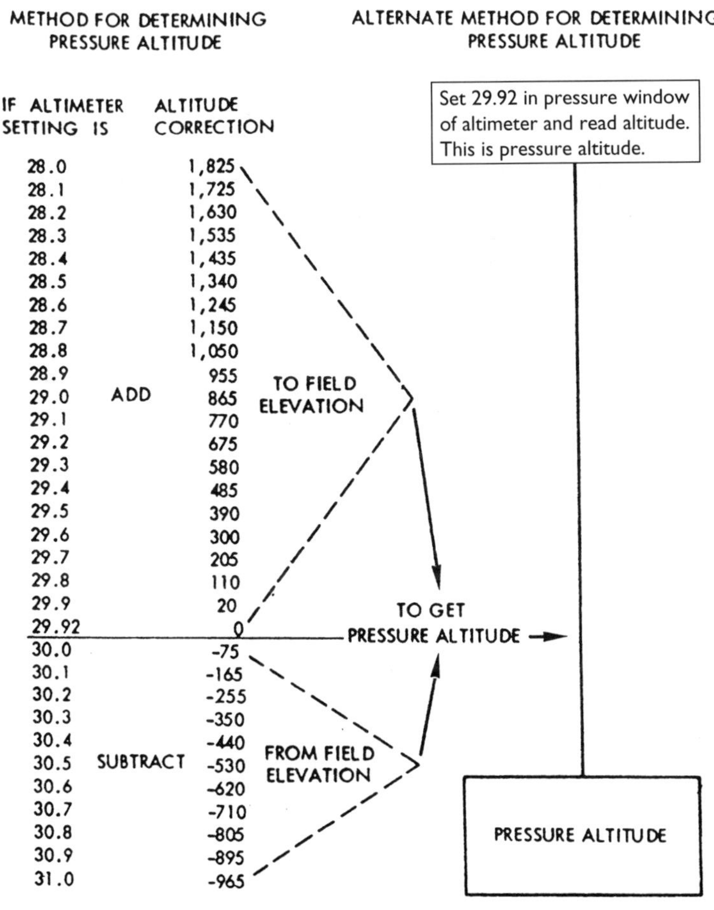

Figure 11.6 Field Elevation Versus Pressure Altitude

The aircraft altimeter is essentially a sensitive barometer calibrated to indicate altitude in ISA. If the altimeter is set to 1013.2mb (29.2in), the altitude indicated is the PRESSURE ALTITUDE – the altitude in ISA corresponding to the sensed pressure.

As atmospheric pressure changes, the Standard Datum Plane may be below, exactly at, or above sea level. Pressure Altitude is therefore important as a basis for determining aircraft performance, as well for assigning FLIGHT LEVELS to aircraft operating at high altitude.

Density Altitude

Density altitude is pressure altitude corrected for NON-STANDARD temperature, the altitude in ISA corresponding to a particular value of air density in the non-standard atmosphere.

Under ISA, air at each level in the atmosphere has a specific density. Under standard conditions, pressure altitude and density altitude identify the same level.

Therefore DENSITY ALTITUDE is the vertical distance above sea level in ISA at which a given density is to be found.

Since density varies directly with pressure – and inversely with temperature – a given pressure altitude may exist for a wide range of temperature, by allowing the density to vary. However, a known density occurs for any one temperature and pressure altitude.

We know that air density has a pronounced effect on both aircraft and engine performance. Regardless of the actual altitude the aircraft is operating, its performance will be as though it were operating at an altitude equal to the existing density altitude.

Density altitude can be calculated by using a standard navigational computer. Apply the pressure altitude and outside air temperature against the scales set in the appropriate windows on the circular sliding scale on the back.

Alternatively DENSITY ALTITUDE can be found by using a Density Altitude Chart as in Figure 11.7.

Speeds

Indicated Airspeed (IAS).

The dynamic pressure of air against an aircraft, or indicated airspeed, is equal to $\frac{1}{2}\rho V^2$, where ρ = density and V = true airspeed.

An airspeed indicator, calibrated to ISA mean sea level conditions records the dynamic pressure as a speed. If, for example, the indicated reading were 200kts, then it means that the dynamic pressure is the same as it would be at a true airspeed of 200kts in standard conditions at mean sea level.

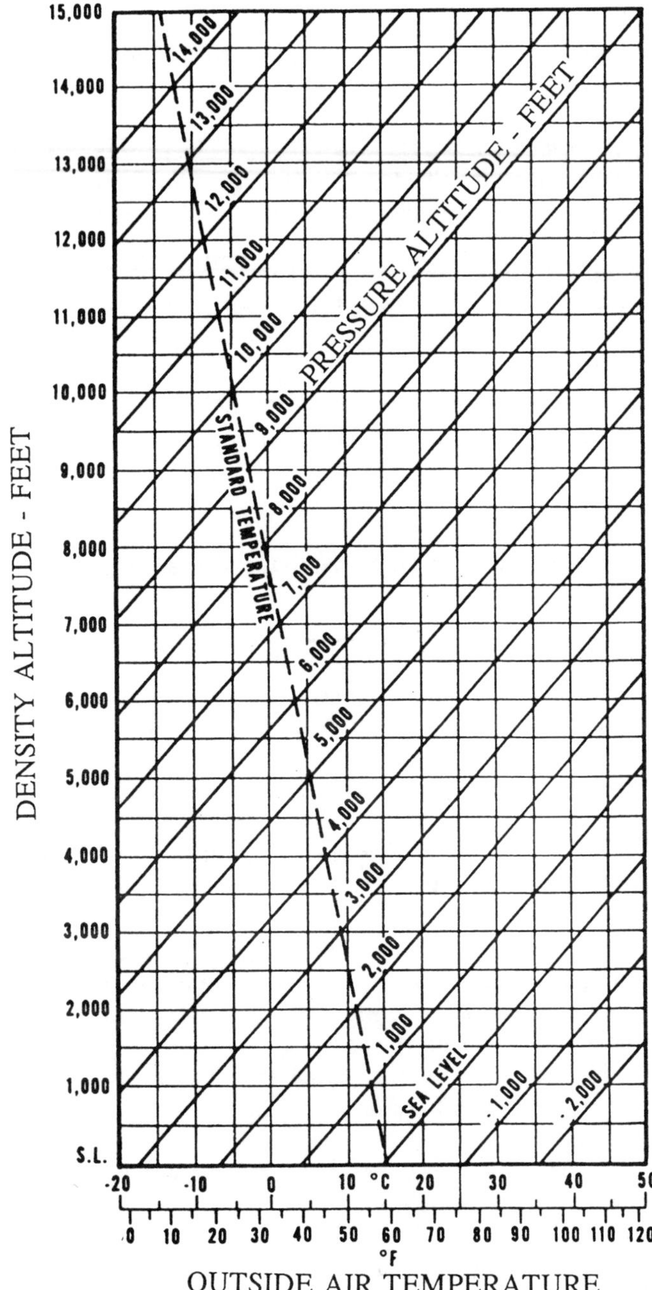

Figure 11.7 Density Altitude Chart

Rectified Airspeed (RAS).
Rectified airspeed is the indicated airspeed, corrected for instrument and position errors (IE and PE).

Equivalent Airspeed (EAS).
Equivalent airspeed is the rectified airspeed corrected for compressibility (C). It should be noted that compressibility is always a subtracted quantity.

True Airspeed (TAS).
True airspeed is the equivalent airspeed corrected for density.

Calibrated Airspeed (CAS).
Some airspeed indicators are corrected for mean sea level compressibility. Calibrated airspeed is the value of this reading, corrected for instrument and position errors.

Mach Number (Mn).
Mach number is the ratio of true airspeed to the local speed of sound (LSS).

Airfield Criteria

It is important that the terminology used when referring to airfields is fully understood, and it is therefore outlined below for reference:

- Take-Off Run Available (TORA) is the actual runway length available for take-off.
- Take-Off Run Required (TORR) is the actual runway length required for take-off allowing for all relevant factors including intended take-off weight.
- Stopway is an area beyond the TORA over which the aircraft can roll and be brought to rest in an emergency without risk of accident. The stopway is normally the same width as the runway it augments but on some runways it may be narrower.
- Clearway is an area beyond the TORA that is clear of obstacles which might affect the safety of the aircraft during take-off. (Obstacles considered significant exceed a height of 50ft). A clearway may be over ground declared as stopway and/or it may be over water, or land not capable of supporting the aircraft weight.
- Emergency Distance Available (EDA) is TORA plus stopway. It is referred to as ED in UK, AIP, or in the USA as Accelerate/Stop Distance Available (ASDA).
- Take-Off Distance Available (TODA) is TORA plus clearway and may

therefore be a different length to EDA and is usually wider. TODA is limited to 1½ x TORA for performance planning.

- Take-Off Distance Required (TODR) is the actual distance required to complete a take-off to a specified height; normally 50ft, (35ft in some performance regulations).
- Landing Distance Available (LDA) is the runway distance available for landing, normally from 50ft, and may be shorter than TORA, e.g. displaced threshold. LDA does not include a stopway.
- Landing Distance Required (LDR) is the actual landing distance required to land and stop from a height of 50ft.

All the above are usually expressed in metres; TORA, TODA and EDA being published as declared distances in UK AIP.

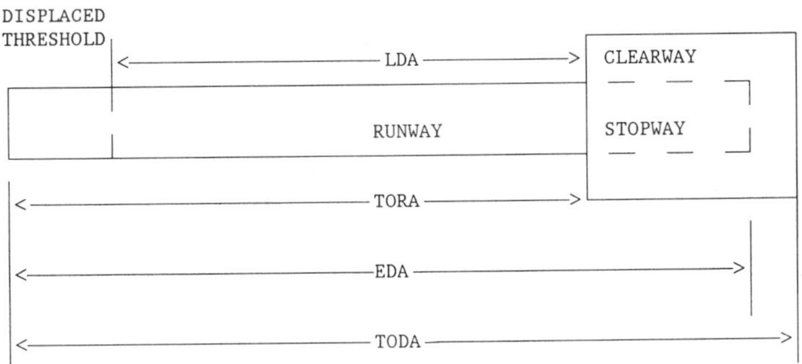

Figure 11.8 Airfield Criteria

Performance Knowledge

Know Your Limitations

Accidents, such as failure to get airborne, collision with obstacles after take-off and over-run on landing continue to occur with monotonous frequency – particularly in the general aviation sector.

Many happen at short strips, often when operating out of wind or where there is a slope. Poor surfaces such as long or wet grass, mud or snow are some of the contributory factors.

In the UK alone there are over 20 performance related accidents per year. Almost all of them could have been avoided if the pilots had been fully aware of the performance limitations of their aircraft. Remember, it is the command pilot's responsibility to check that the aircraft will have adequate performance for the proposed flight.

Obviously it may not be necessary to check the performance aspects before every flight, particularly if you are flying a light twin off a 3000 metre runway. Where you do have to pay close attention to performance is when you *know* the runway length is marginal. This could vary from 500 metres to 1000 metres. The 'go' – 'no-go' decision is then dictated by a number of important variables such as, actual surface wind conditions, obstacles and nett climb performance. However, the overriding factor is the aircraft performance charts.

So Where Do We Find the Information?

The data needed to calculate the performance in any particular set of conditions, may be contained in any one of the following:

- The aircraft Flight Manual.
- For some older aircraft types, the Performance Schedule.
- The Pilot's Operating Handbook or the Owner's Manual. (This is applicable to most light aircraft, and sometimes contains Civil Aviation Authority Change Sheets and/or Supplements giving additional performance data. This may either supplement or override data in the main document, e.g. a 'fleet downgrade'.)
- For some imported aircraft, an English language Flight Manual approved by the airworthiness authority of the country of origin. This will have a supplement containing the performance data approved by the Civil Aviation Authority.

Using the Performance Data

Many light aircraft are certified with unfactored data, which is the performance achieved by the manufacturer using a new aircraft and engine(s) in ideal conditions flown by a very experienced pilot. Also, not all the performance data on every foreign aircraft is checked and verified. In some cases only a single spot check is made.

To ensure a high level of safety on Public Transport flights, both the CAA and FAA have a legal requirement to apply specified safety factors to unfactored data. It is strongly recommended that those same factors be used for private flights in order to take account of:

- Lack of practice.
- Incorrect speeds and techniques.
- Aircraft engine wear and tear.
- Less than favourable conditions.

Performance data in manuals usually makes it clear if factors are included (i.e. Net Performance). If you have any doubt you should consult your local civil aviation inspector.

Any *'Limitations'* given in the Certificate of Airworthiness, the Flight Manual, the Performance Schedule or the Owners' Manual/Pilot's Operating Handbook are mandatory on all flights. So if any advice or information is given to you and it differs from that in the appropriate publication, then you must always comply with the manual or handbook – these are the authoritative documents.

Performance Planning

A useful list of variable factors affecting performance are shown in tabular form at Figure 11.9. These represent:

- The increase in take-off distance to a height of 50 feet.
- The increase in landing distance from 50 feet.

This is in convenient tabular form so that you can photocopy it and attach it to your pilot's clipboard for easy reference.
N.B.When specific factors are given in the aircraft manual, handbook, or supplement, they must be considered the minimum acceptable.

General Advice About Performance

Aircraft Weight

As we saw in chapter 3, you must use the actual aircraft BASIC EMPTY WEIGHT stated on the individual Weight and Balance schedule of the aircraft you intend to fly. (Aircraft basic weights for the same aircraft type can vary considerably, depending on the equipment fitted.)

Fuel Load

Remember that on many aircraft, it may not be possible to carry maximum fuel, fill all the passenger seats *and* the baggage area.

Airfield Elevation

Performance deteriorates with altitude. This is a fact we are faced with – remember to use the pressure altitude at the airfield for your calculations. (This equates to the height the altimeter reads on the ground at the airfield, with the sub-scale set at 1013.2mb or 29.92in.)

Runway Slope

- An uphill slope increases the take-off ground run.
- A downhill slope increases the landing distance.
- Any benefit derived from an upslope on landing or a downslope on take-off should be regarded as an additional performance safety factor.

FACTORS MUST BE MULTIPLIED i.e. 1·2 x 1·3				
	TAKE-OFF		LANDING	
CONDITION	INCREASE IN DISTANCE TO HEIGHT 50 FEET	FACTOR	INCREASE IN LANDING DISTANCE FROM 50 FEET	FACTOR
A 10% increase in aircraft weight, e.g. another passenger	20%	1.2	10%	1.1
An increase of 1,000 ft in aerodrome elevation	10%	1.1	5%	1.05
An increase of 10°C in ambient temperature	10%	1.1	5%	1.05
Dry grass* – Up to 20 cm (8 in) (on firm soil)	20%	1.2	20% +	1.2
Wet grass* – Up to 20 cm (8 in) (on firm soil)	30%	1.3	30% + When the grass is very short, the surface may be slippery and distances may increase by up to 60%.	1.3
A 2% slope*	uphill 10%	1.1	downhill 10%	1.1
A tailwind component of 10% of lift-off speed	20%	1.2	20%	1.2
Soft ground or snow*	25% or more	1.25	25% + or more	1.25
NOW USE ADDITIONAL SAFETY FACTORS (if data is unfactored)		**1.33**		**1.43**

Notes:

1. * Effect on Ground Run/Roll will be greater.
2. + For a few types of aircraft e.g. those without brakes, grass surfaces may decrease the landing roll. However, to be on the safe side, assume the INCREASE shown until you are thoroughly conversant with the aircraft type.
3. Any deviation from normal operating techniques is likely to result in an increased distance.

If the distance required exceeds the distance available, changes will HAVE to be made.

Figure 11.9 Factors Affecting Performance

As we have seen illustrated at several places in this book, 'one-way strips' are not unusual, especially in STOL operations. So there are places where it is not only desirable to land uphill and take-off downhill, but impossible to do anything else because of terrain, obstacles, etc.

Temperature Versus Performance

For those of us who live in a hot climate, or have a hot summer season, we know that our aircraft performance decreases as the temperature increases (see Figure 11.10). In more temperate climates which suddenly experience a hot spell of weather, pilots have been surprised by the loss of power in ambient temperatures of 30°C and above.

Figure 11.10 High Temperature = Low Performance!

Wind

Even a slight tailwind increases the take-off and landing distances more significantly than you would imagine.

If there is a 90° crosswind there is no advantageous headwind component. However, aircraft controllability may be the limitation in this case, depending on wind strength.

Where the data allows adjustment for wind, it is recommended that not more than 50% of the headwind component, and not less than 150% of the tailwind component of the reported (actual) wind be assumed.

To give us a better picture of how this affects both take-off and landing, a few representative percentage figures, backed up by the graph at Figure 11.11, are given below.

Take-Off

On take-off, a headwind allows the aircraft to reach lift-off at a lower groundspeed, while a tailwind means the aircraft must reach a higher groundspeed before lift-off.

- A headwind which is 10% of the take-off airspeed will reduce the take-off distance approximately 19%.
- A tailwind which is 10% of the take-off airspeed will increase the take-off distance approximately 21%.
- In the case where the headwind speed is 50% of the take-off speed, the take-off distance would be approximately 25% of the zero wind take-off distance – a 75% reduction.

LANDING

The effect of wind on landing distance (on deceleration) is identical to the effect of acceleration during take-off.

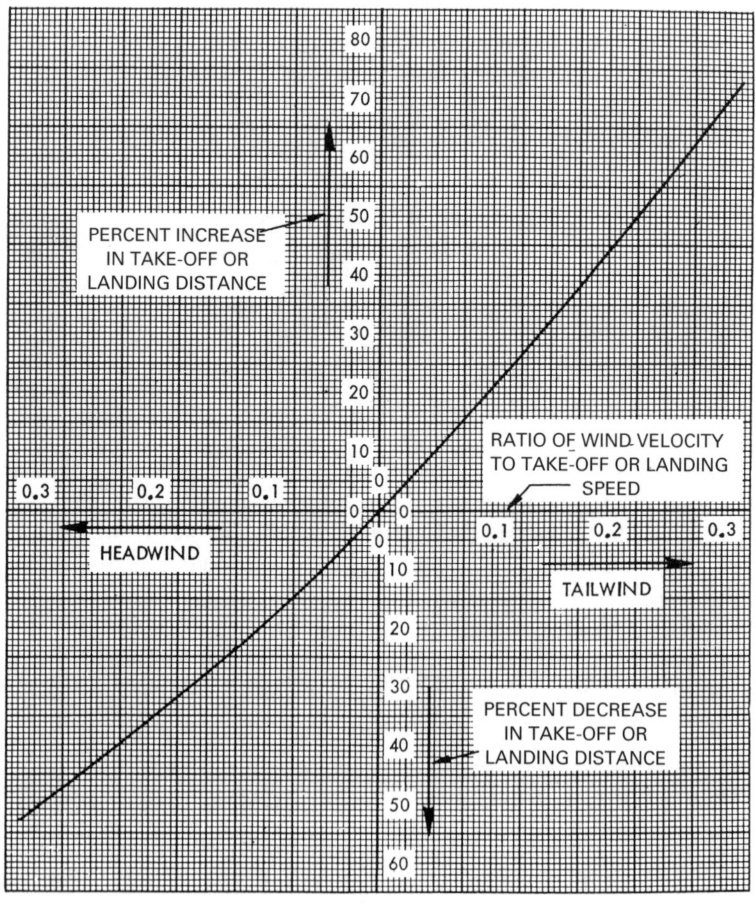

Figure 11.11 Effect of Wind on Take-Off and Landing

- A headwind which is 10% of the landing airspeed will reduce the landing distance approximately 19%.
- A tailwind which is 10% of the landing airspeed will increase the landing distance approximately 21%.

CROSSWIND

On some aircraft types, even a relatively slight crosswind can cause directional problems during take-off. For example, The SHORT'S SKYVAN highlighted in chapter 5 has a square box structure and is 'slab-sided'. Even in slight crosswinds full into-wind aileron must be used to control the aircraft during both take-off and landing.

Do not be tentative about using as much aileron as is necessary (up to full travel) to keep the 'into-wind' wing from rising.

Apply rudder as appropriate to stop any yaw – but only use brakes to keep straight during the very early part of the take-off run when the speed is low. The use of brake during take-off will increase the take-off distance.

KNOW HOW TO USE THE CROSSWIND COMPONENT CHART (Figure 11.12).

As you will see from the SKYVAN *take-off and landing performance graphs*, included later in this chapter, all the relevant factors, including wind, are taken into account for performance calculations.

Turbulence and Wind Shear.

As we have considered in chapter 6, turbulence and wind shear can adversely affect aircraft performance to a considerable extent. Awareness of this problem is essential when working out both take-off and landing distances required.

Cloudbase and Visibility.

If you have to make a forced landing – or fly a low-level bad weather circuit and re-land – you must be able to see obstacles and have visual contact with the ground.

However, the aircraft types most referred to in this book are multi-engine (twin) of the Public Transport category. By way of reference, they fall into the UK CAA performance category C group of aircraft up to 12,500lbs (5700kgs). An aircraft certified in Group C should not need to make a forced landing if an engine fails after take-off and initial climb. Aircraft with a MTWA of not more than 12,500lbs (5700kgs) may be in group C.

Obstructions and High Terrain.

If either obstructions or high terrain are reasonably close to the airfield, check you will have a rate or angle of climb that will be adequate to clear them. Weather conditions involving strong winds (down-draughts),

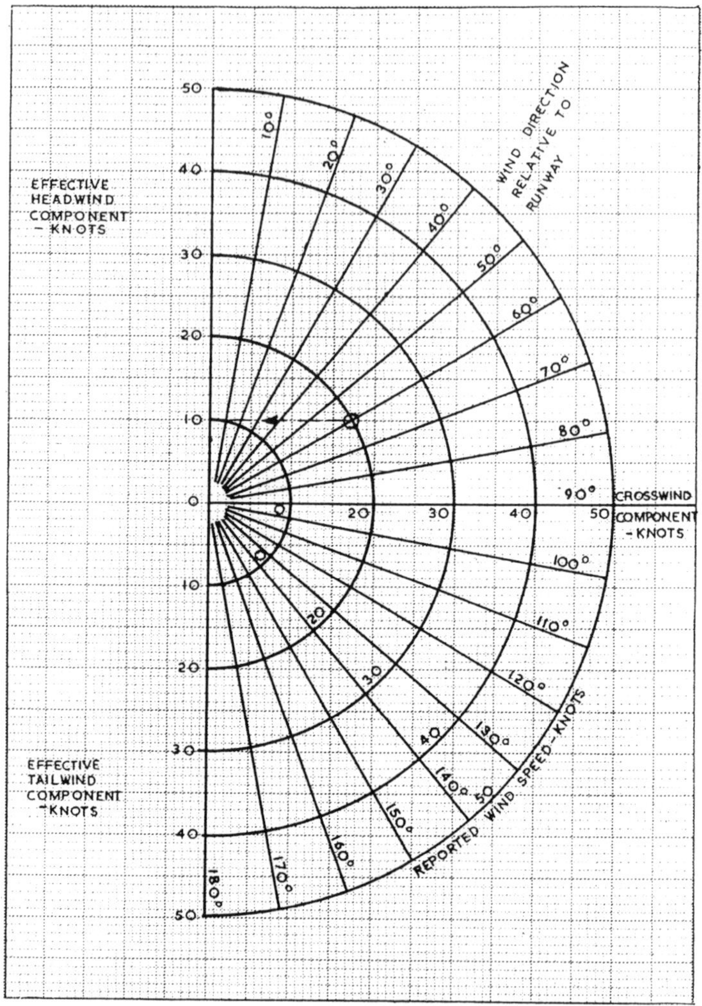

The example illustrated by the arrowed dotted line, shows that for a wind velocity of 20 knots at an angle of 60° to the flight path, the parallel wind component is 10 knots.

This Chart to Convert Wind Velocity, into a Headwind or Tailwind Component.

Figure 11.12 Crosswind Component Chart.

turbulence and wind shear can all contribute to performance problems.

If aircraft performance is marginal, you might consider a 'circling climb-out' over the airfield. By doing this a safe terrain clearance can be reached for easy transition to an en route cruising altitude.

Raindrops, Insects and Ice.

Raindrops, insects and ice all have an appreciable effect on aircraft lifting surfaces, particularly those with laminar flow aerofoils. Stalling speeds are increased and greater distances are required.

Any ice, snow or frost affects *all* aerofoils, including the propeller. It also increases the aircraft weight, so ice must all be cleared immediately before flight. Remember that aircraft de-icing procedures are only good for a maximum of 30 minutes.

Tyre Pressures.

Low tyre pressures (even on one tyre) can have a detrimental effect on the take-off run, as will wheel fairings jammed full of mud, grass, slush, etc.

Performance During Aerobatics.

For those of you with suitable aircraft, and the inclination to indulge in aerobatics – a word of warning. Remember the variations in aircraft weight will directly affect its performance during aerobatics (even steep turns), and outside air temperature/altitude will similarly affect available engine power. 'Hot day' aerobatics require careful planning and thought.

Decision Point and Asymmetric (Emergency) Procedures

Never programme your mind into a 'go-mode' to the exclusion of everything else. Think engine failure – think malfunction. Remember the command pilot's brief (single-pilot operation say to yourself): *'In the event of ANY malfunction during this take-off before* $V_1/V_R/V_2$ (as appropriate)*, I will close the throttles and abort the take-off. After V(?) I will continue to climb straight ahead to 400 feet, identify and deal with the problem.'* (There are all too many variations of this, but it should be kept short and simple.)

With an engine autofeather system in operation (multi-engine aircraft), the drill is simply to control and fly the aircraft to the 400' plateau height before taking any action. The exception to this is an engine fire situation that requires immediate action (use of engine fire bottles after engine shutdown – manual as appropriate).

Manually feather a malfunctioning engine immediately if no autofeather is available, to avoid the excessive drag of a windmilling propeller, or even worse – a seized engine.

Regular practise in asymmetric procedures is essential to stay sharp. When identifying and confirming a failed engine, remember, DEAD LEG – DEAD ENGINE, and reconfirm by point and touch drills – then close the affected engine throttle. If everything keeps 'turning and burning' on the good engine you've got the right one. Then use the emergency checklist.

Do not try the initial identification of a failed engine by instrument indications as they are almost always misleading. Positive, physical identification is the only sure and safe way. But whatever else you have to do, your primary responsibility is to fly the aircraft.

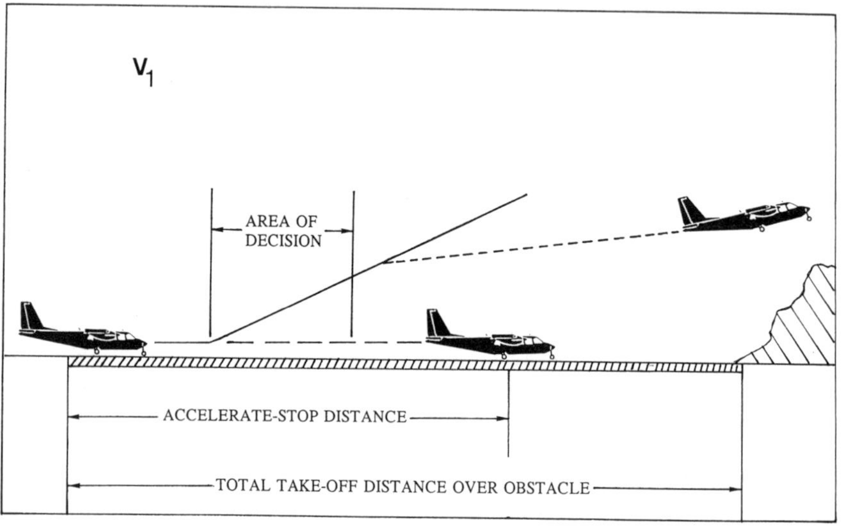

Figure 11.13 Engine failure in Take-Off – Area of Decision.

The take-off flight paths illustrated in Figure 11.13 show that the AREA OF DECISION is governed by:

- the point at which V_Y is reached.
- the point where the obstacle altitude is reached.

An engine failure in this area requires the pilot to make an immediate decision. This decision can be broken down into two clearly defined areas:

- *The 'accelerate-stop distance' – if one engine fails prior to reaching V_2 (for light twins), and V_1 for a larger multi with a guaranteed engine-out performance, then the take-off should be aborted.* 'Accelerate-stop distance' is defined as the total distance required to accelerate the multi-engine aircraft to a specified speed, and, if an engine fails before reaching that speed, the aircraft can be brought to a stop on the remaining runway.

- *The 'accelerate-go distance' – if after an engine failure V_2 has been reached (in a light twin), and V_1 in a larger multi, with a decision to continue the take-off, then the aircraft must be able to maintain a positive gradient of climb on one engine. This also means it can accelerate to $V_{\underline{Xse}}$ if obstacles are a factor, or $V_{\underline{Yse}}$ if no obstacles are involved.* 'Accelerate-go distance', is the total distance required to accelerate the aircraft to a specified speed, and, if an engine fails *after reaching that speed*, the take-off can be continued to a height of 50 feet.

Note: No pilot should make an attempt to maintain altitude at the expense of a SAFE AIRSPEED.

Choose Your Decision Point.

Your decision point will be the spot where you can abort the take-off with sufficient runway remaining to stop the aircraft, (sometimes referred to as the ABORT POINT.)

On multi-engine aircraft if there is an engine failure after lift-off, it may not be possible to reach the scheduled single-engine rate of climb until:

- The landing gear and (take-off) flap have been retracted. (There is appreciable drag generated by the gear itself and the gear doors when they are extended.)
- The best single-engine climb speed has been achieved. In light twins it is referred to as the '*blue line speed*' which is marked on the face of the airspeed indicator. For larger aircraft in our category we would maintain V^2+5kts.

Maintaining Directional Control is Vital

There is the possibility you may have to trade height for speed to achieve the correct single-engine climbing speed, which could prove critical at very low altitude.

Under some limiting conditions (hot and high or marginal performance), an engine failure shortly after lift-off may mean a forced landing is inevitable. Therefore the following points must be considered when deciding the best course of action:

- If flying on asymmetric power it is VITAL that airspeed is maintained above the minimum single engine control speed (V_{mc}).

  A forced landing under control is certainly preferable to losing directional control with the strong possibility of the aircraft rolling inverted at low altitude.

  If you feel you are losing directional control, lower the nose

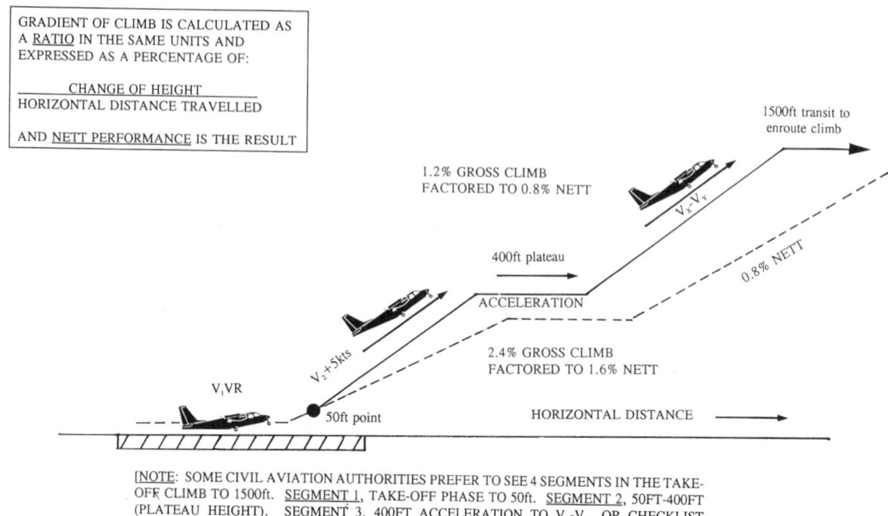

[NOTE: SOME CIVIL AVIATION AUTHORITIES PREFER TO SEE 4 SEGMENTS IN THE TAKE-OFF CLIMB TO 1500ft. SEGMENT 1, TAKE-OFF PHASE TO 50ft. SEGMENT 2, 50FT-400FT (PLATEAU HEIGHT). SEGMENT 3, 400FT ACCELERATION TO V_X-V_Y, OR CHECKLIST ACTION FOR ANY EMERGENCY. SEGMENT 4, CLIMB AT V_X-V_Y TO 1500ft AND TRANSIT TO EN-ROUTE CLIMB.]

Figure 11.14

immediately (if height permits) to regain 'control speed'. But if all else fails reduce power on the 'live' engine, and always maintain a safe speed margin above the stall.

- Performance and stall speed margins will be reduced in turns, so all manoeuvring turns should be kept to around RATE ONE (15°-20° angle of bank), which means you need to leave yourself plenty of airspace when positioning for a forced landing.
- Always use the full runway length. Don't be tempted to take short cuts. There is no point in turning a good length runway into a short one by using an intersection for take-off. (Obviously if the runway is 3000 metres long, that's a different matter). On short fields use any 'starter strip' provided.

Rolling Take-off.

In STOL flying off short, restricted area runways rolling take-off will not be possible. If it is, be careful when turning onto the runway and applying full (take-off) power without stopping. There's no doubt it can reduce the take-off run, but do not impose undue side loading on the undercarriage by rapid turning. It makes it more difficult to maintain directional control – or to stop quickly if you have to. Also your propwash must not hazard other aircraft.

Adverse Runway Surface.

If the ground is soft or the grass is long, and the aircraft is still on the ground and not accelerating as normal, stick to your decision point and abandon the take-off.

With wet or damp grass, particularly if it is very short, you will need a lot more space to stop.

Twin-Engine Climb Peformance.

The two speeds we are closely concerned with during the take-off phase are V_{MC} and V_2. (For larger aircraft in our category there is also V_1 and V_R.

Let us refresh our memories about the first two:

- V_{MC} – MINIMUM SINGLE-ENGINE CONTROL SPEED – *is that speed at which, in the event of sudden engine failure, the pilot can stop the resulting turn within 20 degrees of the original heading, and after recovery hold a straight heading, with not more than 5° of bank and full rudder.*
- V_2 – TAKE-OFF SAFETY SPEED – *is the minimum speed at which, following sudden and complete failure of the critical engine in the take-off configuration, the ability exists to maintain directional control at a safe margin above the stall, regardless of whether the aircraft has sufficient performance to maintain a positive gradient of climb on one engine.*

Surface Versus Take-off Run.

Soft ground, grass, slush or snow increase rolling resistance and therefore the take-off ground run. An example of this problem experienced by the author is at Figure 11.15

When the ground is soft, a heavy aircraft may 'dig in' and never reach take-off speed. Keeping the weight off the nosewheel, or getting the tail up on a tail wheel aircraft may help.

If you have a graph in the Flight Manual or Owner's Manual that shows the EFFECT OF GRASS RUNWAY ON NORMAL TAKE-OFF PERFORMANCE, then use it. For surface and slope, remember that the increases shown are the take-off and landing distances to or from a height of 50 feet. The correction to the ground run will be proportionally greater.

Flap Setting.

We have covered the use of flaps and what they do in some detail in this book. So the only additional comment I will make here is to use flap settings

A 'runway' surface consisting of long grass and soft ground can badly affect aircraft performance. Add to this hot, humid tropical weather, and some careful take-off calculations are essential when using a short improvised airstrip. This particular ranch strip was situated close to the Orinoco River in Venezuela.

Figure 11–15.

recommended in the aircraft manual or pilot's handbook. But check for any Supplement attached to your manual/handbook.

The take-off performance shown in the main part of the manual may give some flap settings which are not approved (for Public Transport operations). Remember that aircraft used for flying training – flying schools, etc, are Public Transport operations.

Do not use flap on hearsay alone. If no flap is recommended in the manual (for all *normal* take-offs) don't use any.

Humidity.

High humidity can have an adverse effect on engine performance, and this is usually taken into account during certification. If you check in the aircraft manual/handbook there may be a correction factor given.

Abandoned (Aborted) Take-off – Engine Power.

Multi-engine aircraft manuals include data on rejected take-off distances. Some quote a minimum engine RPM that should be reached prior to, and during the take-off run. (Note that Static (power check) RPM and take-off RPM will vary with a fixed-pitch-prop piston engine aircraft, according to the type of propeller fitted; if in any doubt check with a qualified aircraft engineer/mechanic.)

Even after the satisfactory completion of the normal pre take-off engine checks, engine power (RPM and manifold pressure) must be maintained during the take-off run. If anything is abnormal (and I include oil pressures/engine temperatures, etc), abandon the take-off while you have room to stop.

If carburettor heat is applicable to your aircraft, use it briefly at the holding point to ensure carb ice is not forming.

Landing Performance – Brief Points to Note

Again in this book we have covered in detail the approach and landing. Therefore, in summary form let's recap on some of the more important points:

- Adjust your approach to make sure you touch down on, or very close to your threshold aiming point. (This is not necessarily the actual threshold of the runway.) This is important if the runway length is marginal. If you've misjudged it make an early decision to go around – don't float half-way down the runway in an indecisive manner because you might leave it *too late*.
- Landing on wet grass or snow, etc, can result in increased ground roll, despite increased rolling resistance. This is due to reduced braking effectiveness through lack of tyre friction. Very short wet grass with a firm subsoil will be slippery and give a 60% distance increase (1.6 factor).
- The landing factors for dry grass are conservative because the pilot cannot see, or always know, whether the grass is wet or covered in dew.
- The landing distances quoted in the Flight Manual/Pilot's Operating Handbook assume the correct approach speed and technique is flown. Use of a higher speed will add significantly to the distance required, whilst a lower speed will reduce the speed margin above the stall.

Safety Factoring for Take-off and Landing

For all flights it is strongly recommended that the appropriate public transport factor be applied.

Take-off

The take-off factor is x 1.33 and applies to all single and multi-engine aircraft with limited performance (Group E in the UK). Aircraft manuals in other performance groups may give factored data.

Every pilot is expected to refer to the Flight Manual for specific information on all aspects of performance planning.

Aircraft Performance with Unfactored Data

Don't forget, where several factors are relevant, they must be multiplied. The resulting take-off distance required (TODR) to a height of 50 feet, can become surprisingly high.

For example, in still air, on a level, dry hard runway at sea level, with an ambient temperature of 10°C, an aircraft requires a measured take-off distance of 390 metres to a height of 50 feet. This should be multiplied by the safety factor of 1.33, giving a TODR of 519 metres.

The same aircraft from a dry, short grass strip (factor of 1.2), with a 2% uphill slope (factor 1.1), at 500 feet AMSL (factor of 1.05) and at 20°C (factor of 1.1), including the safety factor of 1.33 Results in a TODR of 791 metres.

(390 x 1.2 x 1.1 x 1.05 x 1.1 x 1.33 = 791 metres)

You should always ensure that after applying all the relevant factors – including the safety factor – the TODR does not exceed the TODA. If it does, the aircraft weight must be reduced. This can be a combination of off-loading passengers, baggage or fuel.

Climb and Performance

In order that the aircraft climb performance does not fall below the prescribed minimum, some manuals/handbooks quote take-off and landing weights that should not be exceeded at specific combinations of altitude and temperature. (In other words the *weight for altitude and temperature* – WAT – limits.) They are calculated using the pressure altitude and temperature at a specific airfield.

Remember that the aircraft rate of climb decreases with altitude, so don't allow yourself to get into a situation where the terrain out-climbs your aircraft!

Landing

It would be advisable to apply the Public Transport factor for all flights. For landing this factor is x 1.43, so you should be able to land in 70% of the distance available.

Once more, when several factors are relevant they must be multiplied. As in the take-off case, the total distance required may seem surprisingly high. Always ensure that after applying all the relevant factors, including the safety factor, the Landing Distance Required (LDR) from a height of 50 feet does not exceed Landing Distance Available (LDA).

Obstacles

We all know the problems created by obstacles in our take-off and landing flight path. So we must confirm that there is adequate performance available to clear them by a safe margin.

Excessive angles of bank shortly after take-off greatly reduce the rate of climb.

Airfields/Airstrip Runway Distances

Many airstrips, particularly in remote wilderness areas, do not have published runway distances available. Therefore at airfields where no published information exists, distances can be paced out. Accurately measure your pace length, or assume it to be no more than 0.75 metres (2.5 feet).

If you expect to use a particular airstrip frequently, it is better to measure the length accurately with the aid of a piece of cord or thin rope of a specific known length.

Slopes can be calculated if runway elevations at each end are known. For example an altitude difference of 50 feet on a 750 metre (2,500ft) strip shows a 2% slope. The aircraft altimeter can be used to check threshold elevations by taxying to each end of the runway in turn and comparing the difference in height between both ends.

Airfield elevation can be measured by an actual Pressure Altitude calculation, using the aircraft altimeter against the standard pressure of 1013.25mb (29.92in).

Be sure not to mix metres and feet in your calculations.

Aircraft, Engine and Aerodynamic Aspects

The various parts of aircraft performance result from the combination of actual aircraft and engine characteristics. While the aerodynamic aspects of the aircraft generally define the power and thrust requirements at various flight conditions, engine characteristics tell us what power and thrust is available. The matching of aircraft aerodynamics and suitable engines is solely the province of the manufacturer. This provides maximum performance for a specific design/performance combination, e.g., climb, endurance, aircraft range, etc.

Aircraft performance depends on a number of factors:
For take-off:

- The weight of the aircraft.
- Altitude of the airstrip (AMSL).
- Ambient temperature.
- Pressure altitude.
- Wind (direction and speed).

By using these five variables, the pilot can calculate the accelerate-stop distance, normal take-off distance and additional performance items, such as crosswind component.

Landing and stopping distances are plotted on the landing performance chart. Wing flaps have minimal direct effect on aircraft stopping distances, but indirectly they have an appreciable effect, because a large wing flap angle will materially reduce landing speed.

The data presented in the landing chart is based on maximum braking, 40° or more flap extension and a hard-surfaced runway. Theoretically, maximum braking is realised just before the point at which skidding occurs. The chart makes direct allowances for aircraft weight, temperature, pressure, altitude and wind.

The take-off, landing and en route charts for the SHORT'S SKYVAN 3M are presented at Figure 11.16 in the order they would be used for an actual flight. They are typical of those found in Flight or aircraft owner manuals for multi-engine aircraft. But similar types of charts and graphs for light, single-engine aircraft provide the same performance information.

Thoroughly familiarise yourself with the following charts and study the examples given.

Figure 11.16 Take-Off, Landing and En Route Charts for the Short's Skyvan 3M.

MAXIMUM TAKE-OFF WEIGHT FOR ALTITUDE AND TEMPERATURE

Maximum permissible take-off weight for varying altitudes and air temperatures with or without the use of engine anti-icing.

The example illustrated by the arrowed broken line, shows that for an aerodrome at an altitude of 4500ft, with an air temperature of +30°C maximum permissible take-off weight is 12,200-lbs, anti-icing off.

NOTES:

1) For normal operation the maximum take-off weight using 18° may also be determined by take-off field length, flight path, en route or landing considerations.

2) This curve is determined by the one inoperative initial en route climb requirement of 0.8% gradient.

3) Short-field (STOL) operation was covered in 'The Why and How of STOL' section, chapter four.

MAXIMUM TAKE-OFF AND LANDING WEIGHT FOR ALTITUDE AND TEMPERATURE

WITHOUT ENGINE ANTI-ICING

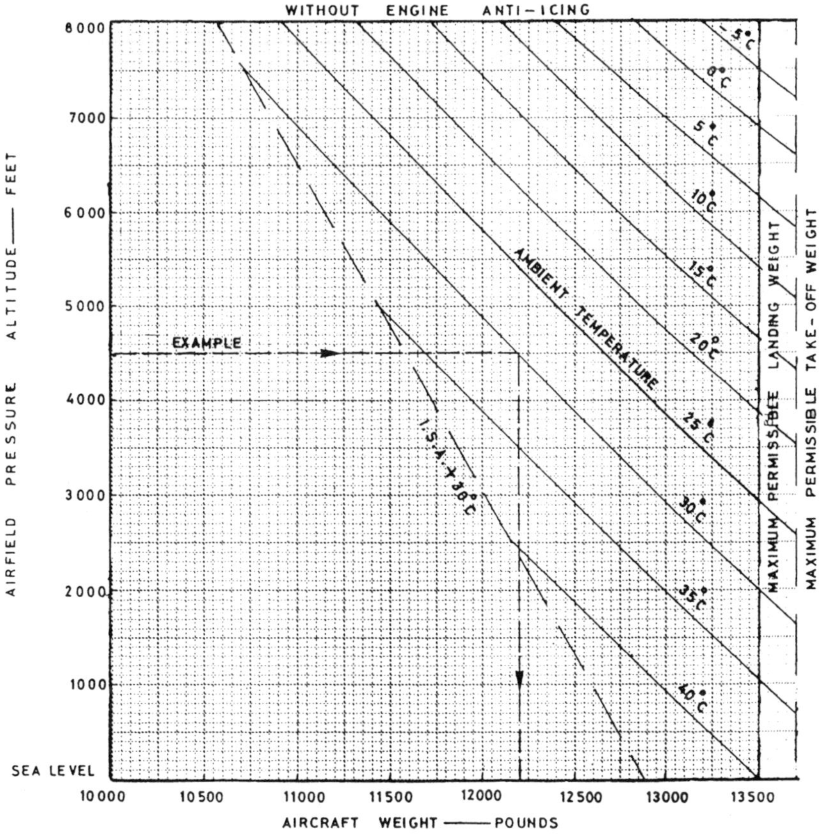

AIRFIELD PRESSURE ALTITUDE —— FEET

8000
7000
6000
5000
4000
3000
2000
1000
SEA LEVEL

EXAMPLE

I.S.A. + 38°C

AMBIENT TEMPERATURE

-5°C
0°C
5°C
10°C
15°C
20°C
25°C
30°C
35°C
40°C

MAXIMUM PERMISSIBLE LANDING WEIGHT

MAXIMUM PERMISSIBLE TAKE-OFF WEIGHT

10000 10500 11000 11500 12000 12500 13000 13500

AIRCRAFT WEIGHT —— POUNDS

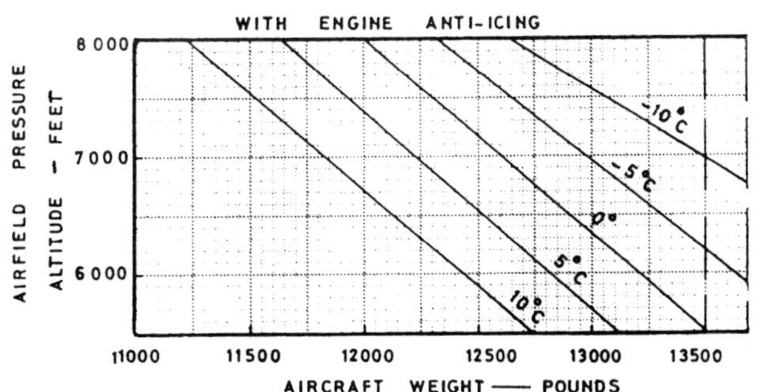

ENROUTE CLIMB SPEEDS

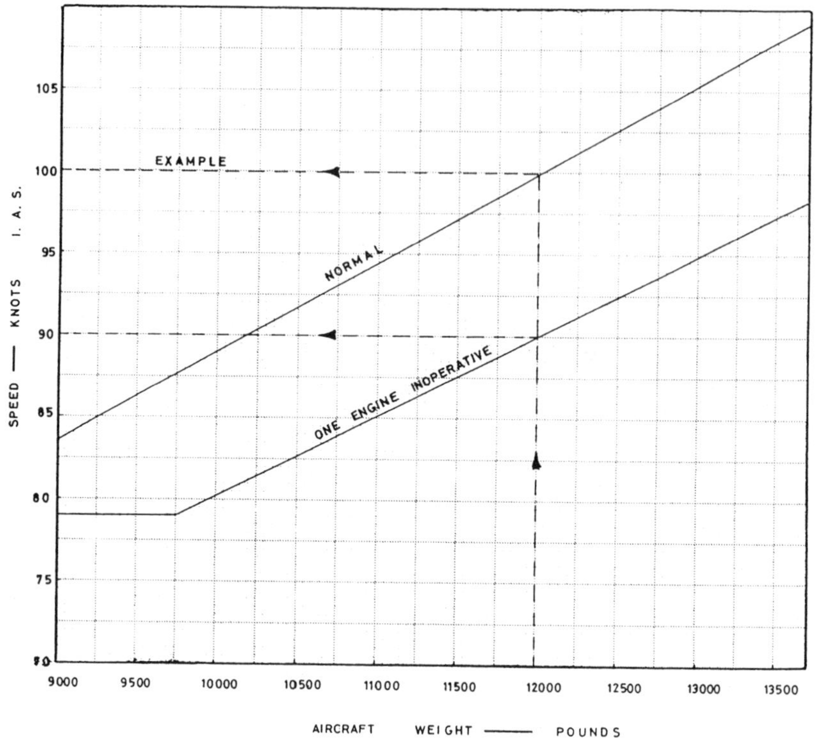

ENROUTE PERFORMANCE CEILING TWO ENGINES OPERATING

The performance ceiling with two engines operating may be obtained from the graph for varying weights and air temperatures.

ASSOCIATED CONDITIONS

Engines	:	Both operating at maximum recommended take-off power.
Engine anti-icing	:	Off (but see note 3).
Cabin heating	:	Off
Wing Flaps	:	Full retracted (0°)
Airspeed	:	Two engine enroute climbing speed.

This example illustrated by the arrowed broken line shows that for a weight of 12,200-lbs in atmosphere of ISA + 25°C, the performance ceiling is 18,600ft.

NOTES

1) The performance ceiling is the maximum altitude which may be assumed when establishing compliance with the operating regulations dealing with enroute flight. It may not be greater than the maximum relight altitude. It does not prohibit flying at a higher altitude, but it is unlikely that the performance ceiling will be achieved unless the power and the airspeed, quoted in the Associated Conditions, are used towards the end of the climb.

2) The ceiling given is that which should give a gross rate of climb 150ft per minute.

3) To take account of the effect of engine anti-icing, reduce the ceiling by 1,500ft when EGT limited.

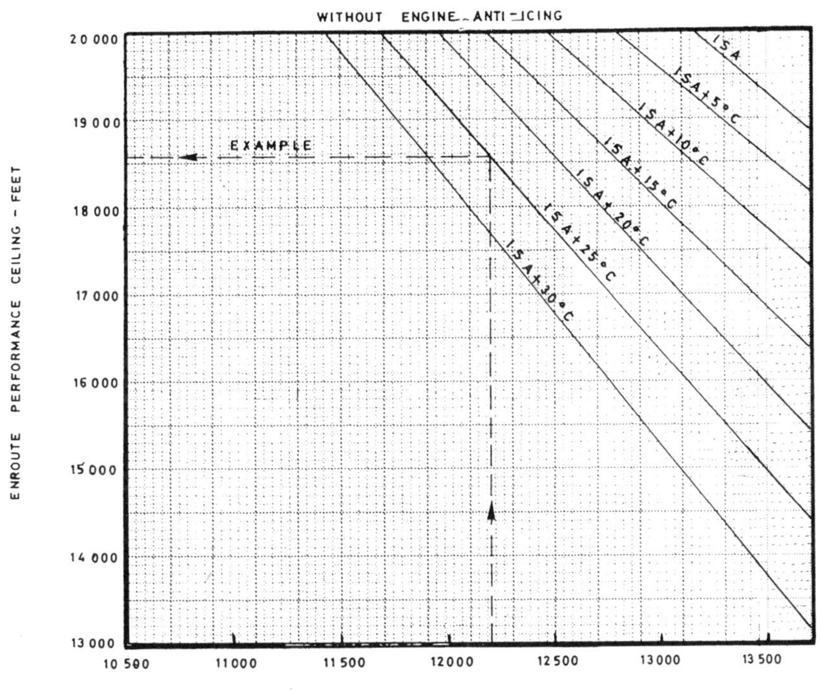

NORMAL TAKE-OFF GROUND RUN REQUIRED

The normal take-off run required which is factor gross distance from rest to the point at which the take-off safety speed is achieved using NORMAL TAKE-OFF (18° FLAP) procedures is shown for varying air temperatures, aerodrome altitudes, weights, reported wind components and uniform runway slopes.

ASSOCIATED CONDITIONS

Engines	:	Both operating at maximum take-off power.
Engine anti-icing	:	Off (but see note 3).
Cabin heating	:	Off
Wing Flaps	:	NORMAL TAKE-OFF (18°)
Speed	:	Rotation initiated at rotation speed V_R. After lift-off, take-off safety speed is achieved by 50 feet.
Runway	:	Hard, dry runway. [See note 4 below].

The example illustrated by the arrow broken lines shows that with an air temperture of 24° C (ISA + 17°C) at an aerodrome altitude of 4000ft and a weight of 12000-lbs with a reported head-wind component of 5 knots and a uniform uphill runway slope of 1% the take-off run required is 2420ft.

NOTES

1) The wind correction grids have been factored by 50% for headwinds and 150% for tailwinds. Reported winds therefore can be used directly in the grids.

2) The scheduled take-off run required is 1.15 times the gross distance to accelerate from rest to the take-off safety speed.

3) To take account of the effect of engine anti-icing, increase the take-off run required by 5% when EGT limited.

4) When operating from grass runway surfaces, the take-off run obtained must be increased by an amount appropriate to the grass conditions. Use should be made of the data given to correctly allow for the effect of the grass runway surface on the take-off performance.

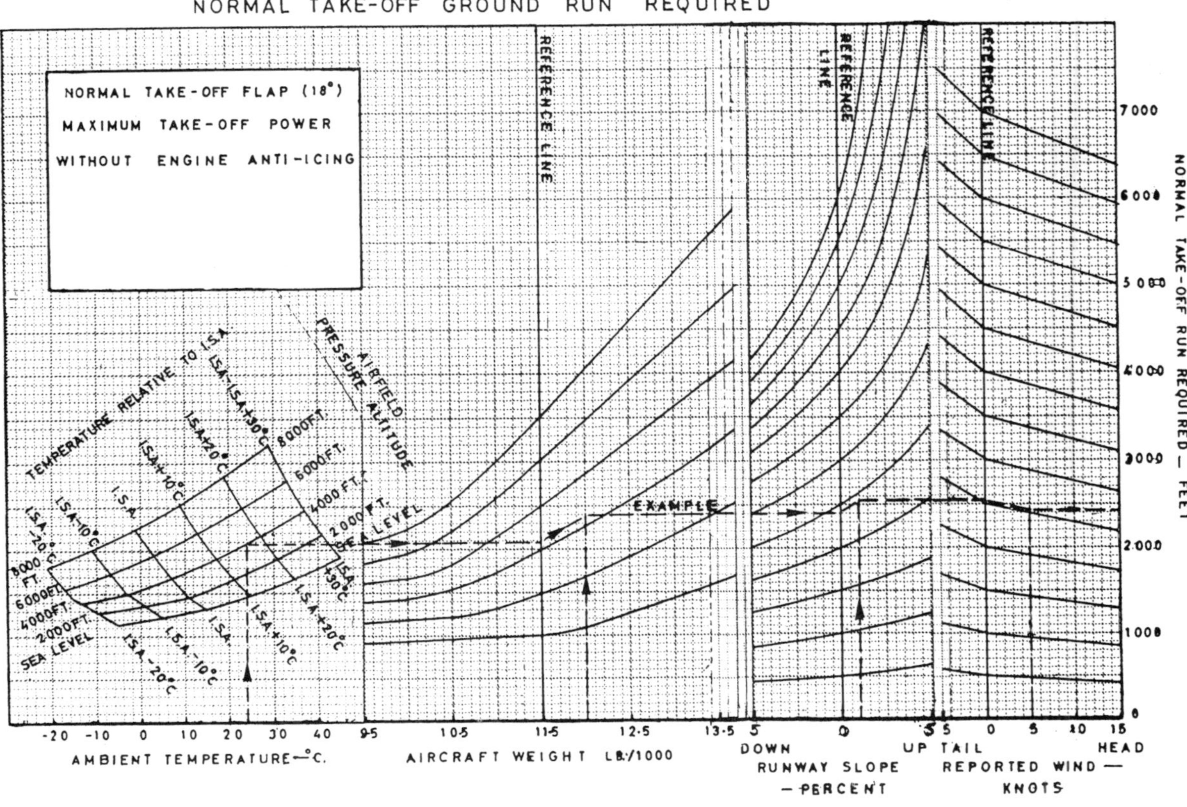
NORMAL TAKE-OFF GROUND RUN REQUIRED
NORMAL TAKE-OFF FLAP (18°)
MAXIMUM TAKE-OFF POWER
WITHOUT ENGINE ANTI-ICING
REFERENCE LINE
REFERENCE LINE
REFERENCE LINE
EXAMPLE
AIRFIELD PRESSURE ALTITUDE
8000 FT.
6000 FT.
4000 FT.
2000 FT.
SEA LEVEL
TEMPERATURE RELATIVE TO I.S.A
I.S.A +30°C
I.S.A +20°C
I.S.A +10°C
I.S.A
I.S.A -10°C
I.S.A -20°C
-20 -10 0 10 20 30 40
AMBIENT TEMPERATURE—°C.
9.5 10.5 11.5 12.5 13.5
AIRCRAFT WEIGHT LB./1000
5 0 5
DOWN UP
RUNWAY SLOPE — PERCENT
5 0 5 10 15
TAIL HEAD
REPORTED WIND — KNOTS
0 1000 2000 3000 4000 5000 6000 7000
NORMAL TAKE-OFF RUN REQUIRED — FEET

NORMAL TAKE-OFF DISTANCE REQUIRED

The normal take-off distance required which is a factored gross distance from rest to a height of 50ft using NORMAL TAKE-OFF (18° FLAP) procedures is shown for varying air temperatures, aerodrome altitudes, weights, reported wind components and uniform runway slopes.

ASSOCIATED CONDITIONS

Engines	:	Both operating at maximum take-off power.
Engine anti-icing	:	Off (but see note 3).
Cabin heating	:	Off
Wing Flaps	:	NORMAL TAKE-OFF (18°)
Speed	:	Rotation initiated at rotation speed V_R. After lift-off, take-off safety speed is achieved by 50 feet.
Runway	:	Hard, dry runway. [See note 4 below].

The example illustrated by the arrow broken lines shows that with an air temperture of 28°C (ISA + 17°C) at an aerodrome altitude of 2000ft and a weight of 12,000-lbs with a reported headwind component of 5 knots and a uniform uphill runway slope of 1% the take-off run required is 2480ft.

NOTES

1) The wind correction grids have been factored by 50% for headwinds and 150% for tailwinds. Reported winds therefore can be used directly in the grids.

2) The scheduled take-off run required is 1.25 times the gross distance to accelerate from rest to the take-off safety speed and to achieve a height of 50ft.

3) To take account of the effect of engine anti-icing, increase the take-off run required by 5% when EGT limited.

4) When operating from grass runway surfaces, the take-off run obtained must be increased by an amount appropriate to the grass conditions. Use should be made of the data given to correctly allow for the effect of the grass runway surface on the take-off performance.

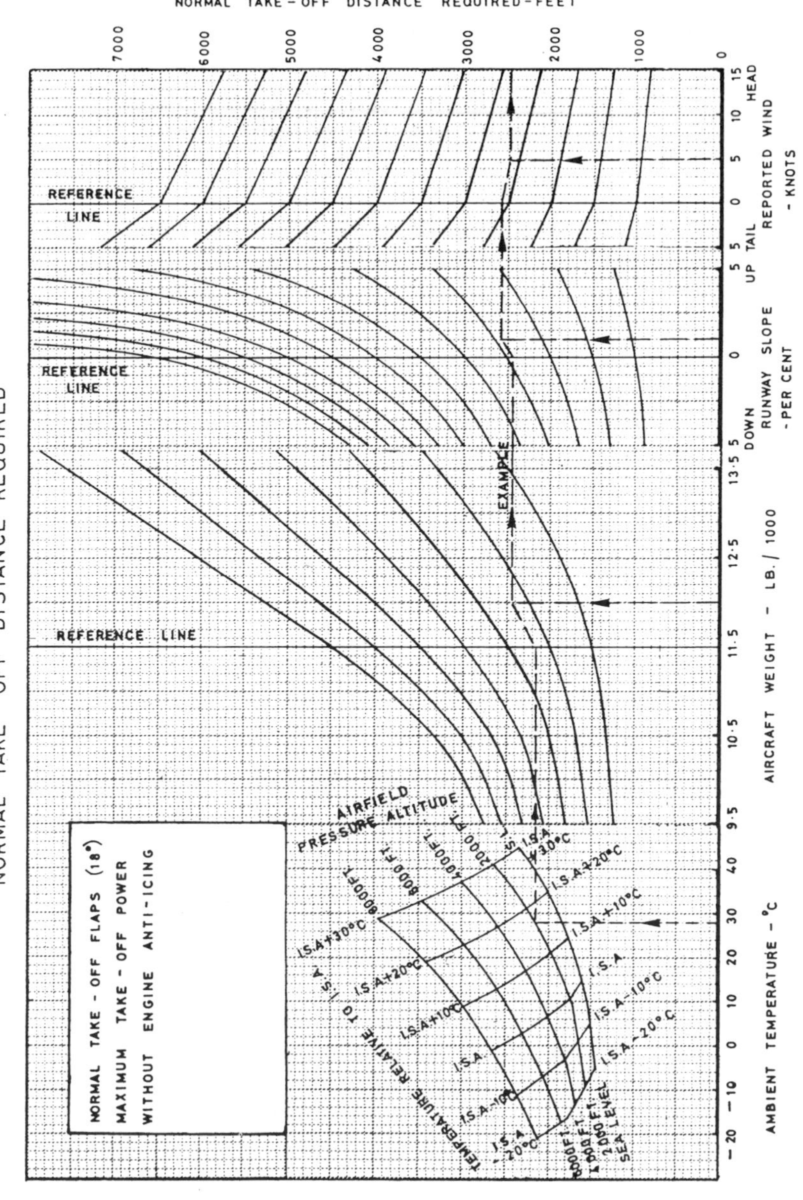
NORMAL TAKE - OFF DISTANCE REQUIRED
NORMAL TAKE - OFF DISTANCE REQUIRED - FEET
7000
6000
5000
4000
3000
2000
1000
0
REFERENCE LINE
REFERENCE LINE
REFERENCE LINE
REPORTED WIND - KNOTS
HEAD
TAIL
15 10 5 0 5
RUNWAY SLOPE - PER CENT
UP
DOWN
5 0 5
AIRCRAFT WEIGHT - LB./1000
13·5 12·5 11·5 10·5 9·5
AMBIENT TEMPERATURE - °C
40 30 20 10 0 −10 −20
EXAMPLE
AIRFIELD PRESSURE ALTITUDE
8000 FT.
6000 FT.
4000 FT.
2000 FT.
SEA LEVEL
TEMPERATURE RELATIVE TO I.S.A.
I.S.A.+30°C
I.S.A.+20°C
I.S.A.+10°C
I.S.A.
I.S.A.−10°C
I.S.A.−20°C
NORMAL TAKE - OFF FLAPS (18°)
MAXIMUM TAKE - OFF POWER
WITHOUT ENGINE ANTI-ICING

EFFECT OF GRASS RUNWAY ON NORMAL TAKE - OFF PERFORMANCE

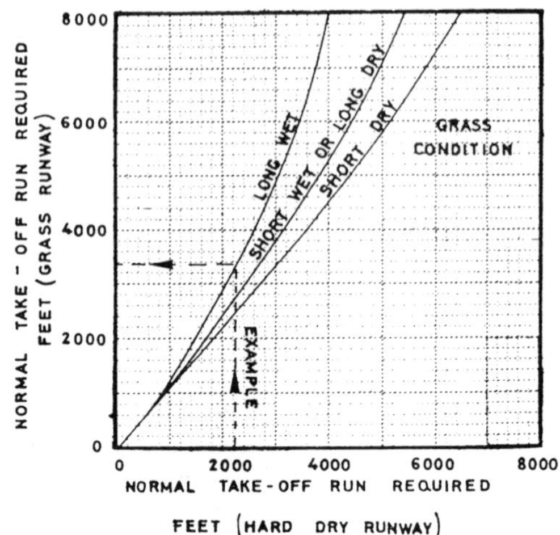

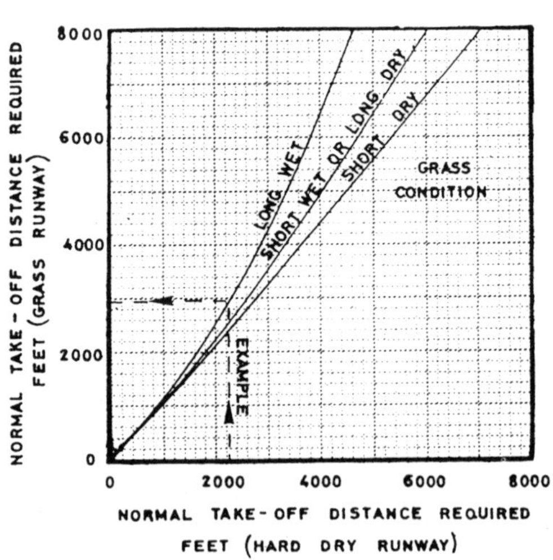

NORMAL LANDING DISTANCE REQUIRED

The landing distance required from 50 feet to rest is shown for varying air temperatures, aerodrome altitudes, weights, reported wind components and uniform runway slopes.

ASSOCIATED CONDITIONS

Engines	:	Both operating at minimum flight power until touchdown, ground idle being selected as soon as the aircraft is on the runway.
Engine anti-icing	:	Off
Cabin heating	:	Off
Wing Flaps	:	LAND (50°)
Speed	:	The aircraft is set up on the approach with 600 feet per minute rate of descent and at the speed (1.3 V_{MS}). At 50 feet the power is reduced to that indicated above. Once on the runway maximum wheel braking without skidding the wheels is applied.
Runway	:	Hard, dry runway. [See note 3 below].

The example illustrated by the arrow dotted lines shows that at an air temperature of 17°C (ISA + 10°C) at an aerodrome altitude of 4000ft and a weight of 12000lbs with a reported headwind component of 8 knots and a uniform uphill runway slope of 1% the take-off run required is 1770ft.

NOTES

1) The wind correction grids have been factored by 50% for headwinds and 150% for tailwinds. Reported winds therefore can be used directly in the grids.

2) The landing distance required includes the factor of 100/70 specified by the operating regulations. This means that the distance obtained may be equated directly with the landing distance available.

3) When landing on a grass surface, the landing distance is the distance obtained and increased by 10%.

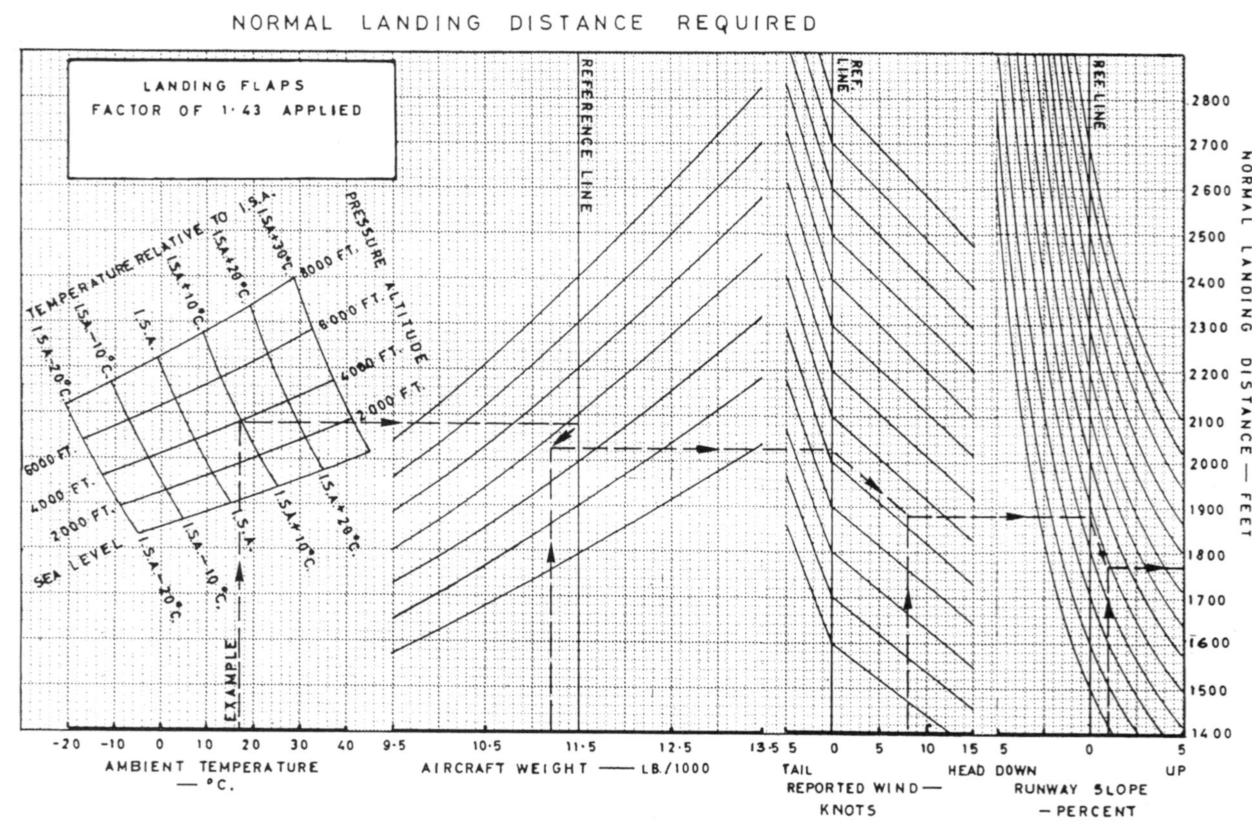
NORMAL LANDING DISTANCE REQUIRED
LANDING FLAPS
FACTOR OF 1·43 APPLIED
TEMPERATURE RELATIVE TO I.S.A.
I.S.A.+30°C.
I.S.A.+20°C.
I.S.A.+10°C.
I.S.A.
I.S.A.-10°C.
I.S.A.-20°C.
PRESSURE ALTITUDE
8000 FT.
6000 FT.
4000 FT.
2000 FT.
SEA LEVEL
EXAMPLE
REFERENCE LINE
REF. LINE
REF. LINE
-20
-10
0
10
20
30
40
AMBIENT TEMPERATURE — °C.
9·5
10·5
11·5
12·5
13·5
AIRCRAFT WEIGHT —— LB./1000
5
0
5
10
15
TAIL
HEAD
REPORTED WIND — KNOTS
5
0
5
DOWN
UP
RUNWAY SLOPE — PERCENT
NORMAL LANDING DISTANCE — FEET
2800
2700
2600
2500
2400
2300
2200
2100
2000
1900
1800
1700
1600
1500
1400

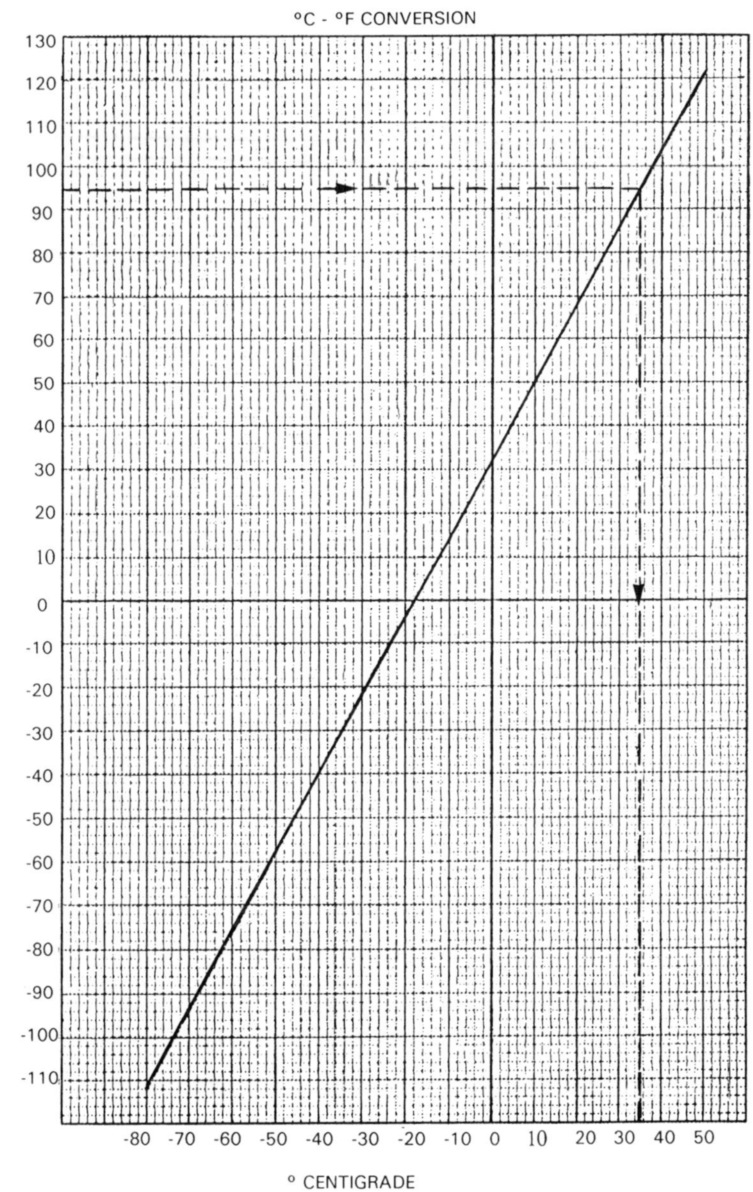
°C - °F CONVERSION
130
120
110
100
90
80
70
60
50
40
30
20
10
0
-10
-20
-30
-40
-50
-60
-70
-80
-90
-100
-110
°FAHRENHEIT
-80 -70 -60 -50 -40 -30 -20 -10 0 10 20 30 40 50
° CENTIGRADE

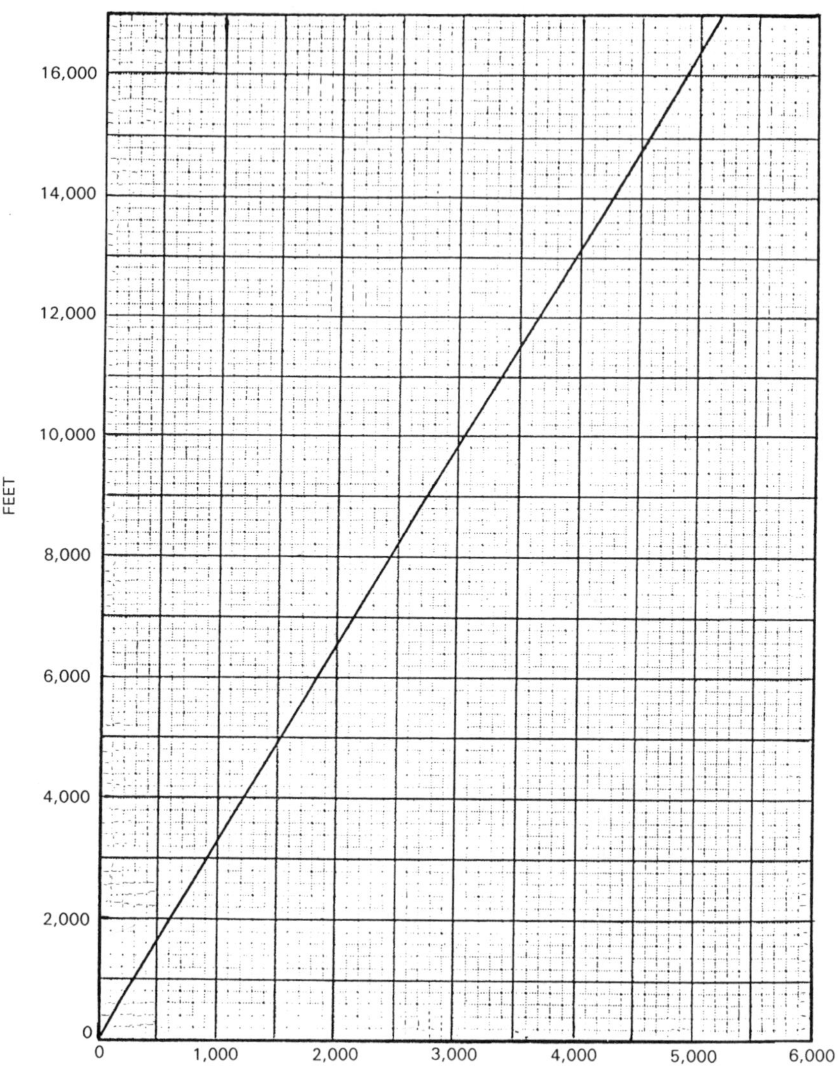
METRES-FEET CONVERSION
FEET
16,000
14,000
12,000
10,000
8,000
6,000
4,000
2,000
0
0
1,000
2,000
3,000
4,000
5,000
6,000
METRES

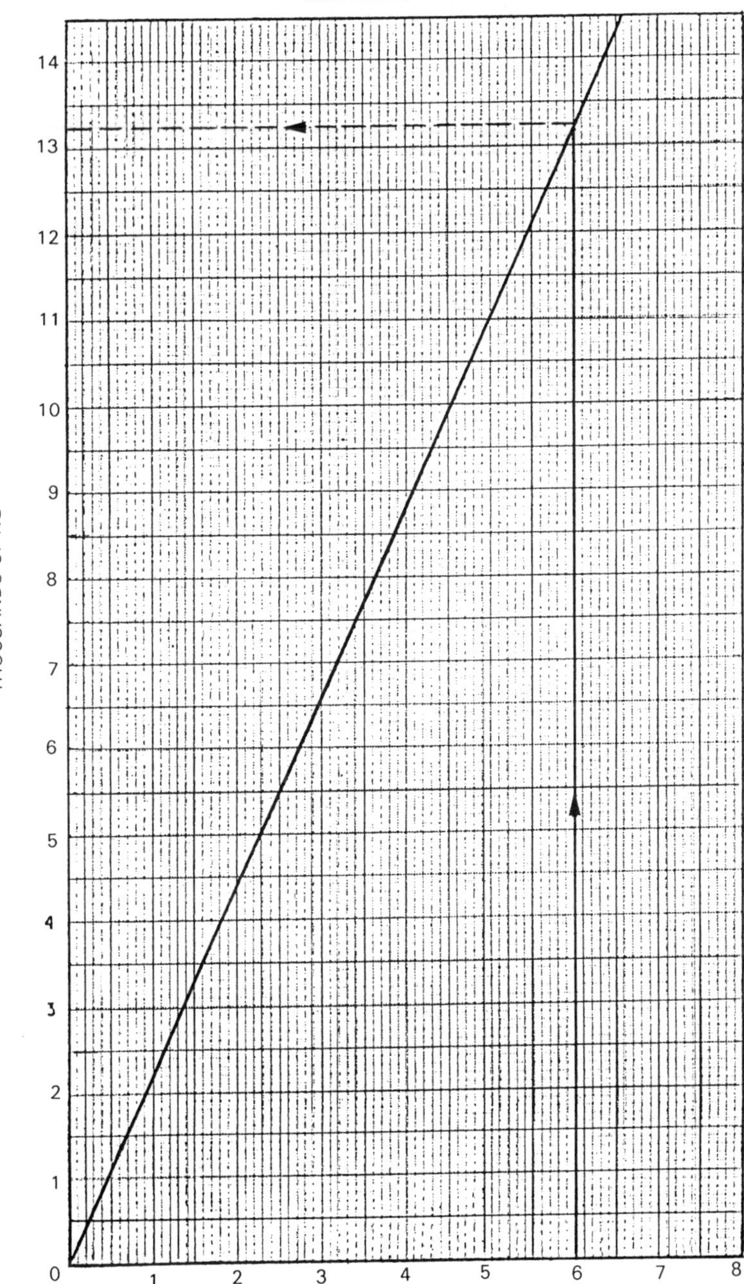
CONVERSION - KG TO LB
THOUSANDS OF KG
14
13
12
11
10
9
8
7
6
5
4
3
2
1
0
1
2
3
4
5
6
7
8
THOUSANDS OF LB

Straight and Level Flight Performance

When the aircraft is in steady level flight, equilibrium must occur. This unaccelerated condition of flight is achieved with the aircraft trimmed for lift equal to weight.

The engine(s) will be set for a thrust to equal the aircraft drag.

The maximum level flight speed for the aircraft will be obtained when the power, or thrust required, equals the maximum power or thrust available from the power-plant (Figure 11.17).

NOTE: The *minimum level flight airspeed* is not usually defined by the thrust or power requirement, since the conditions of stall, stability and control problems predominate.

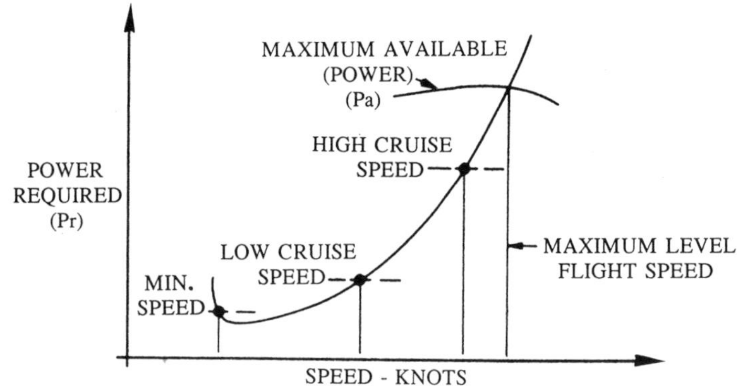

Figure 11.17 Power Versus Speed

The Relationship between Angle of Attack, IAS and Altitude

Assuming that in level flight lift equals weight then:

$$\text{Lift} = \text{Weight} = \tfrac{1}{2}\rho V^2 S C_L$$

i.e. our normal theory of flight formula + angle of attack, where:

ρ	=	density
V	=	TAS
S	=	wing area
C_L	=	a constant coefficient

As for a given weight lift will be constant, then the equation must also be constant. The only variables in the equation are, density, TAS and angle of attack. It must be remembered that the expression $\tfrac{1}{2}\rho V^2$ is dynamic pressure or IAS. In view of this, for a fixed IAS and weight the angle of attack will be constant for any altitude.

Looking at it from a different point of view, if IAS ($\frac{1}{2}\rho V^2$) is increased, then to keep the equation balanced the angle of attack must be decreased and vice versa.

To summarise:

- At a constant weight and IAS, angle of attack is fixed regardless of altitude.
- If IAS is increased, angle of attack must be decreased and vice versa.

For the best aerodynamic efficiency, there is a requirement that the maximum amount of lift will be produced for the least amount of drag. This means flying for the maximum lift/drag ratio which has already been shown to occur at a fixed angle of attack, usually around 4°. For a given weight this will represent a fixed indicated airspeed, regardless of height. However, if the weight decreases due to use of fuel, then it will be necessary to decrease the indicated airspeed to maintain the same angle of attack.

Climb Performance

In our flying we are mostly concerned with engine power output to achieve the best climb performance/weight ratio, so let's consider this now.

We increase the power by advancing the throttles (power levers). This immediately produces a marked difference in the rate of climb. And climb depends on the reserve power or thrust.

Reserve power is that available over and above the requirement to maintain level flight at a given speed. So if an aircraft is equipped with engines which develop 800 (maximum available) HP and the aircraft only requires 500 HP for a particular level flight speed, then the power available for CLIMB is 300 HP.

POWER means horsepower, the common unit of mechanical power. One horsepower is work equivalent to lifting 33,000 pounds vertically by 1 foot in one minute.

THRUST is also a function of work. It means the force which imparts a change in the velocity of a mass. This force is measured in pounds, but has no element of rate or time. It can therefore be said that during a steady climb, the rate of climb is a function of excess thrust.

The Aerodynamics of Climbing

During a climb, the aircraft gains potential energy by virtue of elevation. This is achieved by one, or a combination of two ways:

- Use of propulsive energy above that required for level flight.
- Expenditure of aircraft kinetic energy.

In a climb, although the weight continues to act vertically downwards the lift does not. The lift is now at right angles to the flight path of the aircraft, and weight can now be resolved into two components:

- One supported by the lift.
- The other acting in the opposite direction to the flight path, in the same direction as drag.

From this two things can be seen:

- Firstly, the lift is now less than that required in straight and level flight, W Cos y. (Figure 11.18)
- Secondly, the thrust has to be equal and opposite to the sum of the drag and weight component along the flight path, T=D+W Sin y. (Figure 11.18).

It is still considered sufficiently correct to assume L=D up to about 15° climb angle (Cos 15° =0.9659, error is less than 2%).

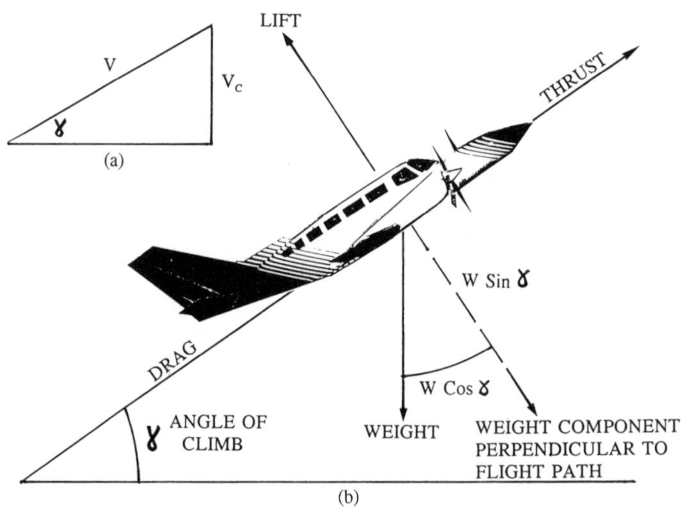

Figure 11.18 Drag and Weight Component in the Climb

Rate and Angle of Climb

The following two mathematical depictions, C1 and C2, show that *rate of climb* is determined by the amount of *excess power*, and *angle of climb* by the amount of *excess thrust* remaining after opposing drag.

RATE OF CLIMB

$$C1 \quad \sin\gamma = \frac{Vc}{V} = \frac{\text{Rate of Climb}}{\text{Speed in Climb}}$$

$$C2 \quad \gamma = \frac{\text{Thrust} - \text{Drag}}{\text{Weight}}$$

$$\text{Therefore } \frac{Vc}{V} = \frac{\text{Thrust} - \text{Drag}}{\text{Weight}}$$

$$\text{Therefore } Vc = \frac{V\,(\text{Thrust} - \text{Drag})}{\text{Weight}}$$

$$= \frac{\text{Power (Available)} - \text{Power (Required)}}{\text{Weight}}$$

$$= \frac{\text{Excess Power}}{\text{Weight}}$$

$$\text{or } \frac{Vt - Vd}{W} \text{ where } Vt = \text{Thrust Horsepower}$$

$$Vd = \text{Drag Horsepower}$$

ANGLE OF CLIMB

From C2 it can be seen that for the maximum angle of climb

$$\text{where } \sin\gamma = \frac{\text{Thrust} - \text{Drag}}{\text{Weight}}$$

the aircraft should be flown at a speed which gives the maximum difference between Thrust and Drag. Alternatively, if climb angle = 0, i.e. level flight, then

$$\frac{\text{Thrust} - \text{Drag}}{\text{Weight}} = 0$$

$$\text{or } \frac{\text{Thrust} - \text{Drag}}{\text{Weight}} = 1$$

So, it can be deduced the factor controlling the angle of climb will be the excess of thrust over drag. (See Figure 11.19).

Power Available and Power Required

The thrust power curve for a piston engine differs from that of a jet as seen in Figure 11.20.

The main reason for this is that the thrust of a jet remains virtually constant at a given altitude – regardless of speed – whereas the piston engine under the same set of circumstances, and for a given BHP, suffers

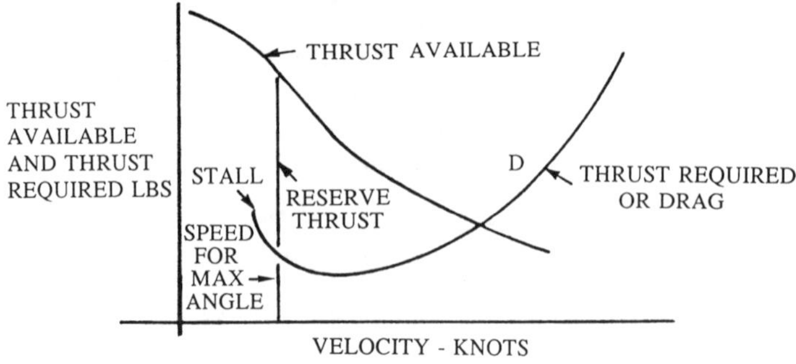

Figure 11.19 Thrust Versus Climb Angle

a loss at both ends of its speed range because of reduced propeller efficiency.

$$THP\ (available) = \frac{Thrust\ (LBS)\ x\ Speed\ (FPS)}{550}$$

The horsepower required to propel an aircraft is found by:

$$Power\ Required = \frac{Drag\ (LBS)\ x\ TAS\ (FPS)}{550}$$

The curve shown in Figure 11.20 can be assumed to apply to both a piston or a jet powered aircraft (i.e. the airframe drag is the same regardless of the power unit used), note the minimum drag speed and minimum power speed. The increase in power required at the lowest speed is caused by rapidly rising effects of induced drag.

Climb Speed

The best climbing speed (highest rate of climb), is that at which the excess power is maximum. So that, after some power is used overcoming drag, the maximum amount of power is available for climbing.

The vertical distance between power available and power required, represents the power available for climbing at that speed.

Note: In Figure 11.20, this speed for the piston engine is 175kts, and the jet approximately 400kts. In the jet there appears to be a fairly wide band of speeds which would still give the same excess power. In practice, the higher speed is used in the interest of engine efficiency. At points X and Y all available power is being used to overcome drag. Therefore these points are the V_{min} and V_{max}.

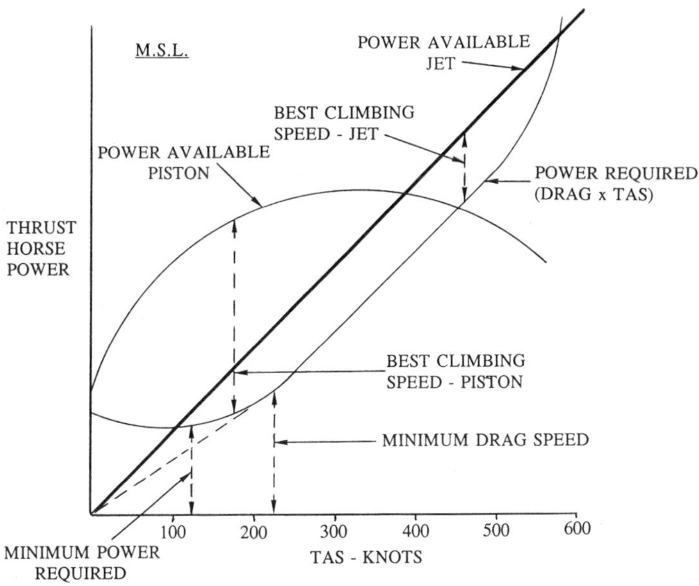

Figure 11.20 Climb Performance Piston and Jet Aircraft

Effect of Altitude

The effect of altitude has been covered elsewhere in this book. However, we can summarise by saying that:

- The THP of both piston and jet engines decreases with altitude, mainly due to decreasing air density.
- At altitude, power required to fly at minimum drag speed is increased.
- The speed for best rate of climb decreases with altitude.

Figure 11.21 a and b give the comparison between piston and jet aircraft.

Flying for Range and Performance

Flying for range is one of the most important parts of the aircraft performance. It's no good having the best STOL (or any other), if it only has the fuel range to fly 60 nm with a reasonable payload.

That's an exaggerated example, of course, but there are aircraft types that have a poor payload to fuel range performance. And there is the other type – the relatively short range aircraft that is pushed into a longer (sector) range unsuitable for its performance. The first example is a manufacturer problem. The responsibility for the second lies mostly with the operator.

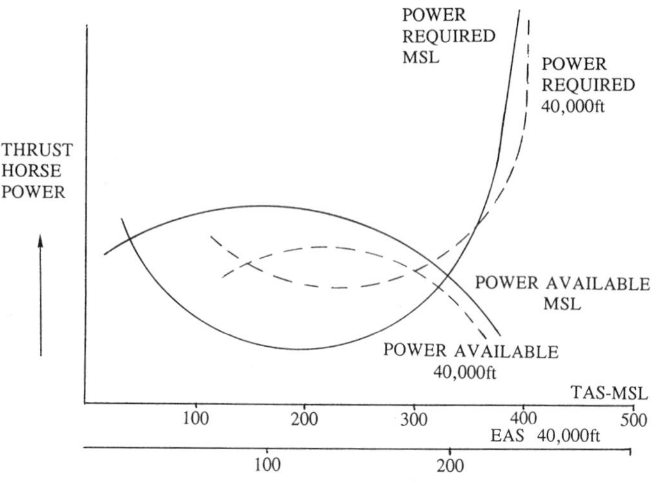

Figure 11.21a Piston Engine

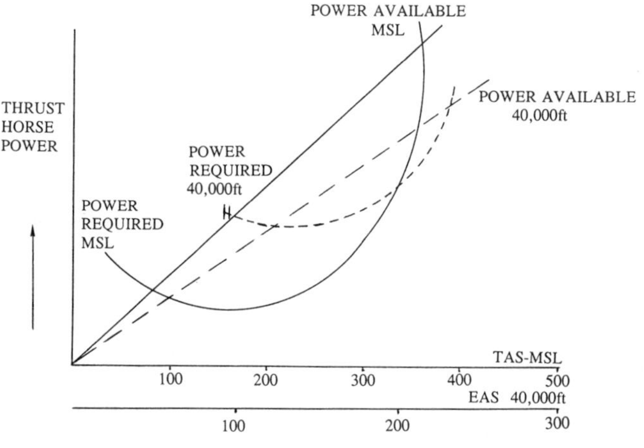

Figure 11.21b Jet Engine

But as we all know, the majority of aircraft types are a performance-operational compromise in some way. However, I'm not going to get involved in those arguments here.

Range performance is the ability of the aircraft to convert fuel energy into flying distance. This can be broken down into two general forms:

- To extract the maximum flying distance from a given fuel load.
- To fly a specified distance with a minimum fuel expenditure.

RANGE PROFILE

CONDITIONS:
1. Takeoff Weight - 7450 Pounds.
2. Cruise Climb to Desired Altitude.
3. Recommended Lean Fuel Flow.
4. Zero Wind.
5. Standard Day.

NOTE:
1. Range computations include fuel required for start, taxi, takeoff, climb, cruise, descent and 45 minutes reserve fuel at the particular cruise power.
2. The distances shown are the sum of the distances to climb, cruise and descend.

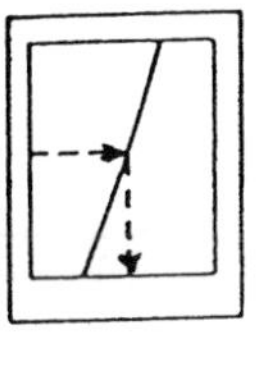

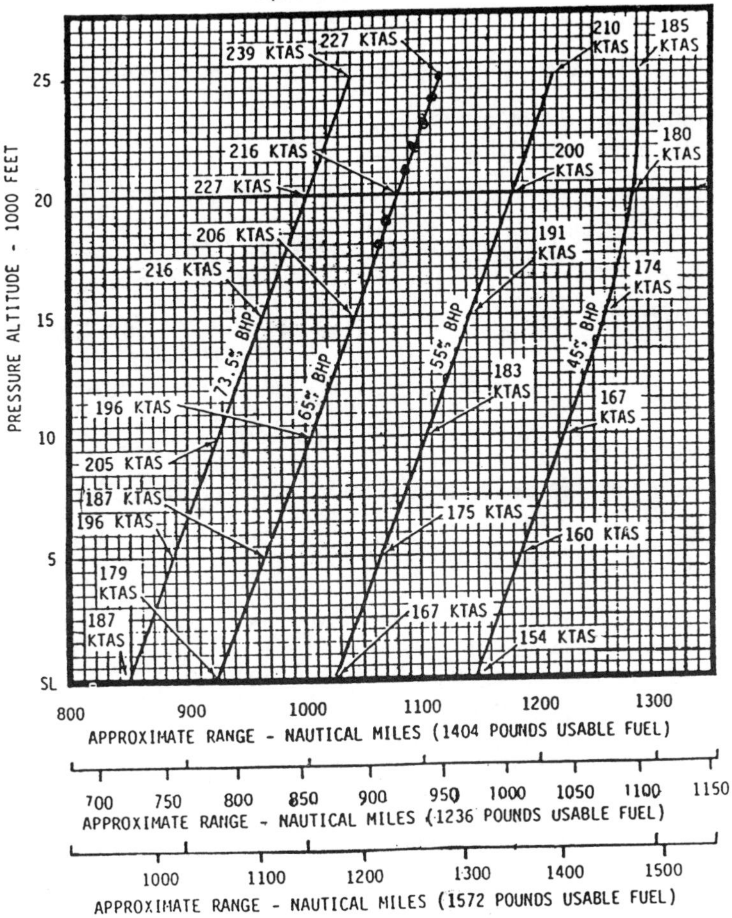

PRESSURE ALTITUDE - 1000 FEET: SL, 5, 10, 15, 20, 25

73.5% BHP: 187 KTAS, 196 KTAS, 205 KTAS, 216 KTAS, 227 KTAS, 239 KTAS

65% BHP: 179 KTAS, 187 KTAS, 196 KTAS, 206 KTAS, 216 KTAS, 227 KTAS

55% BHP: 167 KTAS, 175 KTAS, 183 KTAS, 191 KTAS, 200 KTAS, 210 KTAS

45% BHP: 154 KTAS, 160 KTAS, 167 KTAS, 174 KTAS, 180 KTAS, 185 KTAS

800 900 1000 1100 1200 1300
APPROXIMATE RANGE - NAUTICAL MILES (1404 POUNDS USABLE FUEL)

700 750 800 850 900 950 1000 1050 1100 1150
APPROXIMATE RANGE - NAUTICAL MILES (1236 POUNDS USABLE FUEL)

1000 1100 1200 1300 1400 1500
APPROXIMATE RANGE - NAUTICAL MILES (1572 POUNDS USABLE FUEL)

Figure 11.22 Range Profile

The common denominator for both these operating problems is the SPECIFIC RANGE. That is, the nautical miles of flying distance per pound of fuel.

Specific range can be defined:

$$SPECIFIC\ RANGE = \frac{NAUTICAL\ MILES}{LBS\ OF\ FUEL}$$

$$SPECIFIC\ RANGE = \frac{NAUTICAL\ MILES/HR}{LBS\ OF\ FUEL/HR}$$

$$OR\quad \frac{KNOTS}{FUEL\ FLOW}$$

We must clearly understand the difference between range and endurance.

- Range means flying for distance.
- Endurance means flying for time.

We can now define a separate term – SPECIFIC ENDURANCE.

$$SPECIFIC\ ENDURANCE = \frac{FLIGHT\ HOURS}{LBS\ OF\ FUEL}$$

$$OR\ SPECIFC\ ENDURANCE = \frac{FLIGHT\ HOURS/HR}{LBS\ OF\ FUEL/HR}$$

$$OR\quad \frac{1}{FUEL\ FLOW}$$

If we want maximum endurance there must be a minimum of fuel flow.

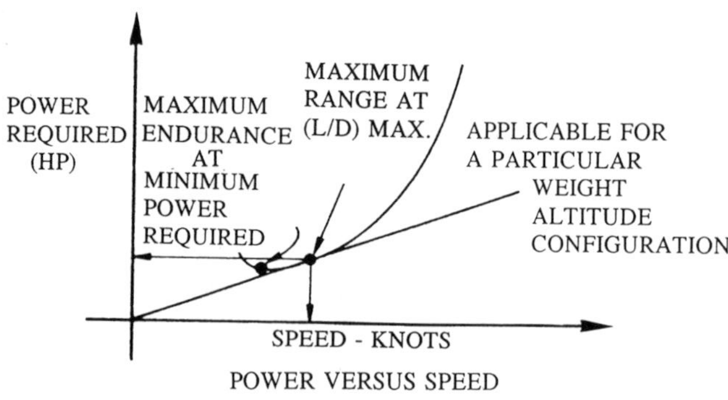

Figure 11.23 General Range Conditions – Propeller Aircraft

While the peak value of specific range would provide maximum range operation, long range cruise is usually recommended at some slightly higher airspeed. Most long range cruise operations are conducted at the flight condition which provides 99% of the absolute maximum specific range.

The values of specific range versus speed are affected by three principal variables:

- Aircraft gross weight.
- Altitude.
- The external aerodynamic configuration of the aircraft.

Cruise Control means the control of the optimum airspeed, altitude and power setting to maintain the 99% maximum specific range condition.

At the beginning of cruise flight, the high initial weight of the aircraft will require specific values of airspeed, altitude and power setting to produce the recommended cruise condition. (Figure 11.24).

CRUISE PERFORMANCE WITH RECOMMENDED LEAN MIXTURE

NOTE:
1. At 20,000 Feet, increase speed by 6 KTAS for each 1000 pounds below 7450 pounds.
2. At 25,000 Feet, increase speed by 6 KTAS for each 1000 pounds below 7450 pounds.
3. Operations at peak EGT may be utilized with power settings within the boxes if the airplane is equipped with the optional EGT system.

ALTITUDE	RPM	MP	-45°C (-48°F)			-25°C (STD TEMP) (-12°F)			-5°C (24°F)		
			PERCENT BHP	KTAS	TOTAL LB/HR	PERCENT BHP	KTAS	TOTAL LB/HR	PERCENT BHP	KTAS	TOTAL LB/HR
20,000 FEET	1900	32.5	78.0	225	271	73.5	224	257	69.0	223	242
	1900	31.0	74.3	220	260	70.0	220	246	65.7	218	231
	1900	29.0	68.8	213	241	64.8	212	228	60.8	211	216
	1900	27.0	63.0	205	223	59.3	204	211	55.7	201	200
	1900	25.0	57.1	196	204	53.8	194	194	50.5	188	183
	1800	32.5	73.2	219	256	69.0	219	242	64.8	217	228
	1800	31.0	69.9	214	245	65.9	214	232	61.8	212	219
	1800	29.0	64.3	207	227	60.6	206	215	56.9	203	204
	1800	27.0	58.8	199	210	55.4	197	199	52.0	192	188
	1800	25.0	53.0	188	191	49.9	185	181	46.9	175	172
	1700	32.5	69.2	214	243	65.2	213	230	61.2	211	217
	1700	31.0	65.5	208	230	61.7	208	219	57.9	205	207
	1700	29.0	60.5	201	215	57.0	200	204	53.5	196	193
	1700	27.0	54.9	192	197	51.7	189	187	48.6	182	177
	1700	25.0	49.6	181	180	46.8	175	171	---	---	---
	1600	31.0	60.0	200	213	56.6	199	203	53.1	195	192
	1600	29.0	55.3	193	199	52.1	190	188	48.9	183	178

Figure 11.24 Cruise Performance Chart

As fuel is consumed and the aircraft gross weight decreases:

- The optimum airspeed and power setting may decrease.
- The optimum altitude may increase.
- The optimum altitude specific range will increase.

It is up to the pilot to see that the proper cruise control technique is used to ensure the optimum conditions are maintained.

Total Range is dependent on both fuel availability and specific range. When flying for range and economy the aircraft will be set up for long range cruise. Using this procedure, the aircraft will be capable of its maximum design operating range – or can fly any distance up to the maximum with extra fuel reserves at destination.

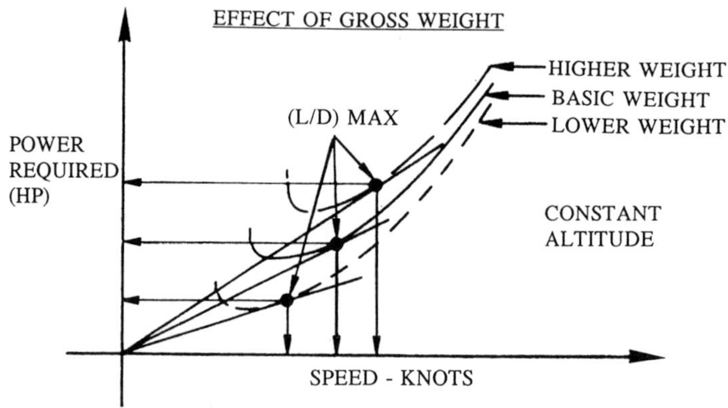

Figure 11.25 Weight Versus Cruise Speed

Note: *The propeller-driven aircraft* – whether piston or turbo-prop, combines the propeller with an engine for propulsive power. In both piston and turbo-prop aircraft cases, fuel flow is dictated by the shaft power put into the propeller, rather than thrust.

Therefore the fuel flow can be directly related to the power required to maintain the aircraft in steady level flight. This fact allows for the calculation of range through analysis of power required versus speed (variation of fuel flow versus speed).

Maximum endurance is obtained at the point of minimum power which requires the lowest fuel flow.

Note: For a given aircraft configuration, the maximum lift-drag ratio occurs at a particular angle of attack and lift coefficient. It is unaffected by weight and altitude.

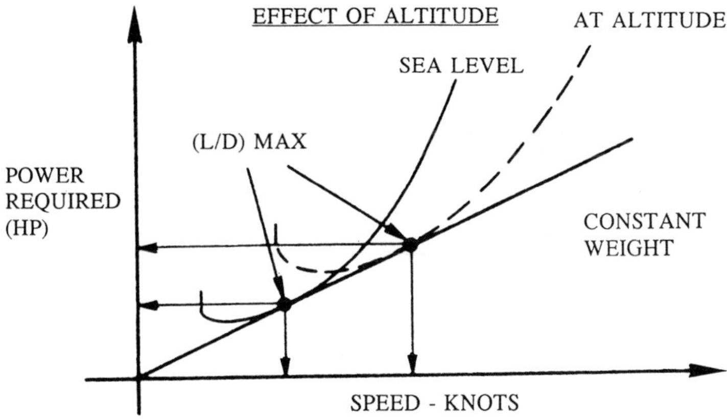

Figure 11.26 Altitude Versus Range

The effect of altitude on the range of a propeller-driven aircraft is shown in Figure 11.26. A flight at high altitude will have a greater true airspeed, and the power required will be proportionally greater than flown near sea level.

Also, the drag of the aircraft at altitude is the same as the drag at sea level, but the higher true airspeed causes a proportionally greater power required. Note that in Figure 11.26, the tangent to the *sea level* power curve is also the tangent to the altitude power curve.

When considering the effect of altitude on specific range, it is true to say that specific fuel consumption and propeller efficiency are the principal factors which can cause a variation of specific range with altitude. Therefore, if compressibility effects are negligible – any variation of specific range with altitude is strictly a function of engine-propeller performance. One advantage of *supercharging* a piston engine, is that the cruise power may be maintained at high altitude with an increase in true airspeed.

The principal differences between the high and low altitude cruise, are the true airspeeds and climb fuel requirements.

The enroute and Performance ceiling can be extracted from graphs contained in the Flight Manual. These can be used in conjunction with the appropriate range and cruise performance charts for complete overall performance planning. Sample graphs from the SKYVAN Flight Manual are provided for study on pages 88 and 202.

An 'Aerodynamics – Forces in Flight' Quiz is available at the rear of the book for revision purposes.

How Load Factors Affect Performance

There is a maximum positive and negative 'G' loading specified for each aircraft type. This is listed in the limitations section of the Flight Manual/Pilot's Operating Handbook.

In fact critical load factors apply to all flight manoeuvres, except unaccelerated straight flight, where a load of 1G is always present. Therefore design load factor limitations determine manoeuvring speeds and the general operating performance/structural integrity of the aircraft.

We know from our study of weight and balance, that if an aircraft is overloaded it degrades not only the structural integrity, but affects the overall performance of the aircraft also. The easiest method of demonstrating the load factor is to see what happens in a turn.

During a turn weight still acts vertically downwards, but a second force, centrifugal force, appears due to the aircraft travelling along a curved path. This centrifugal force has to be opposed by a centripetal force which can only be obtained as a resolved part of the lift force. The lift also has to balance the weight in addition to the centripetal force. So it can be seen that in a turn the lift has to be increased more than weight. See Figure 11.27.

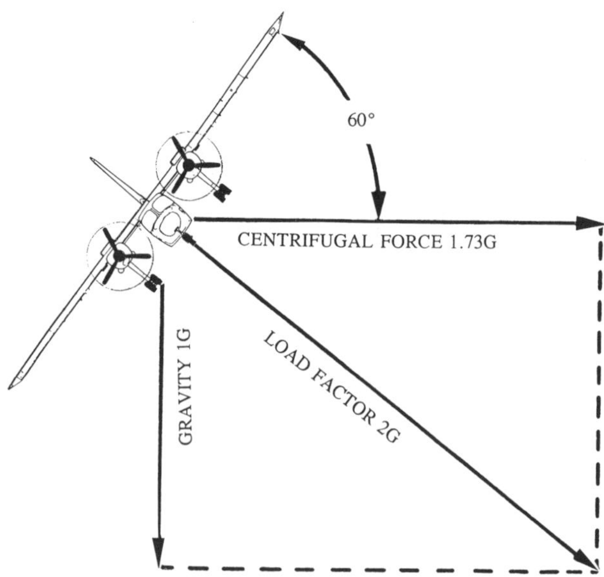

Figure 11.27 Primary Forces causing Load Factor in a Turn

Effect of Weight

If the IAS is maintained at a constant figure, the increased lift can only be obtained by an increase in the angle of attack. This increase in lift will produce more induced drag which will require increased thrust. So as the angle of attack has been increased the wing is closer to its stalling angle – therefore the stalling speed will be increased. Which means that the increase in lift is equivalent to increasing the aircraft's weight.

The amount this is apparently increased is called the LOAD FACTOR, or 'n'. We more commonly refer to this as the 'G' – FORCE. The amount of G-force felt by seat pressure on the pilot depends on the rate of turn.

For instance, if the weight is apparently doubled, 'N' becomes two, and this is called *a 2G turn*. The increase in stalling speed associated with the load factor may be calculated from the following formula:

$$STALLING\ SPEED = NORMAL\ STALLING\ SPEED \times \sqrt{G\ LOAD\ (n)}$$

For example, an aircraft with a normal stalling speed of 100kts carrying out a 2G turn, would have its stalling speed increased by

$$100 \times \sqrt{2} = 140\ kts$$

approximately.

We can see in Figure 11.28 that the load factor in a 60° bank is 2Gs. If we increase this to an 80° bank it reaches 5.76 Gs – a considerable increase. This would certainly over-stress the average general aviation aircraft.

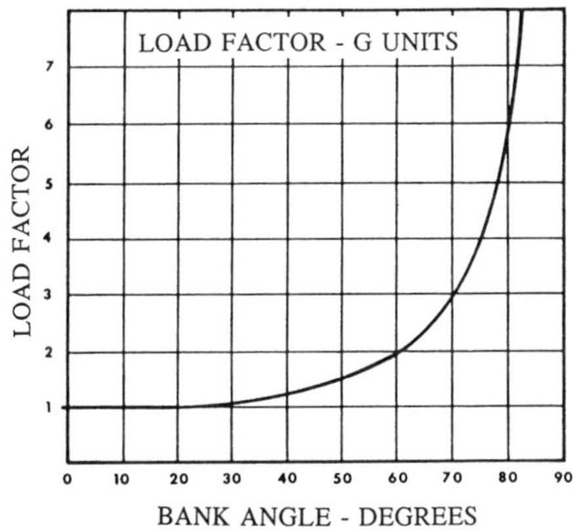

Figure 11.28

Structural Stress – the Hidden Problem

All certified aircraft are designed by the manufacturers to withstand loads imposed by gusts of considerable intensity. Gust load factors increase with increasing airspeed, and the strength used for design purposes usually corresponds to the highest level flight speed.

In extremely rough air – as in thunderstorms or frontal conditions, it is prudent to slow down to the design manoeuvring speed (Va). But regardless of the speed at which we fly, there may certainly be gusts that will exceed the 'load' limits in extreme conditions – this is why we should avoid them.

In the limitations section of your Flight Manual/Pilot's Operating Handbook, there is usually a turbulence penetration speed listed. It should be noted that the maximum 'never exceed' speed (V_{ne}), when in a dive is for smooth air only. High speed dives, or aerobatics involving speeds above Va, should never be practised in rough or turbulent air.

Stress on the structure involves forces acting on many parts of the aircraft. For the unaware – or uninformed, there is a tendency to think of load factors only in terms of their effect on spars and struts. Most structural failure due to excess load factors involve rib structure, which is set within the leading and trailing edges of wings and the tailplane. For fabric-covered aircraft, the critical area is the covering about one-third of the chord aft, on the top surface of the wing.

The main problem for aircraft generally, is the cumulative effect of such loads over a long period of time. They may tend to loosen and weaken vital parts, so that an actual failure may occur some time later when the aircraft is being operated in a perfectly normal manner.

Velocity Versus 'G' Loads (V-g)

The flight operating strength of an aircraft is given on a graph whose horizontal scale is based on load factor. This is called a V-g diagram (velocity versus 'G' loads, or load factor). Each aircraft has its own V-g diagram which applies at a certain weight and altitude.

The curved lines denote maximum lift capability, and are of major importance. The aircraft the diagram at Figure 11.29 represents is not capable of developing more than 1-'G' positive at 54 knots – the wings level stall speed of the aircraft.

Since we know that the maximum load factor varies with the square of the airspeed, the maximum lift capability is 2-'G' at 80 knots, 3-'G' at 97 knots, and 4.4'G' at 119 knots. Any load factor above this line is aerodynamically unavailable. Note that the aircraft cannot fly above the line of maximum lift capability because it will stall.

More or less the same situation exists for negative lift flight. With the exception that the speed necessary to produce a given negative load factor, is higher than to produce the same positive one.

If the aircraft is flown at a positive load factor greater than the positive load limit of 4.4, structural damage will certainly be possible. When operating in

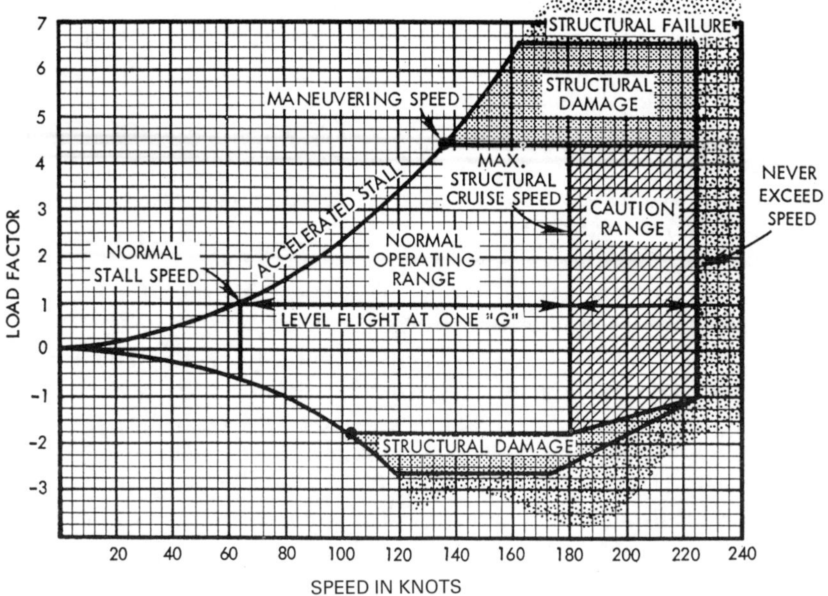

Figure 11.29 Velocity Versus G-Load

this region permanent deformation of the primary structure may take place. If this happens a high rate of fatigue damage is incurred. Operation above the load limit factor must be avoided in normal operation.

The Propeller – Know How It Works

The aircraft we have been discussing in our STOL operations throughout this book are propeller-driven. Whether they are fitted to a piston (reciprocating) or turbo-prop (jet) engine makes no difference. What we are concerned with is how they work and what they contribute to the overall performance of our aircraft.

Fixed pitch propellers are of no real use in a STOL environment, so we will be concentrating on constant speed, variable pitch propellers.

Basic Propeller Principles

The aircraft propeller consists of two or more blades, and a central hub to which the blades are attached. Each propeller blade can be compared to a rotating wing and is cambered like an aerofoil. This produces a force that creates the thrust to pull – or push – the aircraft through the air.

The power needed to rotate the propeller blades is provided by the engine, which rotates the aerofoils of the blades through the air at high speeds. The propeller transforms this rotary power of the engine into forward thrust.

In a cross-section of a typical propeller blade, the chord line is an imaginary line drawn through the blade from its leading to trailing edge. As in a wing, the leading edge is the thick edge of the blade which meets the air as the propeller rotates.

Blade angle is usually measured in degrees. It is the angle between the chord of the blade and the plane of rotation, and is measured at a specific point along the length of the blade (see Figure 11.30).

Because most propellers have a flat blade 'face', the chord line is often drawn along the face of the propeller blade.

Pitch is not the same as blade angle, but because pitch is largely determined by blade angle, the two terms are often used interchangeably. An increase or decrease in one, is usually associated with an increase or decrease in the other. The pitch of a propeller may be designated in inches. A propeller that is 74–48, would be 74 inches in length and have an effective pitch of 48 inches. The pitch in inches is the distance which the propeller would screw through the air in one revolution if there was no slippage.

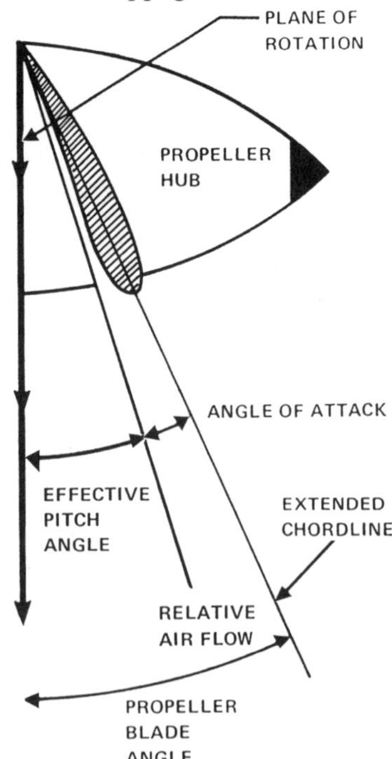

Figure 11.30 Propeller Blade Angle of Attack

PROPELLER SLIP is the difference between the geometric pitch of the propeller and its effective pitch (see Figure 11.31). GEOMETRIC PITCH is the theoretical distance a propeller should advance in one revolution. EFFECTIVE PITCH is the distance it actually advances. Thus, geometric or theoretical pitch is based on no slippage, but actual or effective pitch includes propeller slippage in the air.

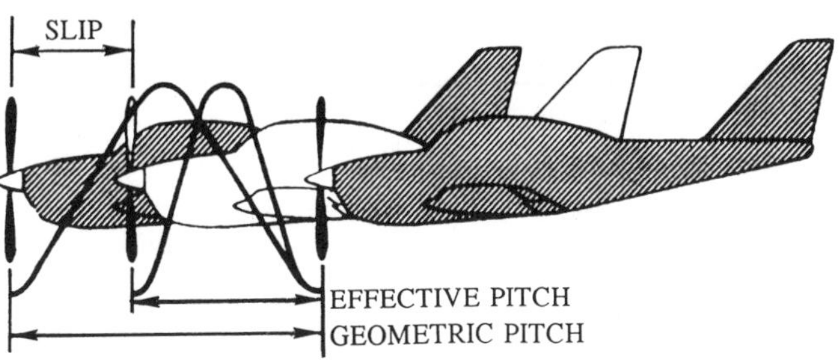

Figure 11.31 Propeller Slippage

PROPELLER EFFICIENCY is the ratio of thrust horsepower to brake horsepower. Efficiency varies from 50%–87%, depending on how much the propeller 'slips'.

Why is a Propeller 'Twisted'?

The answer to the question 'why is a propeller twisted?' starts with the outer parts of the propeller blades. Like all things that turn about a central point, the outer part travels faster than the portions near the hub. I always compare this to a straight line of long-legged, high-kicking chorus girls at a London variety theatre. They start to pivot around a central point, with the girl on the outer edge going so fast you think she will suddenly fly off into the audience. I've always purchased a seat in the front stalls – and hoped!

If the blades had the same geometric pitch throughout their lengths, at cruise speed the portions near the hub could have negative angles of attack, while the propeller tips would be stalled. 'Twisting', or variation in the geometric pitch of the blades, allows the propeller to operate with a relatively constant angle of attack along its length in cruising flight.

To explain it another way, propeller blades are twisted to change the blade angle in proportion to the differences in speed of rotation along the length of the propeller, and so keep thrust more nearly equalised along this length.

How Does a Propeller Get Its Thrust?

The shape of a blade creates thrust because it is cambered, like the aerofoil shape of a wing. In the case of a wing, the airflow over the wing has a lower

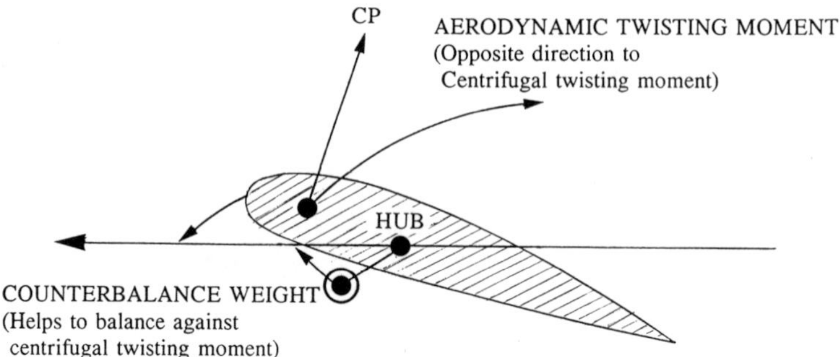

[NOTE: The propeller efficiency can be increased by increasing the number of propeller blades. This increases the solidity of the disc.
CONTRA-ROTATING PROPELLER is one engine with two shafts rotating in different directions.
COUNTER-ROTATING PROPELLER is two engines each rotating in different directions.]

Figure 11.32

pressure, and the lifting force is upwards. With the propeller, which is mounted in the vertical not the horizontal plane, the area of decreased pressure is in front of the propeller, and the thrust force is in a forward direction.

Aerodynamically then, thrust is the result of the propeller shape and the angle of attack of the blade.

Forces Acting on a Propeller Blade

Three main forces act on a propeller blade (see Figure 11.33):

- Centrifugal.
- Bending.
- Torsion.

The forces acting on a rotating propeller are said to be at a maximum in the vicinity of the blade shank. At high rotational speeds these forces will increase, especially that due to the centrifugal action of the blades, tending to pull them out of the hub.

Constant Speed Propellers

A constant speed propeller maintains a selected engine speed by adjusting the blade to meet engine load conditions. For example, as the engine load increases during a climb, the blade angle decreases to prevent the engine from

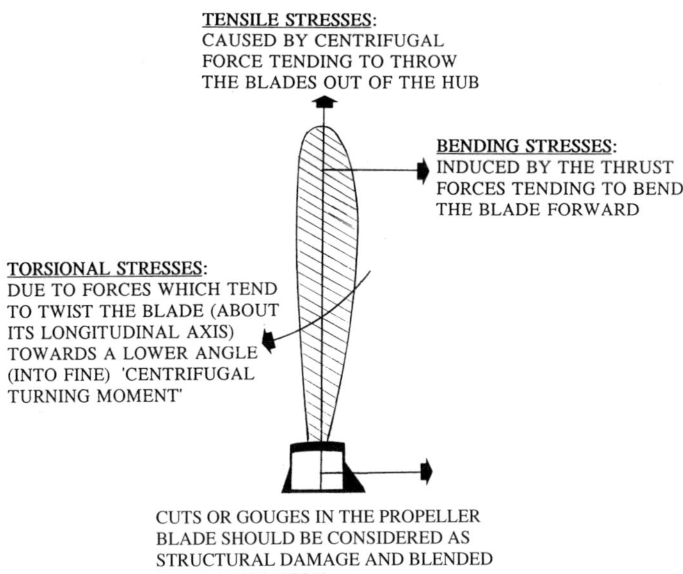

The forces acting on a rotating propeller blade are said to be at a maximum in the area close to the shank of the blades. At high rotational speeds these forces will increase, especially that due to the centrifugal action of the blades tending to pull them out of the hub.

Figure 11.33 The Forces Acting on a Rotating Propeller Blade

slowing down. During high speed flight though, the blade angle increases, adding a load to the engine and preventing it from running faster. This interaction makes a significant contribution to propeller efficiency.

Lift versus drag curves, which are drawn for both wings and propellers, show that the most efficient angle of attack is a small one, and varies from 2°–4° (positive angle). The actual blade angle necessary to maintain this small angle of attack varies with the forward speed of the aircraft.

For comparative interest, I have included a graph showing the differences in propeller efficiency between constant speed and fixed pitch propellers (Figure 11.34).

If a constant speed propeller has blade angle limits of 15° minimum, and 35° maximum, a large increase in efficiency may be gained over fixed pitch propellers with angles of 20° or 25°. Maximum thrust is therefore achieved during take-off when the blade angle is low (fine pitch).

The low blade angle keeps the angle of attack small and efficient with respect to the relative airflow. At the same time it allows the propeller to handle a smaller mass of air per revolution. This light 'load' means the engine

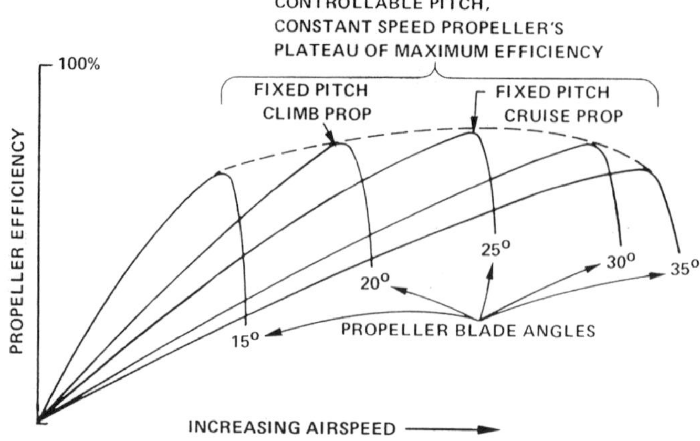

Figure 11.34 Comparison of Propeller Efficiency

can turn at high RPM and convert the maximum amount of fuel into heat energy. (Take-off power also results in the highest engine fuel burn).

As we have said, high RPM also provides maximum thrust, for although the mass of air handled per revolution is small, the number of revolutions per minute is considerable (often close to the maximum engine RPM limitations). The slipstream velocity is also high and, combined with low airspeed, the thrust reaches maximum.

After lift-off, as the airspeed increases, the constant speed propeller automatically changes to a higher angle (coarser pitch). This decreases the engine RPM and reduces fuel consumption whilst keeping maximum thrust.

At cruising altitude in level flight, less power is needed. Although the mass of air handled per revolution of the propeller is greater, this is more than offset by a decrease in slipstream velocity and an increase in airspeed. The angle of attack is still small, because the blade angle has been increased with the increase in (cruising) airspeed.

Summary of Propeller RPM Change Versus Airspeed

RPM	TAS	Initial Tendency	Result
Increase	Constant	Increase in angle of attack	Finer pitch to allow engine to speed up
Decrease	Constant	Decrease in angle of attack	Coarser pitch to increase prop torque – engine slows down

RPM	TAS	Initial Tendency	Result
Constant	Increase	Reduced angle of attack	Increase in pitch to keep RPM constant
Constant	Decrease	Increased angle of attack	Reduction of pitch to keep RPM constant

Torque Reaction and P Factor

Torque reaction involves Newton's Third Law of Physics: 'for every action, there is an equal and opposite reaction'. When this is applied to an aircraft, it means that as the engine parts and propeller are rotating in one direction, an equal force is trying to rotate it in the opposite direction.

To the pilot, 'torque' (which is the left turning tendency of the aircraft) is made up of four elements. These cause, or produce a twisting (rotating) motion around at least one of the aircraft's three axes. The four elements are:

- Torque reaction from engine and propeller.
- Corkscrewing effect of the slipstream.
- Gyroscopic action of the propeller.
- Asymmetric loading of the propeller.

Asymmetrical Thrust

At a high angle of attack in a propeller drive aircraft, asymmetrical thrust is created because the descending propeller blade on the right side of the engine has a greater angle of attack than the ascending blade on the left (Figure 11.35). This produces greater thrust from the right side of the propeller, resulting in a left yaw known as P-factor.

It should be remembered that P-factor creates a left-turning tendency only when the aircraft is flying with a high angle of attack. This is only a minor factor in level cruise flight, since the propeller blades are at the same angle of attack, producing equal thrust.

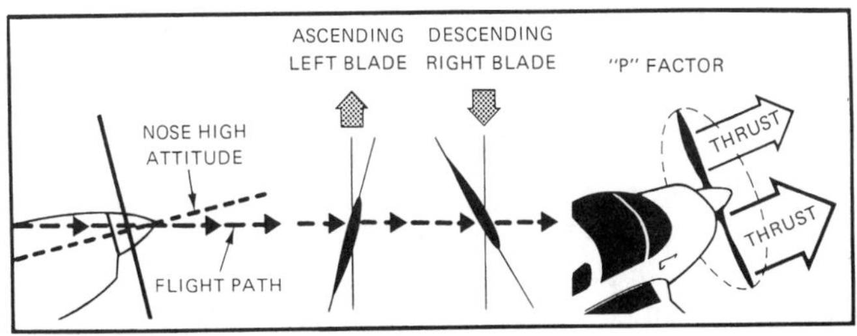

Figure 11.35 Asymmetrical Thrust of Propeller

Power Control

With a fixed pitch propeller, the throttle controls both engine and propeller RPM which is registered on a tachometer. Consequently engine power output, specifically in terms of per cent brake horsepower, is equated only to RPM in cruise performance tables.

One of the major advantages of the constant speed propeller, is that the propeller blade angle changes automatically to maintain a constant RPM. With a constant speed propeller, the throttle is used to control the manifold pressure, while the propeller control is used to adjust RPM. On most light aircraft, the manifold pressure and fuel flow indicators are mounted together in the same instrument case. Typical instruments are shown in Figure 11.36.

Figure 11.36 Power Instruments

Correct Power Change Sequence

When adjusting the throttle and propeller controls, the proper sequence must be followed. If not, it is possible to exceed the maximum allowable pressure within the engine cylinders by using an excessive amount of manifold pressure for a given RPM. Detonation, excessive bearing loads, and even structural failure can result if the correct procedure is not used.

Power adjustments should be made in the sequence illustrated (Figure 11.37).

Propeller Feathering

The constant speed, variable pitch propeller we have been talking about has a fully feathering capability. (See Figure 11.38). This means that if an engine fails, the blade angle can be changed to produce minimum drag.

The drag created when a propeller is windmilling without producing thrust – especially as in an engine failure situation immediately after take-off – causes

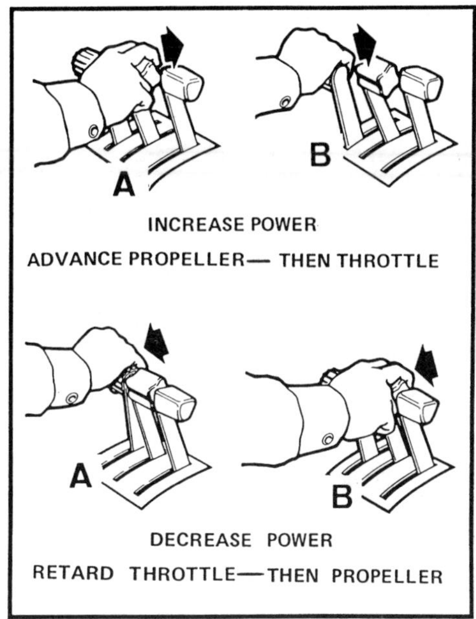

Figure 11.37 Power-Propeller Sequence Change

considerable asymmetric drag and is a serious performance consideration. This is particularly so with a multi-engine aircraft with marginal engine-out capabilities.

In the normal RPM operating range:

- Governor boosted oil pressure moves the propeller blades to the low blade angle (high RPM – fine pitch) position.
- Counterweights and springs in the propeller hub move the blades to high angle (low RPM – coarse pitch).
- When the propeller control lever is moved past the feather detent, oil pressure is removed from the propeller hub.
- Counterweights, aided by springs in the dome, turn the propeller blades past the normal high (coarse) pitch stop to the FEATHER POSITION. (*Counterweights* are important to propeller operation. When the propeller is rotating, the *centre of mass* of the counterweights moves towards the propeller's plane of rotation, tending to *increase* the blade angle. This twisting force attempts to move the blades to the high pitch and feather position).
- The blades are then neatly aligned with the airflow for minimum drag which helps any asymmetric situation.

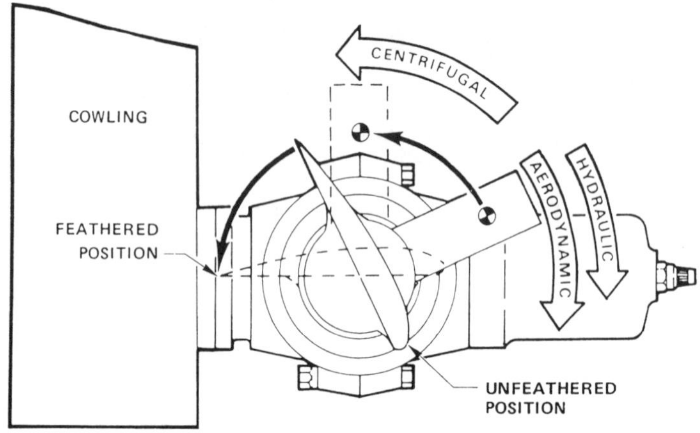

Figure 11.38 Propeller Feathering Mechanism

- If engine oil pressure is lost – or the propeller governor fails to provide oil pressure to the hub – the blades move to the feather position. (This is an added safety feature to ensure the propeller can always be feathered.)

Constant Speed Unit Function Checks

- Exercise and check operation of the CSU by moving RPM lever smoothly over its full governing range. (This should be done at least twice to ensure the circulation of warm oil throughout the system.)
  This check is carried out with the RPM lever set to take-off position (fully fine – low pitch).
- With RPM lever set to governing range, advance throttle slightly and the RPM gauge needle will start to move towards an increase and then return to the selected RPM as the CSU controls the RPM.
- As for the previous item, but with the throttle retarded.
  The above checks must be carried out with the static manifold air pressure – 29.92in Hg standard atmospheric conditions – which is usually approximated to 30in Hg.

Some Useful Tips

A constant speed propeller can be used to adjust drag as well as engine power output.

- With the propeller set for low (fine) pitch, it will produce its greatest drag.
- In high (coarse) pitch the minimum drag will occur.

The pitch and drag relationship has several practical operational advantages:

- When entering the circuit pattern the propeller control can be adjusted to low pitch to increase drag and slow the aircraft.
- For a STOL approach and landing, low pitch will give a steeper approach, with more precise control over the rate of descent by 'fine-tuning' the power to judge an accurate touchdown point.

Turbocharging

Atmospheric pressure variations can have a significant effect on engine power. For example, a decrease in the intake manifold absolute power (MAP) causes a decrease in engine power output. Pressurising the air in the intake manifold as the aircraft climbs to altitude is one solution to the problem of power loss due to decreasing MAP.

For a normally aspirated piston engine power decreases at around 3.3% per 1000 feet (see figure 11.39). Meanwhile a turbocharged engine increases its power at 1.1% per 1000 feet, due to less air pressure on the exhaust outlet.

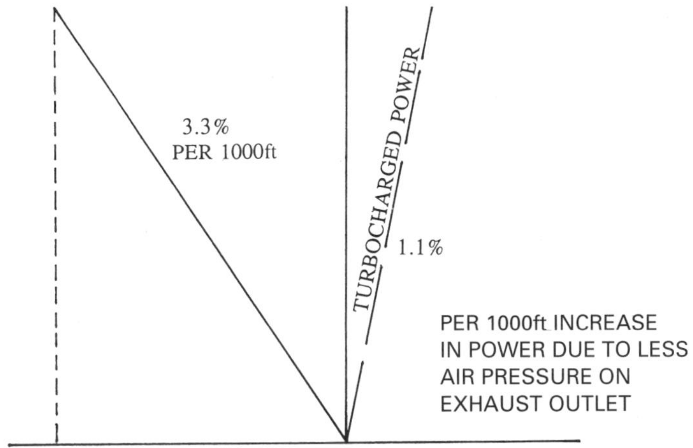

Turbocharging/Supercharging is a means of increasing manifold pressure to maintain sea level pressure to altitude.

Figure 11.39 Comparison of Power Loss Versus Altitude

A turbocharger can be said to be an externally driven supercharger, because the compressor and turbine work together. The compressor is driven by the exhaust turbine, which gets its energy from the engine's hot exhaust gases. It receives ram air from the air inlet or alternate air source (see Figure 11.40).

The air is then pressurised by centrifugal force, with an impeller rotating at up to nine times the engine speed, which increases the air pressure to the

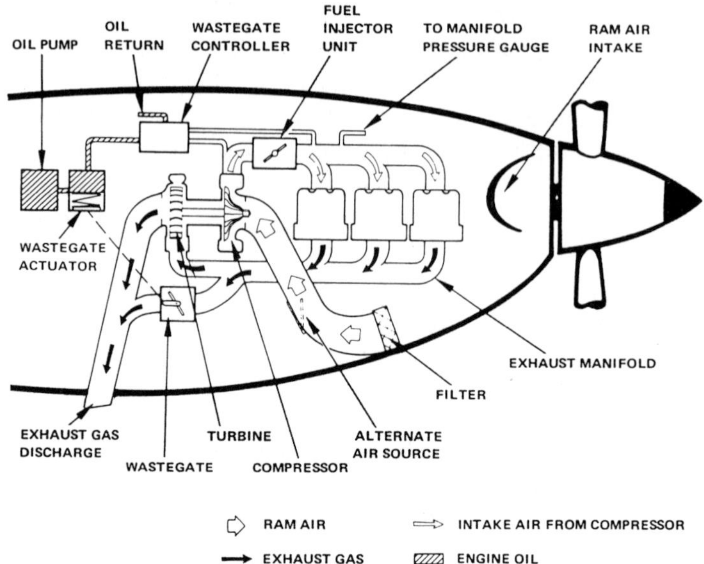

Figure 11.40 Turbocharger

induction manifold. The compressed air is then collected from the ring surrounding the impeller, and directed into the fuel injector unit's throttle valve.

The speed of the turbocharger must be regulated to prevent excessive manifold pressure. This is done by diverting some of the exhaust gases through a waste gate instead of the turbine. The waste gate, controls the turbocharger RPM:

- Close waste gate – increase RPM – increase pressure.
- Open waste gate – reduce RPM – reduce pressure.

The waste gate can be manually controlled. However, with an automatic waste gate controller, the pilot can set the required manifold pressure, and virtually no throttle adjustment is required with changes in altitude. The maximum altitude at which the which the turbocharger can maintain the selected manifold pressure is termed the critical altitude.

OVERBOOST CONTROL. Most engines incorporate a relief valve in the induction system which is set to relieve any excess manifold pressure.

Turbocharger Operation

The turbocharger operation will follow throttle movement, but a built-in time lag exists because it takes time for the system to speed up/slow down, as well as time for the waste gate to move. The throttle should be moved slowly to

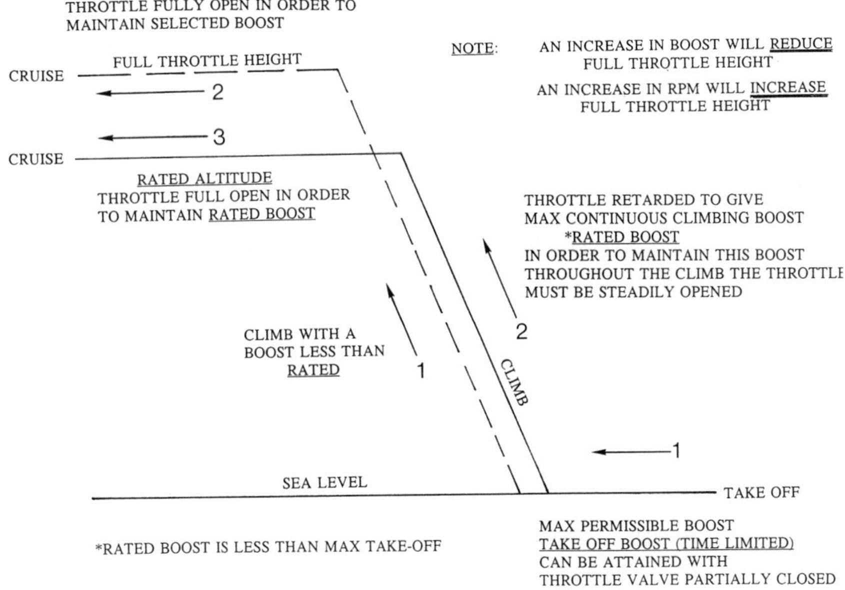

Figure 11.41

prevent the system hunting, as the turbocharger is sensitive and can easily overshoot or undershoot the required datum.

- ABSOLUTE PRESSURE CONTROL – Only one datum pressure selected so that full throttle will not overboost the engine.
- VARIABLE PRESSURE CONTROL – Delivery pressure datum is varied with throttle position to give enough pressure, but not too much.
- DENSITY CONTROL – Tries to maintain delivery air density at SL ISA value (1225gm/m^3), and so has a pressure datum that varies with delivery air temperature. (It is less liable to 'hunt').
- PRESSURE RELIEF VALVE. The inlet-manifold will prevent over-boosting due to surging, control malfunction, etc, by venting manifold as pressure rises.

The Airspeed Indicator

'A vital *performance* instrument, so be aware of what it shows.'

Construction

In principle, the simple ASI can be considered as an airtight box divided by a flexible diaphragm, with pitot pressure fed to one side and static pressure to

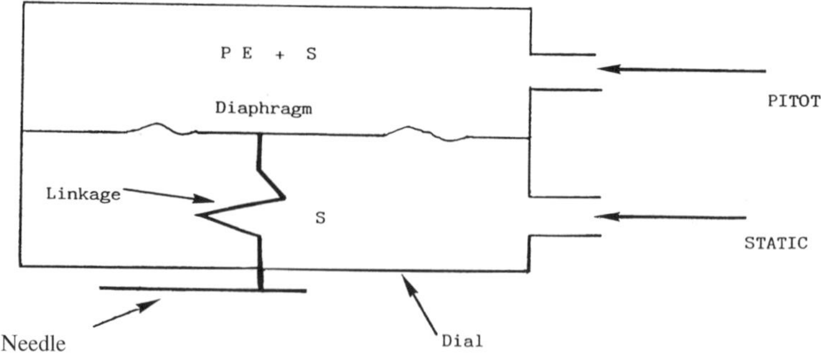

Figure 11.42 Schematic of Simple Airspeed Indicator

the other side. The diaphragm deflects a certain proportion of dynamic (ram) air pressure, which is transmitted through a system to the airspeed indicator needle on the face of the dial (Figure 11.42). Static pressure is common to both sides of the diaphragm, so it does not influence diaphragm movement.

How it Works

The pitot-static system has two major parts, the impact pressure chamber and lines, and the static pressure chamber and lines. The impact chamber contains ram air pressure supplied by the pitot tube. It is usually located on the leading edge of the wing – or on each side of the fuselage beside the cockpit/flight deck. It has a pitot heater to prevent ice formation which would block the tube (anti-ice system). The external static ports also have anti-ice heater elements.

The pitot tube provides dynamic (ram) air pressure for the airspeed indicator, and the static source supplies static pressure to the ASI, VSI and Altimeter. The airspeed indicator reacts to any change between ram (dynamic) air pressure and static (passive) air pressure. The greater the differential between these two pressure readings, the greater the airspeed indication.

The ASI is designed to function correctly at sea level under ISA conditions. So in any different atmospheric condition, altitude or temperature, the true airspeed must be computed.TAS can be found with a navigational computer when the pressure altitude, OAT and CAS are known; as a Rule of Thumb for finding the TAS, use the IAS and add 2% of the IAS for each 1000ft of altitude AMSL.

Basic Aircraft Speeds

Indicated airspeed (IAS) is read directly from the airspeed indicator. This speed will seldom match the actual airspeed of the aircraft throughout the speed and altitude ranges.

Calibrated airspeed (CAS) is indicated airspeed corrected for errors

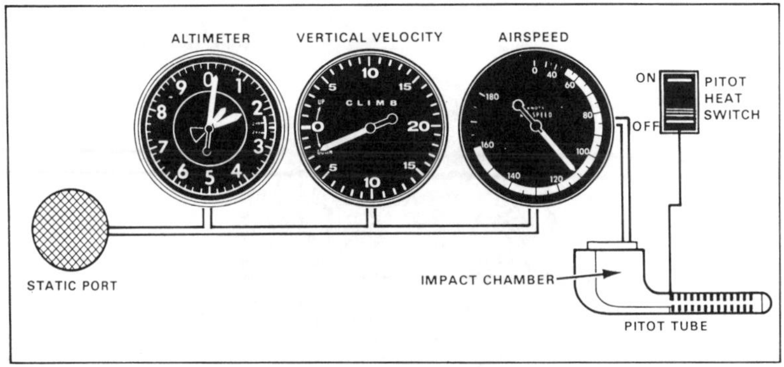

Figure 11.43 Pitot-Static System

resulting mainly from the position of the static source, and to a lesser degree, from pitot tube positions.

True airspeed (TAS) is found by converting IAS, under actual conditions, to an airspeed at a standard temperature and pressure. (Some airspeed indicators incorporate a TAS computer on the face of the (ASI) instrument, which enables the pilot to read TAS directly from the indicator.)

Airspeed Indicator Markings (see Figure 11.44)

V-SPEED		Marking
V_{NE}	–	never exceed (red line).
V_{NO}	–	maximum for normal operations (high speed end of green arc).
V_{FE}	–	maximum for flap extension (high speed end of white arc).
V_{S1}	–	stall, power-off clean configuration (low speed end of green arc)
V_{SO}	–	stall, power-off, landing configuration (low speed end of white arc).
V_A	–	Manoeuvring speed; sometimes referred to as the rough air speed for turbulence penetration. The aircraft will stall before it experiences structural failure (about 4G). (V_A is also expressed as the maximum speed at which full abrupt control travel can be used without exceeding the design load factor.)
V_{LO}	–	Landing gear operating speed; maximum speed for operating the gear mechanism.
V_{LE}	–	Landing gear extended speed; maximum speed for aircraft operation after the gear is down and locked.

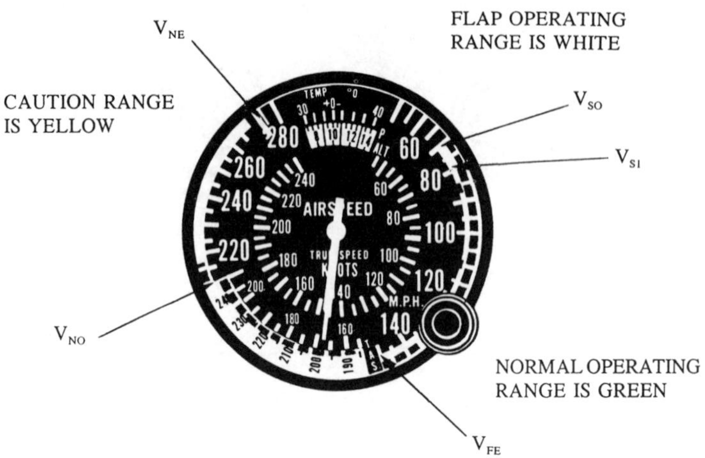

Figure 11.44 Airspeed Indicator Markings

V_X – Best angle of climb speed (useful for obstacle clearance); the airspeed that will give the greatest amount of climb in a given distance.

V_Y – Best rate of climb speed; the airspeed that will give the most altitude gain per minute.

IAS and Stall Speed

It is very important for us to know the indicated airspeeds at which our aircraft will stall in various configurations; flaps up/extended/gear down/banked attitudes (turning).

In our STOL work when 'flying the edge' at the bottom end of the flight envelope, we need to be able to handle our aircraft accurately at low speed close to the stall, and know that the aircraft stalls at the same indicated airspeeds at all altitudes in any given flight condition.

For example, if an aircraft stalls at 60 knots IAS close to sea level in a slow level flight, power-off deceleration, then it will stall at the same IAS at high altitude under identical flight conditions – even though the TAS is greater. (Essential to know for STOL work operating from high altitude airstrips).

Position Error

The IAS is read directly from the ASI. CAS, which is frequently referred to as *true indicated airspeed* (TIAS), is IAS corrected for instrument and position error. There can be quite a large difference between CAS and IAS, especially at low airspeeds, because of installation (*position*) error.

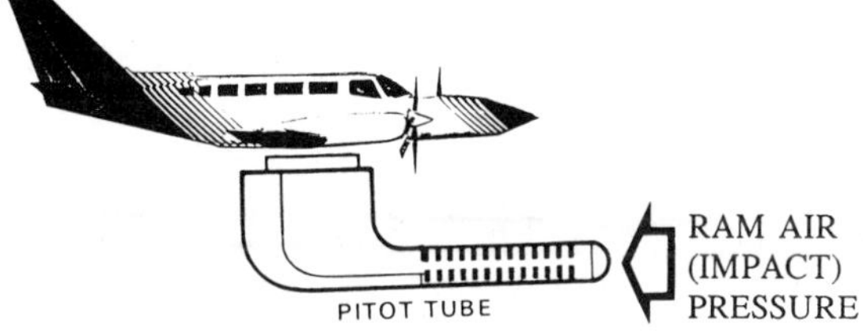

WING AT LEVEL CRUISE ANGLE OF ATTACK ALLOWS RAM AIR TO ENTER THE PITOT TUBE STRAIGHT IN

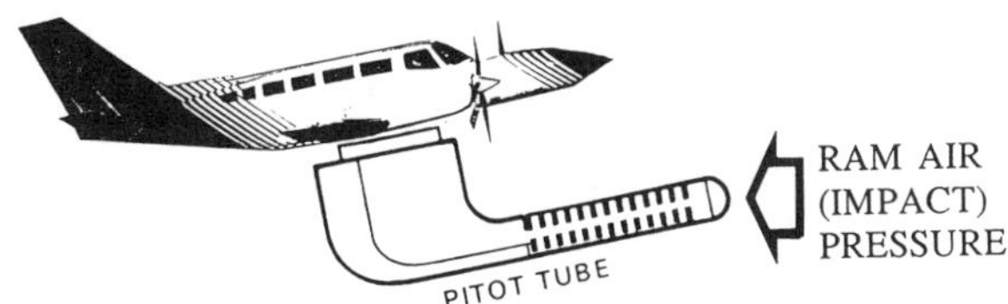

WING AT SLOW FLIGHT (HIGH) ANGLE OF ATTACK ALLOWS RAM AIR TO ENTER THE PITOT TUBE AT AN ANGLE

Figure 11.45 Position Error

Installation error is sometimes called '*pressure*' error. It occurs when the aircraft changes its attitude from normal straight and level flight, (see Figure 11.45). The pitot (ram air) enters the system with a different pressure, caused by the changing aircraft angle of attack. This creates a variation in pitot-static differential pressure. In turn it creates a fluctuation of the internal diaphragm in the airspeed indicator.

How to Avoid Joining the Exclusive Red Faces Club

I WAS TOLD THAT THERE ARE TWO KINDS OF PILOT – THOSE WHO HAVE LANDED WITH THE GEAR UP AND THOSE WHO MIGHT OR WILL – IN THE RIGHT CIRCUMSTANCES. THAT'S THE THEORY, ANYWAY.

Landing with your undercarriage retracted can not only be detrimental to the performance of the aircraft – it can spoil your whole (flying) day! Having said all that, and joking aside, pilots do not deliberately land with the gear up, except in a genuine emergency. And they seldom admit they forgot to lower the gear.

Forgetfulness of this vital item in the pre-landing checklist, happens because pilots become distracted. This can be caused by a whole variety of things. For example:

- A hurried straight-in approach ahead of heavier traffic.
- A go-around, followed by a visual hold close to the field and another tight approach in a busy traffic sequence.
- A practice asymmetric approach with the check pilot saying at the last minute, 'okay, make a touch and go off this one'.
- A flapless approach which diverts/interrupts the normal approach-landing sequence.
- Flying single pilot and talking to ATC and other traffic.
- Instructor-student 'patter', with the instructor concentrating on perhaps advising the student how to improve a bad approach – result, missing the normal gear lowering point, and bingo!

There are many others, of course; weather problems, a hurried instrument approach and so on.

I understand it was manufacturers who came to the conclusion, after much technical deliberation and head scratching, that the average pilot could not concentrate on more than one thing at a time. (That statement is practically inaccurate, but I won't argue about it now.)

So a team of design boffins invented bells, warning horns (they usually sound like a ship's fog warning klaxon), buzzers and/or flashing red lights. This was in the hope of combating the (expensive) problem of inadvertent and unwanted gear-up landings.

Unfortunately – if we all care to admit it – pilots do ignore these devices. (I've known some experienced check and training pilots do it). Perhaps they mistake the warning for a stall warning, or they are so 'switched off' to cockpit noise, that their minds and senses ignore it.

> 'I couldn't hear what the tower controller was saying about my gear being up, because the warning horn was too loud'.

There are also those pilots who decide to get rid of the 'warning horn or bell' distraction by pulling the circuit breaker. The problem is they forget to push it back in! Other pilots use the landing gear as speed brakes to slow down, then retract the gear again in the circuit pattern for some unknown reason, thinking they are lowering it.

To avoid becoming a member of the 'Red Faces Club' requires not only awareness, but above all discipline. Make sure you have three green lights as part of your downwind or final approach check. Now you're going to ask how do I remember to do this? No problem – PUF: PROPS —

UNDERCARRIAGE — FLAPS. (Even if you are flying a fixed gear aircraft, because next time you might not be.)

The challenge and response technique is the best (flying single pilot, say it out loud to yourself). We covered this in chapter 1.

Challenge	Check	Response
Props	Fully Forward	Set max – full line
Undercarriage	Down and locked	Down and locked – three greens
Flaps	Full–A/R	

The mnemonic is a simple one, and if you complete it every time before you land – irrespective of all other checks – you will avoid having to join the Red Faces Club.

Now for the real undercarriage emergency, if it is one. Pilots have declared an emergency because the instrument lights 'dimmer switch' was on DIM for night flight. Also gear bulbs can blow, but there are spares you can use from other lights.

Always be prepared for an emergency by having the emergency checklist handy. Give yourself time to sort out a gear problem. Fly a short distance from the traffic circuit and review the emergency gear extension checklist calmly.

One other thing, don't be afraid to ask for assistance from ATC if necessary, it is an emergency. Also, check your fuel reserves. You don't want to compound the problem through lack of fuel, and build up the stress level so that it impairs your decision-making at a critical time.

Fly the aircraft first – then systematically go through the emergency checklist next. The good news is that if the worst does happen, the chances are you will walk away from a gear-up landing uninjured.

I have only had two gear problems. In the first instance the undercarriage partially collapsed on take-off, and the aircraft slid off the end of the runway into six feet of water. The only problem there was to make sure no-one was drowned!

The second time was in a Citation and it was my first flight straight from the type conversion course. Having only two days previously been dealing with this very problem in the simulator, I overcame the 'emergency' in textbook fashion and landed without further incident.

Afterwards the tower controller said to me, 'How was it then, you didn't sound concerned over the radio?'

'No problem', I replied – but thought, 'why should there be?' because FLIGHT SAFETY is right, the best safety device in any aircraft is a well trained pilot.

Stability Quiz

1. After a disturbance in pitch, an aircraft continues to oscillate at a constant amplitude. It is:
   a. Longitudinally neutrally stable.
   b. Laterally unstable.
   c. Longitudinally unstable.

2. Stability about the longitudinal axis is given by:
   a. Wing dihedral.
   b. Elevators.
   c. Ailerons.

3. Moving the centre of gravity aft will:
   a. Increase longitudinal stability.
   b. Reduce longitudinal stability.
   c. Have no effect on longitudinal stability.

4. Increasing the size of the fin will:
   a. Increase lateral stability.
   b. Decrease lateral stability.
   c. Not affect lateral stability.

5. A high wing position gives:
   a. The same lateral stability as a low wing.
   b. Less lateral stability than a low wing.
   c. More lateral stability than a low wing.

6. Longitudinal stability is given by:
   a. the horizontal tailplane.
   b. the wing dihedral.
   c. the fin.

7. To ensure longitudinal stability in flight, the position of the CG:
   a. Should not be forward of the neutral point.
   b. Should not be aft of the neutral point.
   c. Should coincide with the neutral point.

8. Sweepback of the wings will:
   a. Not affect the lateral stability.
   b. Decrease lateral stability.
   c. Increase lateral stability.

9. After a disturbance in pitch an aircraft oscillates with increasing amplitude. It is:
   a. Dynamically neutral.
   b. Dynamically stable but statically unstable.
   c. Dynamically unstable longitudinally.

10. An aircraft is constructed with dihedral to provide:
    a. Longitudinal stability about the lateral axis.
    b. Lateral stability about the longitudinal axis.
    c. Lateral stability about the normal axis.

11. Stability about the lateral axis is given by:
    a. Wing dihedral.
    b. The horizontal tailplane.
    c. The ailerons.

12. The static margin is equal to the distance between:
    a. The CG and the neutral point.
    b. The CP and the neutral point.
    c. The CG and the CP.

13. The fin gives:
    a. Directional stability about the longitudinal axis.
    b. Directional stability about the normal axis.
    c. Longitudinal stability about the lateral axis.

14. Lateral stability is given by:
    a. The ailerons.
    b. The wing dihedral.
    c. The horizontal tailplane.

Answers to Stability Quiz

1	–	a.	8	–	c.
2	–	a.	9	–	c.
3	–	b.	10	–	b.
4	–	a.	11	–	b.
5	–	c.	12	–	a.
6	–	a.	13	–	b.
7	–	b.	14	–	b.

Aircraft Weight and Balance/ Loading Quiz

Loading and CG — Test Paper 1

1. Calculate the position of the CG of an aircraft, given the following data:

Basic Weight	26 000 lb	Arm 1 ft aft of datum
Pilot Weight	140 lb	Arm 6 ft forward of datum
Navigator Weight	160 lb	Arm 2 ft forward of datum
Cargo 'A' Weight	30 146 lb	Arm 4 ft aft of datum
Cargo 'B' Weight	400 lb	Arm 1 ft forward of datum
Fuel	5 000 galls	Arm on the datum
Oil	50 galls	Arm 1 ft forward of datum
Fuel Specific Gravity	= .72	
Oil Specific Gravity	= .9	

If the aircraft fuel consumption is 204 gallons per hour and the oil consumption is 4 pints per hour, what will be the position of the CG on landing after a flight lasting 4 hours?

2. Calculate the position of the CG of an aircraft, given the following data:

Basic Weight	6 000 lb	Arm 5 inches forward of datum
Fuel	150 galls	Arm 11 inches aft of datum
Oil	8 galls	Arm 6 inches forward of datum
Crew: total weight	340 lb	Arm 40 inches forward of datum
Passengers	340 lb	Arm 36 inches aft of datum
Maximum. All-Up Weight	8 000 lb	
Fuel Specific Gravity	= .72	
Oil Specific Gravity	= .9	

CG limits 4" to ½" forward of datum

Fuel consumption = 40 gal/hour Oil consumption = 2 gal/hour

Is the CG within the limits for take-off and landing?

The flight time is 3 hours.

3. Calculate the take-off CG of an aircraft, given the following data:

Basic Weight	5000 lb	Arm 30 inches aft of datum
Crew: total weight	340 lb	Arm 30 inches forward of datum
Fuel	200 galls	Arm 10 inches forward of datum
Oil	30 galls	Arm 4 inches forward of datum
Passengers	340 lb	Arm 70 inches aft of datum

Fuel Consumption = 50 g.p.h. Total Oil Consumption = 20 gallons
Fuel Specific Gravity .72 Oil Specific Gravity .9

What will be the CG position after a flight lasting 3 hours?

Loading and CG — Test Paper 2

1. Calculate the CG of an aircraft from the following data:

Basic Weight	4 000 lb	Arm 7 inches forward of datum
Fuel load	100 galls	Arm 13 inches aft of datum
Oil	6 galls	Arm 8 inches forward of datum
Cargo in 'B' Hold	340 lb	Arm 42 inches forward of datum
Cargo in 'C' hold	340 lb	Arm 38 inches aft of datum

The CG limits are 3 inches forward to 4 inches aft of the datum.

Fuel Specific Gravity .72 Oil Specific Gravity .9

An extra cargo consignment, weight 100 lb, has to be on-loaded. 'A' hold, 60 inches forward of datum, is empty. So is 'D' hold, which is 60 inches aft of datum. In which hold would you stow the extra freight? What will be the CG after the freight has been on-loaded?

2. Calculate the CG of an aircraft given the following data:

Basic Weight	35 000 lb	Arm 1 ft aft of datum
Crew: 4, each weighing	170 lb	Arm 12 ft forward of datum
Fuel	1800 galls	Arm 5 ft aft of datum
Oil	140 galls	Arm 10 ft forward of datum
Cargo 'A' Hold	500 lb	Arm 16 ft forward of datum
Cargo 'B' Hold	4 000 lb	Arm 1 ft aft of datum
Cargo 'C' Hold	8 000 lb	Arm 6 ft aft of datum
Cargo 'D' Hold	2 500 lb	Arm 40 ft aft of datum

Fuel Specific Gravity .72 Oil Specific Gravity .9

CG limits are 0 ft to 4 ft aft of datum.

Will the Zero Fuel CG be within limits?

3. Calculate the CG of an aircraft given the following data:

Basic Weight	8 250 lb	Arm 6 inches aft of datum
Pilots: 2, each weighing	170 lb	Arm 12 inches forward of datum
Fuel	150 gallons	On the datum
Oil	10 galls	Arm 6 inches forward of datum
Passengers: 10, each weighing	165 lb	Arm 4 ft forward of datum
Baggage	150 lb	Arm 8 ft aft of datum

Fuel Specific Gravity .72 Oil Specific Gravity .9

CG limits are 6 inches aft to 18 inches aft of datum.

Fuel consumed during the flight is 120 gallons.

What will be the CG on landing?

After the landing, the fuel load is adjusted to 150 gallons and the passengers and their baggage are off-loaded. What is the minimum quantity of ballast that must be placed in the baggage compartment to allow the aircraft to be flown back to base?

Loading and CG — Test Paper 3

Given the following data, compile a load sheet and calculate the CG before take-off.

Basic Weight	16 000 lb	Arm 3 in. aft of datum
Crew: 3, each weighing	140 lb	Arm 8 ft forward of datum
Passengers: (forward cabin) 15, each weighing	140 lb	Arm 4 in. aft of datum
Cargo 'A' Hold	4 400 lb	Arm 9 ft aft of datum
Cargo 'B' Hold	655 lb	Arm 11 ft forward of datum
Fuel 1800 gallons at .72 Sp. Gr.		Arm 2 ft aft of datum
Oil 60 gallons at .9 Sp. Gr.		Arm 6 inches forward of datum
Passengers (aft cabin): Nil		Arm 6 ft aft of datum

Maximum All-Up Weight Limit = 38 000 lb

CG limits 9 inches to 19½ inches aft of datum

770 gallons of fuel and 14 gallons of oil will be used during the flight; will the CG be within limits for landing?

If the cargo in A and B holds is unloaded when the aircraft reaches its destination, what will be the Arm of the CG? Will it be within limits?

If 6 of the passengers move back to the aft cabin, which has an arm of +6 feet, will the aircraft be safe to take-off? The fuel tanks will not be refilled before take-off.

Loading and CG — Test Paper 4

Given the following data, compile a load sheet and calculate the CG of the Aircraft.

Basic Weight	2 700 Kg	Arm 36 inches aft
Fuel	150 galls at .72 Sp. Gr.	Arm 50 inches aft
Oil	15 galls at .9 Sp. Gr.	Arm 30 inches aft
Crew	150 Kg	Arm 2 inches forward
Passengers Row 1	150 Kg	Arm 40 inches aft
Passengers Row 2	75 Kg	Arm 80 inches aft
Passengers Row 3	Nil	Arm 120 inches aft
Cargo in Front Hold	65 Kg	Arm 60 inches forward
Cargo in Rear Hold	10 Kg	Arm 140 inches aft

Maximum Take-off and Landing Weight = 4000 Kg.

CG limits 34.6 inches to 40.3 aft of datum.

Fuel Consumption for the flight will be 380 kg.

Oil Consumption for the flight will be 20 kg.

Will the CG be within the limits for take-off and landing?

If not, how must the freight load be redistributed to position the CG at its most forward limit for landing?

Weight and CG — Test Paper 5

Compile a trim sheet using the following data:

Basic Weight	2 500 Kg	Arm 2.5 inches aft of datum
Crew	150 Kg	Arm 200 inches forward of datum
Fuel	500 Kg	Arm 50 inches forward of datum
Oil	50 Kg	Arm 75 inches forward of datum
Load (forward hold)	400 Kg	Arm 225 inches forward of datum
Load (aft hold)	100 Kg	Arm 100 inches aft of datum

Answer the following questions using the trim sheet you have compiled as a basis for each answer. (Treat each question as a separate item).

1. What is the zero fuel weight?
2. What is the take-off CG?
3. You are required to move the take-off CG one inch forward. How much weight will have to be transferred from one hold to the other to achieve this?

4. During the flight 380 Kg of fuel are used and 20 Kg of oil. What will be the position of the CG on landing?
5. You are required to move the take-off CG one inch forward. How much weight will have to be on-loaded? In which hold would you stow the load?
6. The forward CG limit is 36 inches from the datum, if an extra 50 Kg was loaded into the rear hold before take-off would the CG be within limits?

Answers to Aircraft Weight and Balance/Loading Quiz

Loading and CG **Test Paper 1 Answers**

Item	Weight lb	– Arm in	+	– Moment lb/in	+
Basic Weight	5 000		30		150 000
Crew	340	30		10 200	
Fuel	1 440	10		14 400	
Oil	270	4		1 080	
Passengers	340		70		23 000
Total Weight	7 390		Total Moments	25 680	173 800
				+ 148 120 lb/in	

Total Weight = 7 390 lb

CG after 3 hours = 20" aft of datum

Item	Weight lb	– Arm	in +	– Moment	lb/in +
Take-off weight	7 390			25 680	173 800
Fuel burnt	1 080	10			10 800
Oil used	180	4			720
Total weight burnt off	1 260	Adjusted Moments		25 680	185 320
Total weight after burn-off	6 130	Resultant Moment		+ 159 640 lb/in	

Total Weight = 6 130 lb

CG after 3 hours = 26.04" aft of datum

Loading and CG

Test Paper 2 Answers

Item	Weight lb	– Arm	in +	– Moment	lb/in +
Basic Weight	4 000	7		28 000	
Fuel	720		13		9 360
Oil	54	8		432	
Cargo 'B'	340	42		14 280	
Cargo 'C'	340		38		12 920
	5 454	Total Moments		42 712	22 280
		Resultant Moment		–20 432 lb/in	

Total Weight = 5 454 lb

CG = 3.75" forward of datum

CG arm is forward of the forward limit, therefore the extra cargo must be placed in 'D' Hold, 60 inches aft of datum.

Item	– Weight lb +	– Arm in	+	– Moment lb/in	+
Weight as above	5 454			42 712	22 280
Cargo on-loaded	100		60		6 000
Weight with load in 'D' hold	5 554 lb	Adjusted Moments		42 712	28 280
		Resultant Moment		– 14 432 lb/in	

Total Weight = 5 554 lb

CG = 2.6 " forward of the datum
CG is now within the forward limit of 3 inches.

Item	Weight lb	– Arm in	+	– Moment lb/ft	+
Basic Weight	35 000		1		35 000
Crew	680	12		8 160	
Fuel	12 960		5		64 800
Oil	1 260	10		12 600	
Cargo in 'A'	500	16		8 000	
Cargo in 'B'	4 000		1		4 000
Cargo in 'C'	8 000		6		48 000
Cargo in 'D'	2 500		40		100 000
Total Weight	64 900	Total Moments		28 760	251 800
					+ 223 040 lb/ft

Total Weight = 64 900 lb

CG = 3.43 ft aft of datum
CG is within limits for take-off with fuel load of 12 960 lb and oil 1260 lb.

Item	– Weight lb	+	– Arm in	+	– Moment lb/ft	+
Weight on take-off		64 900			28 760	251 800
Fuel Weight	12 960			5	64 800	
Zero Fuel Weight	51 940		Adjusted Moments		93 560	251 800
			Resultant Moment		+ 158 240 lb/ft	

Total Weight = 51 940 lb

CG with zero fuel = 3.05 ft aft of datum

Zero fuel CG is within limits. Therefore the CG must be within limits during all phases of the flight.

Loading and CG

Test Paper 3 Answers

Item	Weight lb	– Arm in	+	– Moment lb/ft	+
Basic Weight	16 000		/		4 000
Crew	420	8		3 360	
Passengers	100		$^1/_3$		700
Cargo 'A'	4 400		9		39 600
Cargo 'B'	655	11		7 205	
Fuel	12 960		2		
Oil	540	fi		270	
	37 075	Total Moments		10 835	70 220
		Resultant Moment		+ 59 385 lb	

Total Weight = 37 075 lb

CG = 1.6 feet aft of datum

Take-off CG = 19.2 inches aft datum, i.e. WITHIN LIMITS

Item	– Weight lb	+	–	Arm in +	–	Moment lb/ft +
Take-off Weight		37 075			10 835	70 220
Fuel Burn-Off	5 544			2	11 088	
Oil Consumed	126		½			63
Weight after Burn-Off	31 405				21 923	70 283
		Resultant Moment			+48 360 lb/ft	

Total Weight = 31 405 lb

CG Arm = 1.53 feet
Landing CG 18.47 inches aft of datum, i.e within limits

Item	– Weight lb	+	–	Arm in +	–	Moment lb/ft +
Landing Weight		31 405			21 923	70 283
Cargo 'A'	4 400			9	39 600	
Cargo 'B'	655		11			7 205
Weight after Cargo unloaded	26 350	Adjusted Moments			61 523	77 488
		Resultant Moment			+15 965 lb/ft	

Total Weight = 26 350 lb

CG Arm = .60 feet
After unloading CG = 7.2 ft aft of datum (outside the limits)

Item	− Weight lb	+	− Arm in	+	− Moment lb/in	+
Weight after Cargo Off		26 350			61 523	77 488
Passengers Forward	840			1/3	280	
Passengers aft		840		6		5 040
Total Weight (Unchanged)	26 350	Adjusted Moments			61 803	82 528
		Resultant Moment			+20 725 lb/ft	

Total Weight = 26 350 lb

CG Arm = .78 feet

CG Arm after moving 6 Pax = 9.3 inches aft (within limits)

Loading and CG

Test Paper 4 Answers

The second part of the question: 'How must the freight be redistributed to position the CG at its most forward limit for landing', is another way of saying, 'find the weight which must be moved in order to move the position of the CG through a given distance'. The 10 foot beam will give us the answer.

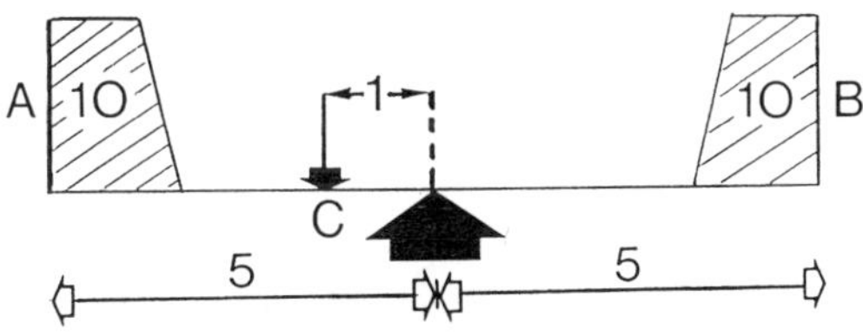

Figure Quiz 1

We want to position the CG at point 'C', 1 foot ahead of its present position. Multiplying the total weight (20) by the distance to move (1 foot) gives us a value of the unbalanced moment.

$$\text{The weight (which we require)} = \frac{\text{Unbalanced moment (20)}}{\text{distance (1)}}$$

= $\frac{20 \times 1 \text{ (= MOMENT)}}{\text{Distance between loads}}$

= $\frac{20}{10}$ = 2 Units of weight

Proof A becomes 12 units
B becomes 8 units
12 x 4 = 48 (moment units)
8 x 6 = 48 (moment units)

NOTE: Weight x arm = moment = Unbalanced Moment

$\frac{\text{Unbalanced Moment}}{\text{Distance Between Loads}}$ = Weight

Loading and CG

Test Paper 4 Answers

Item	Weight Kg	– Arm in	+	– Moment kg/in	+
Basic Weight	2 700		36		97 200
Fuel	491		50		24 550
Oil	61		30		1 830
Crew	150	2		300	
Passenger R1	150		40		6 000
Passenger R2	75		80		6 000
Passenger R3			120		
Cargo Front	65	60		3 900	
Cargo Rear	10		140		1 400
Total Weight	3 702			4 200	136 980
		Resultant Moment			+132 780 Kg/in

Total Weight = 3 702 Kg

∴CG for take-off = 35.8 inches aft of datum

Item	– Weight + Kg		– Arm + in		– Moment + Kg/in	
Take-off Weight		3 702			4 200	136 980
Fuel Burn-Off	380			50	19 000	
Oil Consumed	20			30	600	
Weight after Burn-off (Kg)	3302	Adjusted Moments			23 800	136 980
		Resultant Moment			+113 180 Kg/in	

Total Weight = 3 302 Kg

CG for take-off = 34.27 inches aft (outside limits)
CG after burn-off is forward of forward limit
Difference between position of actual CG and desired CG

= 34.6 in –34.27 in
= .33 in

Unbalanced moment = .33 in x 3302 Kg

Weight to move = $\frac{\text{moment}}{\text{distance}}$

= $\frac{.33 \times 3302}{\text{Distance between front and rear holds}}$

= $\frac{.33 \times 3302}{200}$

Weight = 5.45 Kg which must be moved from front to rear
Your answer should be proved by compilation of a trim sheet.

Item	– Weight Kg	+	– Arm in	+	– Moment Kg/in	+
Take-off Weight		3 700			148 750	16 250
Fuel Burn-Off	380		50			19 000
Oil Consumed	20		75			1 500
	3300		Adjusted Moments		148 750	36 750
			Resultant Moment		– 112 000Kg/in	

Total Weight = 3 300 Kg

= –33.9 in (ahead of datum)

∴CG on landing = 33.9 in ahead of datum

Loading and CG

Test Paper 5 Answers

Item	Weight Kg	– Arm in	+	– Moment kg/in	+
Basic Weight	2 500		2.5		6 250
Crew	150	200		30 000	
Fuel	500	50		25 000	
Oli	50	75		3 750	
Load (Fwd hold)	400	225		90 000	
Load (Aft hold)	100		100		10 000
	3 700	Total Moments		148 750	16 250
		Resultant Moment		+ 132 500 Kg/in	

Total Weight = 3 700 Kg

CG = –35.8 in (forward of datum)

Ans. 1	Zero Fuel Weight	=	3200 Kg
Ans. 2	Take-off CG	=	–35.8 in (forward of datum)
Ans. 3	Required CG	=	1 inch forward of –35.8 in
		=	–36.8 in
Total movement required		=	1 in

Total Unbalanced moment = 3700 x 1 (Kg in)
Total distance to move = aft hold to front hold
= +100 in to –225 in
= 325 in
Weight to move = $\frac{3700}{325}$
Weight to transfer = 11.35 Kg. from aft to forward.

Required movement is forward so extra weight must go into front hold.

CG (trim sheet) = –35.8 in
CG required = –36.8 in
Total unbalanced moments = Weight (trim sheet) x distance to move CG
= 3700 x 1 (Kg in)
Arm of front hold = –225 in
Required CG Arm = –36.8 in
Difference = 188.2 in
Weight required = $\frac{3700 \text{ (Moment)}}{188.2 \text{ (Distance)}}$
= 19.75 Kg

Weight to onload in FORWARD hold = 19.75 Kg.

Ans. 6

Item	– Weight Kg	+ Weight Kg	– Arm in	+ Arm in	– Moment Kg/in	+ Moment Kg/in
All up weight		3 700			148 750	16 250
Wt. in rear hold		50		100		5 000
Wt. after extra load	3 750	Total Adjusted Moments			148 750	21 250
		Resultant Moment			127 500 Kg/in	

Total Weight = 3 750 Kg

CG = –34 in (ahead of datum)

Forward limit is quoted for this example as –36 in CG is within limits.

Lift and High-Lift Devices Quiz (Including the Stall and Definitions)

•LIFT

•HIGH-LIFT DEVICES

•THE STALL

•DEFINITIONS

Lift Quiz

1. For the same angle of attack a cambered wing will:
   a. Give less lift than one with no camber.
   b. Give the same lift as one with no camber.
   c. Give more lift than one with no camber.

2. If the angle of attack is increased the Centre of Pressure will:
   a. Move rearward.
   b. Remain stationary.
   c. Move forward.

3. The lift/drag ratio of a wing section at its stalling angle of attack is:
   a. Of a negative quantity.
   b. Low.
   c. High.

4. For a cambered wing section the zero lift angle will be:
   a. Positive.
   b. Negative.
   c. Zero.

5. The Centre of Pressure is:
   a. The Centre of Gravity of the wing.
   b. The point on the chord line at which the resultant lift force may be said to act.
   c. The point of maximum pressure on the under surface of the wing.

6. The airflow over a wing causes:
   a. A decrease in speed and a decrease in pressure over the upper surface, and an increase in speed and a decrease in pressure over the lower surface.
   b. An increase in speed and a decrease in pressure over the upper surface, and a decrease in speed and an increase in pressure over the lower surface.
   c. An increase in speed and an increase in pressure over the upper surface, and an increase in speed and an increase in pressure over the lower surface.

7. The optimum angle of attack of an aerofoil is the angle at which:
   a. The highest lift/drag ratio is produced.
   b. The aerofoil produces zero lift.
   c. The aerofoil produces maximum lift.

8. All the factors that affect the lift produced by an aerofoil are:
   a. Angle of attack, air density, velocity, wing area.
   b. Angle of attack, air temperature, velocity, wing area.
   c. Angle of attack, velocity, wing area, aerofoil shape, air density.

9. A wing section suitable for high speed would be:
   a. Thin with little or no camber.
   b. Thick with high camber.
   c. Thin with high camber.

10. The airflow over the top surface of an aerofoil produces:
    a. A smaller proportion of the total lift than the airflow past the lower surface.
    b. An equal proportion of the total to that produced by the airflow past the lower surface.
    c. A greater proportion of the total lift than the airflow past the lower surface.

11. If the airspeed over a wing at a constant angle of attack is double:
    a. The lift will be doubled.
    b. The lift will increase four times.
    c. The lift will increase eight times.

12. A cambered aerofoil section set at zero angle of attack in an airstream will:
    a. Produce negative lift.
    b. Produce lift.
    c. Produce no lift.

13. The stalling angle of attack of a typical aerofoil is approximately:
    a. −1°.
    b. 15°.
    c. 5°.

14. If the density of the air is increased, the lift will:
    a. remain the same.
    b. decrease.
    c. increase.

15. The maximum lift/drag ratio of an average transport aircraft would be about:
    a. 50.
    b. 1.5.
    c. 20.

Answers to Lift Quiz

1	–	c.	6	–	b.	11	–	b.
2	-	c.	7	-	a.	12	-	b.
3	-	b.	8	-	c	13	-	b.
4	-	b.	9	-	a.	14	-	c.
5	-	b.	10	-	c.	15	-	c.

HIGH-LIFT DEVICES – QUIZ

1. A split flap is:
   a. A flap divided into inner and outer sections to allow for wing flexing.
   b. A flap where the upper wing surface is fixed and the lower surface lowers to form the flap.
   c. A flap divided into sections which open to form slots through the flap.

2. If flaps are raised while speed and attitude are kept constant:
   a. The aircraft will maintain height.
   b. The aircraft will gain height.
   c. The aircraft will sink.

3. When a leading edge slot is opened, the stalling speed will:
   a. Remain the same but will occur at a higher angle of attack.
   b. Increase.
   c. Decrease.

4. Lowering a flap to its landing setting will:
   a. Give a lower unstick speed but longer distance to unstick.
   b. Give a lower unstick speed and shorter distance to unstick.
   c. Give a higher unstick speed but shorter distance to unstick.

5. The principal purpose of a flap is:
   a. To cause the wing to give more lift at a given angle of attack and airspeed.
   b. To adjust the position of the CP relative to the CG.
   c. To trim the aircraft laterally.

6. The type of flap which extends backwards from the trailing edge as it is lowered is:
   a. A split flap.
   b. A Kreuger flap.
   c. A Fowler flap.

7. If the flaps are lowered but airspeed is kept constant, to maintain level flight:
   a. The attitude must be held constant.
   b. The nose must be raised.
   c. The nose must be lowered.

8. If a flap is lowered from its take-off position to its landing position:
   a. There will be a large increase in lift and a small increase in drag.
   b. There will be a large increase in lift and a large increase in drag.
   c. There will be a small increase in lift and a large increase in drag.

9. Lowering a flap to its take-off setting will:
   a. Cause a decrease in drag.
   b. Cause an increase in drag.
   c. Have no effect on the drag.

10. With the flaps lowered, the stalling speed will:
    a. Increase.
    b. Decrease.
    c. Increase but occur at a higher angle of attack.

11. A Kreuger flap is:
    a. A flap which extends from the upper wing surface to increase drag.
    b. A leading edge flap.
    c. A flap which extends rearwards from the trailing edge.

12. A leading edge slat is a device for:
    a. Increasing the stalling angle of the wing.
    b. Decreasing the drag of the wing.
    c. Decreasing the stalling angle of the wing.

13. Lowering a flap to its landing setting will:
    a. Give a large increase in drag and a lower stalling speed.
    b. Give a large increase in drag but a higher stalling speed.
    c. Give a smaller increase in drag but a lower stalling speed.

14. The type of flap which increases wing area is:
    a. A split flap.
    b. A Fowler flap.
    c. A plain flap.

15. The purpose of a leading edge droop is:
    a. To give a more cambered section for high speed flight.
    b. To increase wing camber, and prevent separation of the airflow when trailing edge flaps are lowered.
    c. To increase the wing area for take-off and landing.

Answers to High-Lift Devices – Quiz

1	–	b.	6	–	c.	11	–	b.
2	-	c.	7	-	c.	12	-	a.
3	-	c.	8	-	c.	13	-	a.
4	-	a.	9	-	b.	14	-	b.
5	-	a.	10	-	b.	15	-	b.

The Stall – Quiz

1. A typical stalling angle of attack is:
   a. 30°.
   b. 15°.
   c. 5°.

2. An aircraft wing stalls at:
   a. A constant true airspeed.
   b. A constant angle of attack.
   c. A constant indicated airspeed.

3. In a steady turn an aircraft experiences 3G, the stalling speed will be:
   a. Above the normal stalling speed.
   b. Below the normal stalling speed.
   c. The same as the normal stalling speed.

4. At altitudes above sea level the IAS stalling speed will be:
   a. The same as at sea level.
   b. Less than at sea level.
   c. Greater than at sea level.

5. A stall warning must be set to operate:
   a. At a speed just below stalling speed.
   b. At a speed just above stalling speed.
   c. At the stalling speed.

6. At angles of attack above the stalling angle:
   a. The lift decreases and the drag decreases.
   b. The lift decreases and the drag increases.
   c. The lift increases and the drag increases.

7. A wing is stalled when:
   a. The lift produced is less than the weight.
   b. The airflow has separated from most of the upper surface.
   c. The lift is zero.

8. A fixed spoiler on the leading edge of the wing at the root will:
   a. Prevent a root stall.
   b. Induce a root stall.
   c. Give a shorter landing run.

9. With engine power on, an aircraft will stall:
   a. At the same speed as with power off.
   b. At a lower speed than with power off.
   c. At a higher speed than with power off.

Answers to the Stall – Quiz

1	–	b.	4	–	a.	7	–	b.
2	-	b.	5	-	b.	8	-	b.
3	-	a.	6	-	b.	9	-	b.

Aerodynamics Definitions – Quiz

1. The angle of attack is:
   a. The angle between the chord and the longitudinal axis.
   b. The angle between the wing and the lateral axis.
   c. The angle between the chord and the direction of the airflow.

2. Directional control is obtained by:
   a. The rudder.
   b. Elevators.
   c. Ailerons.

3. The wing span is the distance:
   a. From leading edge to trailing edge.
   b. From wing tip to wing tip.
   c. From wing tip to fuselage centre line.

4. The taper ratio is:
   a. The ratio of root incidence to tip incidence.
   b. The ratio of the wing root thickness to tip thickness.
   c. The ratio of tip chord to root chord.

5. An aircraft has a span of 30 feet and a wing area of 300 square feet. Its aspect ratio is:
   a. 10.
   b. 30.
   c. 3.

6. The chord line is:
   a. A line tangential to the wing surface at the leading edge.
   b. A line equidistant from upper and lower surface.
   c. A straight line from leading edge to trailing edge.

7. The dihedral angle is:
   a. The inclination of the wing to the vertical axis.
   b. The upward inclination of the wing to the lateral axis.
   c. The inclination of the wing to the longitudinal axis.

8. A wing has a span of 50 feet and an area of 200 square feet. Its mean chord would be:
   a. 2.5 feet.
   b. 4 feet.
   c. 10 feet.

9. Wash-out is:
   a. A decrease in chord from root to tip.
   b. An increase in incidence from root to tip.
   c. A decrease in incidence from root to tip.

10. A wing of 40 inch chord has a thickness/chord ratio of 10%. The thickness would be:
    a. 10 in.
    b. 0.4 in.
    c. 4 in.

11. In a symmetrical aerofoil section the mean camber line is:
    a. A straight line coincident with the chord.
    b. Coincident with the upper surface of the section.
    c. A curve.

12. The aspect ratio is:
    a. The ratio between the span and the mean chord.
    b. The ratio between the square of the span and the mean chord.
    c. The ratio between the span and the wing area.

13. Yawing is a rotation about:
    a. The normal axis.
    b. The longitudinal axis.
    c. The lateral axis.

14. A wing whose tips were lower than the root would be described as having:
    a. Wash-out.
    b Wash-in.
    c. Anhedral.

15. Longitudinal control is obtained by:
    a. Rudder.
    b. Ailerons.
    c. Elevators.

16. Yawing is caused by:
    a. The elevators.
    b. The rudder.
    c. The ailerons.

17. The thickness/chord ratio is:
    a. The ratio of the maximum wing thickness to the chord.
    b. The ratio of the wing span to the mean chord.
    c. The ratio of wing thickness at the root to the thickness at the tip.

18. When the aircraft is in straight and level flight the normal axis is:
    a. Horizontal.
    b. Vertical.
    c. Lateral.

19. Rolling is a rotation about:
    a. The longitudinal axis.
    b. The normal axis.
    c. The lateral axis.

20. Wing loading is:
    a. The ratio of the lift to the aircraft weight.
    b. The ratio of the weight of the wing to the area of the wing.
    c. The ratio of the total aircraft weight to the wing area.

21. When an aircraft is in level flight the normal axis is:
    a. Horizontal from front to rear.
    b. Horizontal from side to side.
    c. Vertical.

22. The Mean Camber Line is:
    a. A line equidistant from upper and lower surface.
    b. The line made by the upper surface of the wing.
    c. A straight line from leading edge to trailing edge.

23. Lateral control is obtained by:
    a. Rudder.
    b. Elevators.
    c. Ailerons.

24. Pitching is a rotation about:
    a. The longitudinal axis.
    b. The lateral axis.
    c. The normal axis.

25. The elevators control the aircraft about:
    a. The lateral axis.
    b. The longitudinal axis.
    c. The normal axis.

Answers to Aerodynamics Definitions – Quiz

1	-	c.	7	-	b.	13	-	a.	19	-	a.
2	-	a.	8	-	b.	14	-	c.	20	-	c.
3	-	b.	9	-	c.	15	-	c.	21	-	c.
4	-	c.	10	-	c.	16	-	b.	22	-	a.
5	-	c.	11	-	a.	17	-	a.	23	-	c.
6	-	c.	12	-	a.	18	-	b.	24	-	b.
									25	-	a.

Aerodynamics Forces in Flight Quiz

1. Horsepower is measured in units of:
   a Foot pounds.
   b Foot pounds per minute.
   c Pounds.

2. When an aircraft is climbing, the requirements to maintain equilibrium are:
   a Thrust equals the weight component perpendicular to the flight path, and lift equals the weight component along the flight path.
   b Thrust equals the sum of the drag and the weight component along the flight path, and lift equals the weight component perpendicular to the flight path.
   c Thrust equals the weight component along the flight path, and lift equals the sum of the drag and weight component perpendicular to the flight path.

3. If an aircraft maintains a constant radius of turn but the speed is increased:
   a The bank angle must be increased.
   b The bank angle must be decreased.
   c The bank angle will remain constant.

4. In straight and level flight the following forces act on an aircraft:
   a Thrust, lift, drag.
   b Thrust, lift, drag, weight.
   c Thrust, lift, weight.

5. For a glider having a maximum L/D ratio of 20 the flattest glide angle that could be achieved in still air would be:
   a 1ft in 10ft.
   b 1ft in 40ft.
   c 1ft in 20ft.

6. If the temperature is above ISA, the service ceiling will be:
   a Higher than in ISA conditions.
   b The same as in ISA conditions.
   c Lower than in ISA conditions.

7. In a ‘power on’ glide at a steady speed thrust is:
   a Less than the drag.
   b Exactly equal to the drag.
   c Greater than the drag.

8. For an aircraft in straight and level balanced flight, if the tailplane is producing a down-load, the centre of pressure must be:
   a On the CG.
   b Aft of the CG.
   c Forward of the CG.

9. An aircraft flying at 150kt IAS at 10 000ft compared to an aircraft of the same weight flying at the same IAS at sea level will have:
   a The same angle of attack.
   b A smaller angle of attack.
   c A larger angle of attack.

10. An aircraft has a stalling speed of 100kt IAS. In a steady turn it would stall:
    a At 100kt IAS.
    b At a speed greater than 100kt IAS.
    c At a speed of less than 100kt IAS.

11. Thrust is measured in units of:
    a Foot pounds per minute.
    b Pounds.
    c Foot pounds.

12. An aircraft flying straight and level at a steady IAS begins a banked turn, keeping the IAS constant:
    a The drag will remain constant.
    b The drag will increase.
    c The drag will decrease.

13. In a glide the lift force is:
    a Greater than the weight.
    b Equal to the weight.
    c Less than the weight.

14. As height increases, if the angle of attack and IAS are kept constant:
    a The lift decreases.
    b The lift increases.
    c The lift remains constant.

15. In a climb the lift force is:
    a Greater than the weight.
    b Equal to the weight.
    c Less than the weight.

16. To maintain steady level flight, as the angle of attack is increased the airspeed must:
    a Be increased.
    b Be decreased.
    c Remain constant.

17. During a glide the following forces act on an aircraft:
    a Drag, thrust, weight.
    b Lift, weight, thrust.
    c Lift, drag, weight.

18. During a turn the lift force is resolved into two forces, these are:
    a Centripetal force and a force equal and opposite thrust.
    b Centripetal force and a force equal and opposite weight.
    c Centripetal force and a force equal and opposite drag.

19. An aircraft flies at 150kt IAS at sea level. If it then flies at 150kt IAS at 10 000ft the drag will be:
    a Less.
    b Greater.
    c The same.

20. In a climb at a steady speed the thrust is:
    a Exactly equal to the drag.
    b Greater than the drag.
    c Less than the drag.

Answers to Aerodynamics Forces in Flight Quiz

1	–	c.	6	–	c.	11	–	b.	16	–	b.
2	–	b	7	–	a	12	–	b	17	–	c
3	–	a	8	–	b	13	–	c	18	–	b
4	–	b	9	–	a	14	–	c	19	–	c
5	–	c	10	–	b	15	–	c	20	–	b

Definitions & Glossary of Terms

The definitions and terms given here are in wide general use in aviation. Some definitions which are used in general aviation but are not included in this book are also to be found in this glossary. There are many others, but they would fill an entire section of this book all by themselves so I have had to be selective.

Aerofoil — A surface designed to produce lift when driven through the air.

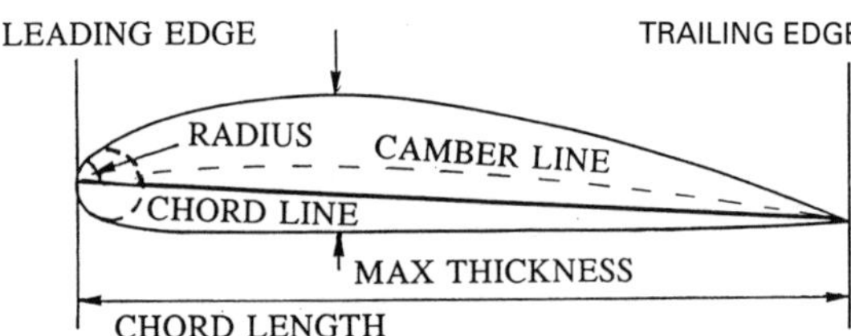

Figure Glos.1 Aerofoil Section

Aileron — A horizontal control surface hinged to the main plane near the wing tip, attached to the outboard trailing edge of the mainplanes (wings), it controls the rolling motion about the longitudinal axis. If the control column is moved to the *right*, the right aileron moves up and the left moves down. This causes a roll to the right.

Airframe — An aircraft less its engine(s). The body of an aircraft as distinct from its engine.

Angle of Attack — The angle between the chord line of the wing and the direction of the relative airflow. (Sometimes called the *aerodynamic angle of incidence*).

ANGLE OF INCIDENCE	The angle (about 3°-4°) at which the aerofoil is attached to an aircraft fuselage when the aircraft is in the rigging position. [The aerodynamic angle of incidence = the angle of attack.]
ANHEDRAL	The *downward* inclination of the wing to the plane through the *lateral* axis.

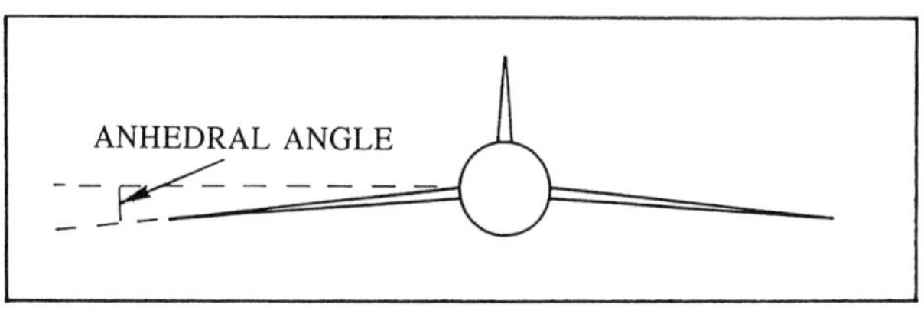

Figure Glos. 3

ASPECT RATIO	The ratio of wing span to mean chord. Alternatively span² to wing area. $\left[\textit{ASPECT RATIO} = \frac{\textit{SPAN}^2}{\text{AREA}} \right]$
AUW	All-up weight refers to the actual aircraft weight at the specified stage of flight.
BONDING	Connecting all metal parts of the aircraft to secure good electrical continuity and so avoid the undesirable effects from 'Static' electricity.
BULKHEAD	A transverse partition which completely separates one compartment from another. The most common example is the fireproof bulkhead behind the engine.
CAMBER	Curvature of the surface of an aerofoil.
CANTILEVER	A beam fixed rigidly at one end only.
CENTRE OF GRAVITY	The point at which the total weight is considered to act irrespective of the size or shape.

CHAFING	Two parts rubbing, producing wear.
CHORD LINE	The chord line of an aerofoil is the *straight line* joining the leading edge to the trailing edge. It is normally used as a reference line when measuring the angular position of the wing relative to the airflow.
CLUSTER	Many items joined together, e.g. tubes welded in a cluster.
COCKPIT (FLIGHT DECK)	The accommodation provided for the pilot(s) or other flight crew members.
CONTAMINATION	Material soiled by being mixed with or coming into contact with undesirable matter.
CORRELATION	Co-related mixing of controls, i.e. blade pitch to throttle opening.
CORROSION	That effect caused by chemical interaction on metal reducing its size and strength, e.g. rust.
DATUM LINE	A line fixed by the designer from which measurements are made when rigging or truing the aircraft.
DIFFERENTIAL AILERON CONTROL	A mechanical device incorporated in the aileron system whereby the upmoving aileron will operate through a larger angle than the down moving aileron.
DIHEDRAL LINE	The angle at which both port and starboard planes are inclined upwards to the lateral axis.

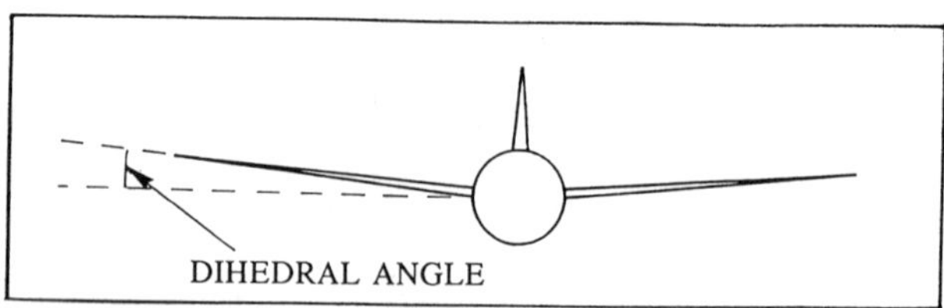

Figure Glos. 2

DRAG	The resistance to motion along the line of flight.
ELEVATOR	A horizontal control surface hinged to the rear of the tailplane, and controls the pitching moment about the lateral axis. A backward movement of the control column moves the elevator up and causes the nose of the aircraft to pitch up.
FAIRING	Additions to any structure to reduce drag.
FATIGUE	The diminishing resistance to fracture caused by fluctuating stresses.
FIN	A fixed vertical surface affecting the stability of an aircraft.
FLAP	A movable auxiliary surface controlled by the pilot for increasing the effective camber of the main plane.
FLUTTER	A rapid unstable oscillation due to alternating forces.
FRETTING	Wearing away of the surface material when one part is knocking against another.
FRISE TYPE AILERON	An aileron designed and pivoted so that when it is raised its nose projects below the main plane. The nose does not project above the main plane when the aileron is lowered.
FUSELAGE	The main structural body of an aircraft to which the main planes, tail unit, etc, are attached.
IAS/EAS/TAS	In the UK, IAS is normally corrected for Pressure and Instrument error (P & IE) to give Rectified Air Speed (RAS) which in turn is converted to TAS using the navigation computer. A correction for compressibility is then applied if the resulting TAS is in excess of 300kt. (Equivalent Air Speed (EAS).
IOAT	Indicated Outside Air Temperature is the temperature indicated in the cockpit and is OAT

	plus any adiabatic compression (ram) rise. IOAT is also known as Total Air Temperature (TAT).
KEEL SURFACE	The complete surface which is seen in side elevation.
LATERAL DATUM LINE	An imaginary line through the aircraft's centre of gravity usually considered to be parallel to a line joining the wing tips.
LONGERONS	The main longitudinal members of the fuselage.
LONGITUDINAL AXIS	An imaginary line running through the aircraft's centre of gravity fore and aft.
MAIN PLANE	The main supporting surface of an aircraft.
MEAN CAMBER LINE	A line which joints the leading edge to the trailing edge, such that it is equidistant from the upper and lower surfaces of the aerofoil. If it is *curved* the aerofoil is described as *cambered.*
MEAN CHORD (GEOMETRIC)	The wing area divided by the span.
MONOCOQUE	The form of stressed skin used in a fuselage or nacelle in which the curved skin carries the whole or greater part of the main load.
MSA	Minimum Safe Altitude is the minimum altitude for safe flight on the intended route and will be detailed in the operations manual.
MTWA	Maximum Take-Off Weight Authorised refers to the structural limitation quoted in the relevant performance data.
OAT	Outside Air Temperature is the ambient temperature at the airfield or altitude specified, normally expressed in C but may be given as an ISA deviation.
PROPELLER	A screw designed to convert the power developed by the engine into forward thrust.

Rib	Member which maintains the shape of a plane or control surface.
Rudder	Vertical control surface, attached to the rear edge of the (vertical) fin, and causes the aircraft to yaw about the normal (vertical) axis. Forward movement of the right rudder pedal moves the rudder to the right, causing a yaw to the right.
Semi-Monocoque	A type of construction in which longitudinal and transverse members relieve the skin of some of its load.
Servo-Control	A control designed to assist the pilot's effort.
Skin Friction	Resistance to motion due to friction between the air and the surface of a solid body moving through it.
Span	The overall distance from wing tip to wing tip.
Spar	A principal longitudinal member of a plane or of a control surface.
Spoilers	May be used in addition to ailerons. When the spoiler is operated it causes a loss of lift on the side it is raised, thus causing a roll to that side. Movement of the control column to the right causes the right spoiler to rise, while the left one remains unaffected. (Spoilers have been known to be used instead of ailerons).
Stabilator or Moving Tail	This is sometimes used in place of a separate elevator control.
Stall	An aerofoil is said to be stalled when its angle of attack is so increased that streamlined airflow can no longer occur. Turbulent flow and loss of lift result.
Stressed Skin	Any construction which relies wholly or in part on a skin (with or without reinforcement) to carry main load and provide stiffness.

STRUT	A structural member intended to resist compression in the direction of its length.
SWEEP ANGLE	(Wing sweep). The angle between the lateral axis and the ¼ chord line (may be referred to the leading edge).
TAIL PLANE	A fixed horizontal surface situated at the rear of an aircraft affecting the longitudinal stability.
TAIL UNIT	The rear portion of an airframe; includes tail plane, fin, rudder and elevators.
TAPER RATIO	The ratio of the tip chord to the root chord.
TENSILE LOAD	That force tending to stretch the material.
THICKNESS/CHORD RATIO ('FINENESS RATIO')	This is the ratio of the maximum thickness of the cross-section to the chord, and is usually expressed as a percentage.
TORQUE	'Twisting moment', the turning effect of force.
TRAILING EDGE} TRIM TAB }	A small tab attached to the trailing edge of a control surface, usually adjustable in flight to correct the trim of the aircraft under varying speeds and loads.
UNDERCARRIAGE	The main alighting gear of an aircraft, together with wheels, skids or floats. The undercarriage may be fixed or retractable.
WASH-IN	An *increase* in angle of incidence from root to tip.
WASH-OUT	A *decrease* in wing angle of incidence from root to tip.
WING AREA	The area enclosed by the wing outline and extending through the fuselage to the centreline.
WING LOADING	The total weight of the aircraft divided by the wing area.

V-Speeds ('V' = Velocity)

V_A Design manoeuvring speed. Sometimes called the 'turbulence penetration speed'. This is the maximum speed at which full control movement or deflection may be made without experiencing structural failure. In rough air the aircraft will stall before the structural integrity (about 3.8Gs) is challenged. Use 1.7 V_{SO} if not specified.

V_B Design speed for maximum gust intensity.

V_C Design cruising speed.

V_D Design diving speed.

V_F Design flap speed.

V_{FE} Maximum flap extended speed. Upper limit of the white arc on the airspeed indicator.

V_{LE} Maximum landing gear extended speed. Maximum speed for aircraft operating after the gear is down and locked, this is the maximum speed for flight in this configuration.

V_{LO} Maximum landing gear operating speed.

V_{MC} Minimum control speed with the critical engine inoperative. This is determined at sea level with maximum allowable power, rearmost allowable CG flaps in take-off position, gear up and the inoperative engine windmilling. V_{MC} depends on and varies with power and CG.

V_{MCA} Minimum control speed, take-off climb.

V_{MCG} Minimum control speed, on or near ground.
(Be aware of the difference between V_{MC} and V_{MCA}, they are often confused and used incorrectly. *See NOTE at the end of this glossary.)

V_{MCL} Minimum control speed, approach or landing.

V_R Rotation speed.

V_1 Take-off decision speed.

V_{MU} Minimum unstick speed.

V_{LOF} Minimum lift-off speed.

V_2 Take-off safety speed.

V_{2min} Minimum take-off safety speed.

V_3 Steady initial climb speed with all engines operating.

V_{RA} Rough air speed.

V_{MO}/M_{MO} Maximum operating limit speed.

V_H Maximum speed in level flight with maximum continuous power.

V_{NE} Never-exceed speed, the red line on the airspeed indicator.

V_S Stalling speed or the minimum steady flight speed at which the aircraft is controllable.

V_{SO} Stalling speed or the minimum steady flight speed in the landing configuration, gear down and locked and flaps fully extended. The lower limit of the white arc on the airspeed indicator.

V_{S1} Stalling speed or the minimum steady flight speed obtained in a specified configuration. 'Stalling speed clean', gear up and flaps retracted. The lower limit of the green arc on the airspeed indicator.

V_X Speed for best angle of climb. Used to clear obstructions. This speed, to the exclusion of all others, results in the greatest altitude gain in a given distance. This particular airspeed generally increases in value with an increase in altitude.

V_Y Speed for best rate of climb. Used for normal operations, this speed, to the exclusion of any other, results in the greatest altitude gain in a given amount of time. The particular airspeed necessary to obtain V_Y generally decreases from a specified value with an increase of altitude.

V_T Maximum aerotow speed (JAR-22 only).

V_T Threshold speed.

V_{Tmax} Maximum threshold speed.

V_W Maximum winch-launch speed (JAR-22 only).

V_{AT} Target threshold speed. A target threshold speed is a speed at which the pilot aims to cross the runway threshold when landing. The speeds may be related to the all-power-units-operating condition ($V_{AT}2$).

V_{REF} Is used frequently as an alternative to V_{AT}.

V_D/M_D Design driving speed.

V_{DF}/M_{DF} Demonstrated flight diving speed.

V_F1 Design flap speed for procedure flight conditions.

V_{FC}/M_{FC} Maximum speed for stability characteristics.

NOTE: V_{MCG} is often used incorrectly in the take-off speeds context. It has been stated in several publications that, 'a take-off should be abandoned (aborted) if an engine failure occurs below V_{MCG}'. As a matter of technical/aerodynamic fact, any take-off should be aborted below V_2 for light twins, and V_1 for larger aircraft. Any lower speed is not applicable and invalid in relation to take-off speeds. V_1 and V_2 are the key in any take-off decision making, with the proof lying in the fact that the aircraft must have the capability in:

- V_2 (take-off safety speed) to have a positive gradient of climb on one engine.
- V_1 ('go-no go' decision speed) be able to accelerate to V_2, and thereafter have a positive gradient of climb – or a guaranteed gradient of climb on one engine.

In special memory of a mentor and dear friend who passed away as I was in the final stages of writing this book:

Hector Taylor, F.R.Ae.S, AFC, MBE

Member of the UK Panel of Examiners

An officer and a gentleman who gave so much to aviation over many years.
I will simply think of him as having returned to his squadron.

Index